Colche

D0297788

Our dedicated line for renewals is (01206) 5 . . .55
hest time to call is during our evening sessions (5p.m. to
on Mondays, Tuesdays, Wednesdays & Fridays.

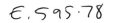

E. 595.78

STACK .

The Butterflies of Essex

by

David Corke

with a status report on all Essex Lepidoptera
by
Brian Goodey

Lopinga Books

in association with

Essex
Wildlife
Trust

BUTTERFLY
CONSERVATION

ENVIRONMENT AGENCY

Published by Lopinga Books

(David Corke), Tye Green House, Wimbish, GB-Essex, CB10 2XE

First published 1997

ISBN 0 9530362 0 0

British Library Cataloguing-in-Publication Data

A catalogue record for this book is available from the British Library

Printed by Healeys Printers Ltd, 49-55 Fore Street, Ipswich IP4 1JL

CONTENTS

FOREWORD

In 1987 I was pleased to write the foreword of Brian Sawford's splendid book *The Butterflies of Hertfordshire*. Ten years on and now it is the turn of Essex and its butterflies, ten years in which butterflies and their conservation have moved even more into the limelight.

For me, it is the common-place sights and sounds of the natural world which bring joy: the first brimstones and peacocks still marking the awakening of every year, while the red admirals and commas enjoying over-ripe fruit mark harvest festival. It is good to know that these delights exist still, even in the most developed parts of Essex.

From spring to autumn the world of butterflies is there, inviting exploration of its secrets. It is a delight that has clearly attracted the wildlife enthusiasts of Essex as over five-hundred of them have spent so many enjoyable hours butterfly-watching to make this book.

David Corke's compilation and analysis of all their work makes a major contribution to the knowledge of the butterflies of Essex; highlighting their problems which have, if anything, increased in the ten years since the study in neighbouring Hertfordshire.

This book is not just a chronicle of disappearing species; remedies exist and some, like the restoration of the heath fritillary to Essex, are already well underway. As we protect the world of the butterfly we protect other wildlife and landscapes and help save a countryside for future generations.

Gordon Beningfield

(President, Butterfly Conservation)

October 1997

INTRODUCTION & ACKNOWLEDGEMENTS

A butterfly atlas

One of the main purposes of this book is to provide a tetrad distribution map for each species of Essex butterfly: something that has not been done before. In this Essex is behind its neighbours: Suffolk's book appeared in 1986 (Mendel & Piotrowski), Hertfordshire's in 1987 (Sawford), London's also in 1987 (Plant) and Kent in 1993 (Philp). Cambridge has an atlas of the main species (Bennett & Perrin, 1994) and already Suffolk has produced a new set of maps (Stewart, 1997) while Hertfordshire and Middlesex started an annual butterfly report with maps in 1996 (second volume Murray, 1997). Mapping and monitoring is not a once and for all task but a continuing part of butterfly conservation.

Essex has not been ignoring its Lepidoptera: it is just the detailed tetrad maps that are new. *A Guide to the Butterflies and Larger Moths of Essex* was one of the first county faunas to be published in book form when it appeared in 1975 (Firmin et al.). It was brought up to date in the 1980s and extended to cover the microlepidoptera in the Essex Field Club's double volume *The Smaller Moths of Essex* (Emmet, 1981) and *The Larger Moths and Butterflies of Essex* (Emmet, Pyman & Corke, 1985). These volumes contained 10km-square maps for all species: a first for any British county. These volumes, together with the long series of butterfly studies that appeared in the Essex Field Club's publications and, more recently in those of the Colchester Natural History Society, have provided an excellent baseline with which to compare the present status of the butterflies (and moths) of Essex.

Moths and butterflies

This book also contains Brian Goodey's summary of the current status of all the moths of Essex: especially emphasising the changes that have happened to the distribution and abundance of some species since they were mapped in the 1980s. Why then is this book called simply *The Butterflies of Essex*? It *is* primarily about the butterflies where our knowledge is much more detailed and where the rarer species are excellent indicator species to use as guides to the success of conservation management. Also 'butterfly' is a much more popular, positive word than 'moth': most European languages sensibly have one (popular) word for butterflies and moths in general, reserving the equivalent of our 'moth' for the unpopular clothes moths; making it much easier to 'sell' moth conservation to the public. So this book is mainly about butterflies in the normal, English, sense but with a detailed checklist of the 'butterflies of the night'.

Co-operating organisations

In 1991 the Cambridge and Essex branch of Butterfly Conservation and the Essex Wildlife Trust worked together to launch the Essex Butterfly Action project. It is primarily from that project that this book developed and so it is appropriate that these two wildlife charities will share the royalties. The following organisations have co-operated in supplying records for use in this book and my thanks are extended to them:

Butterfly Conservation (Cambridge & Essex branch)
Butterfly Conservation (national gardens survey)
Colchester Natural History Society
Colchester Museum
Essex Field Club

Essex Lepidoptera Panel
Essex Moth Group
Essex Wildlife Trust
Epping Forest Conservators
Institute of Terrestrial Ecology
London Natural History Society
Saffron Walden Museum
Southend Museum

Financial help

I thank the Environment Agency for grant aid towards this publication. A generous donation from Iris Newbery allowed the inclusion of the colour plates section. Financial help for the Essex Butterfly Action project, was provided by Butterfly Conservation, the Peoples' Trust for Endangered Species, the Vincent Wildlife Trust and the University of East London.

Illustrations and maps

The photographs were all taken in Essex and made freely available by the photographers who are credited in the captions. Iris Newbery ARPS acted as co-ordinator and photographic editor for the colour plates section.

Gordon Beningfield very generously gave permission to use his lovely painting which adorns the cover.

The software that was used to create the maps is DMAP for Windows written by Dr Alan Morton.

Authorship

I thank Brian Goodey for preparing the complete checklist of Essex Lepidoptera. He, Iris Newbery and Colin Plant checked and commented helpfully on drafts of this publication. My wife, Elaine, acted as copy editor, design consultant and tolerated well the amount of time I spent at the computer.

Although this book is produced in co-operation with, and in aid of, the Essex Wildlife Trust and the Cambridge and Essex branch of Butterfly Conservation, the opinions (and mistakes) in it are mine alone.

The individual recorders

Over 500 people maintained detailed records of butterflies in their gardens or selected habitats in the Essex countryside, while a smaller number of specialists searched for the rarer species and undertook controlled attempts to re-establish some of the species lost to Essex. I estimate that the recording effort equates roughly with two working lifetimes!

The huge amount of data that resulted from these surveys has enabled this to be more than a series of distribution maps and status reports. The chapters giving the results of the garden surveys, butterfly behaviour studies and debating the causes of butterfly declines all contain new scientific information that will, I hope, add to our understanding of the ecology of butterflies in general.

I hope that *The Butterflies of Essex* will join the *Flora of Essex* (Jermyn, 1974) and *Breeding Birds of Essex* (Dennis, 1996) as a tool for wildlife conservation and an inspiration for continued monitoring of our county's wildlife. If it does so, it will be through the combined efforts of everyone who contributed records to the surveys. This is your book, I hope you enjoy it and if I have accidentally omitted any of the recorders from the following list I offer my sincere apologies.

David Corke, Wimbish, October 1997

List of Recorders

Abbott, A.C.	Barber, J.	Brandis, Janet	Burnham, L.M.	Chrome, David
Adams, W.J.	Barnes, B.	Branson, Ellen	Burrage, Karen	Churcher, B.C.
Ager, G.	Barnes, D.	Brereton, L.C.	Burrow, H.J.	Clark, M.
Airey, L.	Barnes, S.	Briggs, Pauline	Burvill, Family	Clift, K.
Akib, N.	Barnett, P.	Brill, M.J.	Butler, D	Clowes, Ian
Aldridge, D.J.	Barratt, S.R.	Brooks, A.M.	Butler, Dilys	Cobb, B.M.
Aldridge, P.C.	Beagley, C.	Brooks, S.R.	Butler, Phil	Cobbett, O.
Allbrook, B.R.	Beal, D.J.	Broughton, U.	Cable, J.A.	Collins, C.
Alldus, P.	Bealey, Family	Brown, C.G.	Cable, M.J.	Collop, D.
Allen, B.R.	Beard, B.C.	Brown, E, P.	Caldow, B.	Colvin, F.& B.M.
Allington, H.J.	Bearham, Sheila	Brown, G.B.	Campion, M.I.	Cook, Kenneth
Anderson, C.	Beauchamp, J.	Brown, Michael	Canning, J.	Cooke, P.
Andrews, J.	Behn, Joan	Brown, P.N.	Cardy, Barbara	Cooper, D.
Andrews, R.C.	Benham, Maura	Brown, Pauline	Carlile, Cathie	Cooper, F.
Arben, C.S.	Bensley, Molly	Browne, Penny	Carmic, H.&.H.	Cooper, W.
Archer, J.R.	Bent, Angela	Bruce, E.	Carter, Sue	Corcoran, W.J.
Ashby, J.	Birnage, Sue	Bruce, R.V.	Castleden, L.S.	Cornish, Paul
Ashley, J.M.	Blamire, Val	Buckner, Edna	Cattanach, J.& N.	Cotgrave, Iris
Ashworth, B.R.	Blunden, J.	Bugler, Family	Cerrino, A.	Court, Greta
Austin, S.H.	Blyth, W.G.	Burchfield, D.S.	Chambers, M.	Crawshaw, J.
Bacon, E.S.	Bonnage, David	Burden, C.	Chandler, G.	Crees, K.
Bailey, G.	Boreham, S.	Burge, M.	Chapman, Sally	Crome, D.A.
Bainton, P.	Borrows, Family	Burgess, Alfred	Chinery, Barbara	Crowhurst, Janet
Baker, D.	Bowdrey, J.P.	Burke, H.B.	Chinery, Joan	Cumming, N.
Baker, M.	Bradbro, Stella	Burman, Peter	Chivers, Ben	Cusack, Linda

Custard, J.	Firmin, Joe	Green, Pat	Horsley, Ralph	Ling, Julie
Cutts, K.G.	Fleet, B.	Green, R.A.	Horswill, A.	Linney, E.A.
Dallisson, Mavis	Fleet, J.	Greenland, Ray	Hoskin, Neal	Little, William J.
Davies, Margaret	Fleming, Stuart	Greenslade, R.	Howard, P.	Littleboy, Norman
Davis, A.P.	Fletcher, G.H.	Grice, Peter	Howard, Sue	Lloyd, M.
Davis, F.E.	Folkes, Helen	Griffin, C.	Hudgell, S.	Looker, Joy
Davis, J.	Fone, J.	Griffiths, Vicky	Hudson, R.	Lucas, Gordon
Davis, M.J.	Foott, Gwen	Griffiths, Y.	Hunford, Don	Luke, P.
Davis, Stephen	Ford, B.W.	Grimsey, D.	Hunt, Felix	Lumbsden, S.
Davy, J.R.	Ford, E.M.	Gunton, Tony	Hunt, Peter	Lunn, S.
Davy, John	Ford, G.D.	Gustard, J.	Hunt, Stella	Mabbit, R.
Dawson, Julian	Foreman, R.	Hales, Valerie	Hunwick, Pam	Mace, E.
Daynes, O.	Frampton,	Hall, Thomas	Hurley, D.F.	MacNeil, B.
Dennis, J.	Family	Hallam, S.	Imrie, Yolande	Malindine, M.
Dewick, A.J.	Francis, D.L.	Hammond, Edna	Ison, Family	Malone, C.
Dewick, Stephen	Franklin, Roy	Hammond, W.J.	Jackson, B. & M.	Malone, S.
Diamond, J.M.	Fredericks, R.	Hansen,	Jackson, M.	Manley, S.
Dickinson, T.	Fremlim, Maria	Richard.	Jackson, S. & I.	Mansfield, Mrs
Digby, D.	Froom, Oliver	Hanstead, Norma	Jackson-Baker, M	Marden, D.
Dispaine, M.E.	Frostick, J.M.	Harden, P.	Jessen, L.W.	Marsh, J.
Diver, I.	Fulford, Deborah	Hardy, M.	Johnson, F.R.	Marsh, Raymond
Dobson, K.	Fuller, L.R.	Harries, S.M.	Johnson, Roy	Marshall, Jo
Doidge, J.W.	Gannaway, M.	Harrington, B.	Jones, A.E.	Martin, H.V.
Douch, Monica	Gardiner, Jane	Harris, .D.	Jones, Ann	Mason, Ann
Douch, Peter	Geeves, D.	Harris, A.J.	Jones, G.I.	Mason, C.F.
Dowling, O.	Gentle, A.E	Harris, Mary	Jopling, Family	Massey, S.
Down, D.G.	Gershon, M.J.	Harris, Pauline	Jordan, D.F.	Matson, B.N.
Downie, Alan	Gerussi, R.	Harrison, K.A.	Joslin, Trevor	McCadden, Les
Drake, Mollie	Gibbard, H.	Harrison, Sophie	Joyce, J.L.& A.	McGhie, B.H.
Drew, S.	Gibbs, R.B.	Harrison, V.	Judd, Margaret	McLaren, J.
Durrant, Marita	Gibbs,	Harvey, Margaret	Kelly, Patricia	Mead, R.J.
Eastcott, B.	R.G.&.K.J.	Hatler, C.D.	Kennet, J.	Mead, Rosemary
Eaton, L.	Gibson, C.	Hawes, Roger	Kent, Ruth	Meadows, M.
Edney, M.F.	Gibson, C.A.	Hazell, M.	Kerbey, J.R.	Merritt, L.
Edwards, K.	Giddings, P.	Heath, David	Kett, W.H.	Michell, R.M.
Edwards, Mary	Gilbert, Bob	Hemingway, Mr	Kibble, R.J.	Millar, A.G.
Edwards, Sylvia	Gilbert, D.E.	Henry, M.D.	King, Pat.	Miller, M.
Emerson, Joy	Gilbert, D.T.	Heywood, M.J.	Kirk, S.J.	Miller, N.
Emery, D.	Girling, C.W.	Hide, H.J.	Knott, B.	Millwood, J.& A.
Emery, John	Glover, Julia	Hill, A.M.	Knowles, J.	Milnthorpe, Mary
English, Alan	Goff, David	Hills, R.	Lacey, R.C.	Minshull, R.
Erdman, Anne	Golder, R.	Hills, S.I.	Lacy, E.S.	Minton, V.
Erdman, D.	Gomm, Peter.J.	Hilton, P.	Lacy, W.E.	Monks, P.
Erridge, Pat	Goodey, Brian	Hinchcliff, Molly	Lake, M.	Moore, Juliet
Evans, A.C.	Gooding, E.M.	Hitching, H.J.	Lamb, E.	More, E.B.
Evans, Martin	Gorham, A.	Hobby, Family	Lane, H.	Morley, C.
Evans, S.	Grant, F.	Hobden, Marion	Langridge, S.	Morris, R.
Fancy, H.	Gray, C.W.	Hockley, C.	Lawrence, A.R.	Morton, M.T.
Feathers, S.	Gray, P.L.	Hodges, Family	Layton, S.	Morton, Tom
Feldwick, L.	Greatorix, Jane	Hogg, M.A.	Lee, Dorothy	Moss, R.G.
Ferguson, Jean	Gree, D.&.S.	Homewood, D.	Lescott, A.	Munroe, Linda
Filbee, Tony	Green, G.R.	Hoosan, Brenda	Levett, Mike	Munson, Paula
Fill, Helen	Green, Jean	Hopkirk, Joyce	Lewis, A.	Murphy, E.
Finbow, V.	Green, P.W.	Horobin, S.	Lilley, Elaine	Murray, Dorothy

Murray, F.	Price, G.D.	Seago, Robert	Threadgood, J.	Wingrove, E.
Murray, J.W.	Pryor, E.	Sell, Geoffrey	Thurgood, T.W.	Wisbey, G.
Murray, Sally	Pryor, G.	Senior, B.& J.W.	Topsfield, A.N.	Wood, Brian
Murrell, J.R.	Pugh, R.S.	Shanle, S.J.	Torino, Susie	Wood, John
Newbery, Iris	Pullen, C.	Sharp, C.	Tremethick, M.	Wood, Julia
Newell, S.	Purches, L.	Sheppard, Betty	Trotter, Lesley	Woodcock, Jane
Nicholls, R.	Purvis, Joan	Shove, M.	Trundle, P.	Woodhouse, A.
Nickson, A.E.	Pyman, Geoff	Simmonds, Mr	Tudge, T.W.	Woods, D.W.
Nickson, M.A.E.	Quigley, A.	Simpson, E.	Tully, N.	Wooldridge, Ken
Nicol, R.	Ragdal, E.S.	Sims, L.A.	Turner, Sheila	Wootton, G.V.
Nightingale, P.	Randall, R.H.L.	Sinclair, Ann	Ulrich, Ken	Wordley, A.
Nisbet, Dennis	Ransom, Helen	Sinden, R.A.	Upton, G.	Worn, Richard
Norman, Elsie	Rawlings, C.A.	Smith, A.R.	Vaughn, Peter	Worster, Elaine
Norton, John	Rawlins, M.	Smith, D.M.	Veal, Vyvian	Wort, J.
Nott, U.	Raybould, A.	Smith, G.Corley	Veen, Lynda van	Wren, Keith
Nott, W.M.	Rayner, N.M.	Smith, Graham	Vicary, Gavin	Wrenn, Margaret
Nottingham, D.J.	Read, Jack D.	Smith, Helen	Vincent, D.G.	Wright, B.
Nunn, Family	Redstone, Family	Smith, M.	Wade, B.J.	Wright, D.V.S.
Nunn, J.R.	Reed, J.S.	Smith, Pauline	Walker, Suzanne	Wright, F.P.
Oakley, Ken	Reed, P.	Smith, Peter	Ward, J.	Wyatt, Bernard
Offord, V.	Reel, Kelvin	Smith, T.J.	Ward, Judith	Wyatt, R.
Oldman, J.	Reid, Thelma	Smith, Wendy	Ward, Sue	Yeldham, C.
Orriss, M.	Reilly, L.G.	Soper, Derek	Ward, W.H.C.	Younge, Evelyn
Osborne, John	Revell, A.	Southgate, Carol	Warren, J.	
Palmer, J.	Revell, P.	Spencer, Family	Watson, T.H.	
Palmer, Jack W.	Rice, B.	Spinner, Mary	Watt, P. & T.	
Palmer, P.A.	Richardson, W.	Spooner, J.M.	Watts, B.R.	
Palmer, Peter	Rickenbach, Mr	Spooner, Terry	Webb, Charles	
Papworth, M.	Roast, Suzanne	Springall, D.	Webb, D.T.	
Parker, L.C.	Robinson, P.	Squier, J.A.	Webster, W.	
Parkins, J.	Robson, R.A.	Squire, Family	Weir, D.	
Parr, Norman	Rodie, Marion	Stebbings, W.	Weir, F.J.	
Parry, D.	Rogers, C.	Stevens, Alan	Weller, M.A.	
Parsons, Evelyn	Rookard, Fiona	Stewart, Family	Westover, Fleur	
Patient, M.E.	Rookard, Joan	Stichbury, W.J.	Whitaker, J.S.	
Peach, Elizabeth	Rose, Gwynneth	Stiff, E.J.	White, Kate	
Pearce, E.M.	Rose.I.	Still, Anne	White, Maureen	
Pearce, J.	Rose.Ian	Stock, Christine	Whitlam, M.	
Pearce, Jane	Ross, D.M.	Stott, Clive	Whitlam, R.	
Pegrum, H.L.	Rostron, John	Strutt, G.M.	Whitmore, R.H.	
Penny, Ian	Routledge, Dawn	Suckling, M.	Whitnall, D.	
Pepper, G.	Rowe, J.	Sunnuck, J.	Wickenden, S.	
Pepys, L.G.	Rowley, M.	Swann, Mary	Wiegand, H.	
Perrin, Val	Rush, R.J.	Tayler, Margaret	Wiffen, C.	
Perry, D.M.	Rushbrooke, B.A.	Taylor, J.S.	Wilbourne, J.	
Philbrick, N.	Russell, Bryan	Taylor, Lesley	Wildig, Aisla	
Pinner, Eileen.	Sadgrove, Alan	Telfer, Philip	Wilkinson, N.B.	
Plant, Colin	Salinger, D.	Thomas, Peter	Willgress, B.	
Poole, Keith & Pat	Sargeaunt, H.B.	Thompson, E.B.	Willia, Christine	
Potter, B.M.	Saunders, D.	Thompson, I.F.	Williams, Mrs	
Potter, Hazel	Savage, J.	Thompson, V.L.	Williams, R.	
Potts, Pauline	Sawkins, D.	Thornton, G.	Williams, Ted	
Poutney, Tom	Scott, D.	Thorogood, John	Willsmer, M.	
Poyser, J.	Seabrook, Vera	Thorogood, R.	Wing, G.	

Chapter 1   **ESSEX LEPIDOPTERISTS**

An elderly amateur entomologist, remembering his Essex boyhood in the early
20th century, wrote "Any keen young student of butterflies would do well to take
my advice and live almost anywhere in the south or centre of England rather than
Essex" (Wykes, 1979). Fortunately for Essex a good number of entomologists,
young and old, professional and amateur, have ignored his advice. In this chapter
I want to concentrate on those Essex residents whose studies have contributed to
advances in the knowledge of Lepidoptera at the national or international level.
Those who contributed to the knowledge of the Essex fauna by compiling lists for
the whole county are also mentioned briefly: it is they whose work is the basis of
all the historical part of the systematic accounts in this book.

Most county butterfly and moth books include a chapter of this type and all those
I have read have required that the people mentioned should be dead. I cannot see
why, and fortunately for Essex we have some living entomologists of great
stature: they get a mention too.

John Ray (1627-1705)   In Essex 1627-1644; 1679-1705

John Ray was not just an entomologist, nor even just a naturalist, but a polymath.
The son of a blacksmith, he was born at Black Notley near Braintree in a cottage
which survives today. He won a scholarship to Cambridge at 16 where, after
graduation, he became a fellow of Trinity College. He studied and taught Latin,
Greek, Hebrew and mathematics while filling in his spare time with natural
history: his botanical studies around Cambridge became important to him while he
recovered from an illness in 1650.

After leaving Cambridge, he undertook many travels, at home and abroad,
studying natural history. In 1673 he married and four years later returned to
Essex, where he lived for the rest of his life. It is during this phase of his life,
collecting insects around Braintree in the company of his children and
corresponding with other naturalists, that his most important work on butterflies
was done.

It was not until 1710, five years after his death, that *Historia Insectorum.* was
published. This included the first published records and descriptions of 29 species
of British butterflies: about half the British total. That he did not have only a
scientist's view of butterflies is shown by this quotation (in translation) from
Historia Insectorum:

You ask what is the use of butterflies? I reply to adorn the countryside and delight the eyes of men: to brighten the countryside like so many jewels.

A more complete account of Ray's life is given in a booklet by an Essex resident (Baldwin, 1986), which also gives detailed references to other works.

Henry Doubleday (1808-1875) In Essex all his life

Henry Doubleday lived in Epping, the son of a grocer he became a grocer in his turn. A general naturalist, he developed a special interest in butterflies and moths and corresponded widely. The number of his publications did not reflect the great extent of his knowledge and much knowledge died with him: including all that which could have been gleaned from his collection (now in the Natural History Museum, London) had he labelled his specimens (in his day this was not normally done).

His *Synonymic list of British Lepidoptera* (1849) though short, was a major work: a full checklist of all the butterflies and moths known in Britain with cross references to the various names by which they were known. It became a vital tool for all British lepidopterists.

He and his brother Edward published observations on the Lepidoptera from his vicinity (important sources for the historical records in this book). He also invented the technique of 'sugaring' trees to attract moths, having observed moths congregating around discarded sugar boxes at his shop.

A biography of Henry Doubleday, written by Robert Mays (1978), a present day Essex lepidopterist devoted to the history of natural history, gives a complete account of his life.

Frederick William Frohawk (1861-1946) In Essex 1903-1911; 1917-1923

F.W. Frohawk was a talented artist who made his living by painting illustrations of wildlife. His two periods in Essex were in Rayleigh and Thundersley, where he undertook the greater part of the most important project of his life: rearing every species of British butterfly and painting, for the first time, a record from life of every stage in the life-cycle of each species. Those species he could not collect locally were obtained from correspondents elsewhere in Britain (or abroad for extinct species). His colour paintings, with his own detailed text, eventually appeared in 1924 as a two volume masterpiece. The original paintings are now in the collection of the Natural History Museum and are so good that they were copied for a much more recent butterfly book (Howarth, 1973). Frohawk's youngest daughter (Valezina) has fond memories of her childhood at Uplands, Thundersley and is herself a butterfly enthusiast. Her christian name derives from the scientific name of a beautiful variety of the silver-washed fritillary. Now Viscountess Bolingbroke, Valezina is a vice-president of Butterfly Conservation.

Dr June Chatfield (1987) has provided a delightful biography of Frohawk with much detail of his time in Essex.

Figure 2.1 A pencil sketch by F.W. Frohawk of "eight pearl-bordered fritillaries in full sun, sketch from life 5.45pm May 20th 1921, Hadleigh Essex". The original of this drawing is owned by Graham Hart who generously loaned it for reproduction. F.W. Frohawk's daughter, Valezina, Viscountess Bolingbroke, kindly agreed to its inclusion.

Arthur Maitland Emmet MBE (living)   In Essex early 1960s onwards

After a career in the Army and later as a classics master, Maitland Emmet retired to Essex in the early 1960s to care for his elderly mother. A butterfly and moth enthusiast throughout his life, in retirement his interest in the smallest moths developed to the point where he is recognised as a world authority on the leaf-mining Nepticulidae. This renown has resulted in his being elected a vice-president and then honorary fellow of the Royal Entomological Society as well as periods as president of the British Entomological and Natural History Society and the Amateur Entomological Society. The Zoological Society of London awarded him the Raffles Medal for contributions to zoology by an amateur.

While in Essex he took on an editorial role in the production of *The Moths and Butterflies of Great Britain and Ireland*. Now senior editor he has seen seven volumes published and is working on the eighth. 'MOGBI' is universally recognised as the most important series of volumes on British Lepidoptera ever published, volume 7 part 1 being a definitive work on British butterflies (Emmet & Heath, 1989) The publisher, Basil Harley, himself a keen naturalist, lives in Essex and founded his own publishing company to produce 'MOGBI' and related titles on entomology and natural history.

Maitland Emmet used his classics skill and love of crossword-type puzzles to track down the meaning of the scientific names of all the British butterflies and moths (Emmet, 1991). The resulting book was named 'book of the year' by the novelist A.S. Byatt.

Paul Whalley (living)   In Essex 1930s and 1981-1988

Born in Essex he was evacuated in wartime and did not return to Essex until well into his career as a professional entomologist. He worked at the Natural History Museum, studying fossil butterflies and moths and various families of tropical moths. As well as his scientific papers on fossil Lepidoptera his major contributions to the study of living butterflies have been two books: the first popular book to emphasise the ways to study butterfly behaviour in the field (1980) and a beautifully illustrated mini-field guide covering all the butterflies of Europe (1982).

Paul Whalley served as secretary of the Royal Entomological Society. He has now retired to Anglesey and recently edited *The Butterflies of Gwynedd* (1997) and has served as chairman of the prestigious Joint Committee for the Conservation of British Insects (JCCBI).

Compilers of previous Essex lists

Although many naturalists have studied the butterfly and moth fauna of particular regions of Essex and recorded their observations in valuable publications, there have been five compilations of status reports for Essex butterflies:

E. A. Fitch (1891) wrote an excellent paper in the *Essex Naturalist*: it was clearly intended to be the first part of a complete history of Essex Lepidoptera but only the butterfly section ever appeared. A farmer, Fitch lived in the Brick House, Maldon from 1874 until his death in 1911. An obituary says "as an entomologist he was one of our great disappointments" (Morley, 1912) referring to his excellent early work on parasitic Hymenoptera to be followed by a long life in which his entomology consisted only of active involvement with local studies and societies.

Fitch is believed to have handed his unpublished notes on the moths of Essex to William H. Harwood who incorporated them in his section on the Lepidoptera in the *Victoria County History of Essex* published in 1903. This was the first complete status report on the county's butterflies and moths. Harwood was a professional naturalist with an deep knowledge of the natural history of his native Colchester area. He made his living collecting and breeding insects for collectors such as the Hon. Charles Rothschild. Some of the rare varieties that he discovered were illustrated by Frohawk in his publications.

Joe Firmin is a naturalist and journalist based in the Colchester area. In the 1970s, when the then Essex Naturalists' Trust (now Essex Wildlife Trust) created the Essex Lepidoptera Panel, he became its chairman: a post he has held ever since. The first task the Panel set itself was the publication of *A Guide to the Butterflies and Larger Moths of Essex* which appeared in 1975.

A set of provisional maps was issued by the Essex Biological Records Centres in 1982 (Payne & Skinner).

Geoffrey Pyman MBE was the Essex Field Club's recorder of Lepidoptera when the Panel was formed and he played a major part in the production of the 'Guide'. A founder member of the Essex Wildlife Trust, he has played an immensely important role in the study and conservation of the wildlife of his native county. He was co-author (with Emmet) of *The Larger Moths and Butterflies of Essex* which appeared in 1985. He remains an active member of the Essex Lepidoptera Panel but has handed the task of county recorder to Brian Goodey who presents the latest status report in chapter 9 of this book.

Chapter 2   MONITORING ESSEX BUTTERFLIES

Monitoring involves some standardised assessment of butterfly populations. A variety of techniques have been used in Essex surveys since 1967 and all have contributed data to this book. The comparisons with years before these standard surveys relies on the information in published studies and checklists: usually accurate as to the species identified but sometimes a little imprecise as to the exact locality and, at best, with subjective abundance indications.

Dot-mapping

The first monitoring technique, by far, was the national Lepidoptera Distribution Mapping Scheme, run from the Biological Records Centre (BRC) at Monks Wood. This collected records from an army of volunteers and produced maps for each species at a 10 km-square scale. The main results are in Heath, Pollard & Thomas (1984) with more up-to-date maps appeared in Emmet & Heath (1989). Although these maps only a broad indication of Essex records, both in terms of grid-squares and groups of years, the original detailed database is maintained so more precise information is available for particularly interesting records.

The national recording scheme wound down after 1984, as BRC concentrated on other groups of organisms, although a second national scheme (run by Butterfly Conservation) started recording in 1995, with a view to producing a Millennium Atlas in the year 2000. The relevant records in this book are being transferred to this new database. The local branch of Butterfly Conservation and the Essex Field Club maintained records of species and local lists submitted by Essex butterfly enthusiasts throughout the 1980s and 1990s.

Butterfly transects

In 1976 a very different kind of monitoring project started where the abundance of butterflies was recorded rather than just their distribution. This used a carefully standardised system of recording and required the surveyed areas to be walked on an identical route twice a month through the butterfly season. This survey method has been the most important of all recent studies of butterfly abundance and has been used, in some counties, for locally based surveys to supplement the national scheme. The results from the areas in the national scheme have been published for 1976-85 (Pollard, Hall & Bibby, 1986) and Pollard & Yates, (1993) for the years to 1991.

Only three of the national monitoring sites are in Essex and that no one has initiated local butterfly transects (often called 'Pollard Walks' to the annoyance of Dr Ernie Pollard who devised the standard technique) for other parts of Essex. In contrast the Butterfly Conservation branch covering Hertfordshire and Middlesex has 38 of these butterfly transects, only one of them part of the national scheme. The Institute of Terrestrial Ecology has generously made available the complete data set for the three Essex sites and the results are summarised in chapter 8.

Essex Butterfly Habitat Survey

During the years 1991-93 roughly a hundred volunteers agreed to take part in surveys in a wide variety of Essex habitats. We considered using the standard 'Pollard Walk' system but rejected it for several reasons:

- It is designed to make comparisons over a series of years, following fluctuations in the indices at single sites.

- It requires regular, twice monthly, visits.

- It does not record what the butterflies were doing when seen.

Instead a system specific for this survey was used, essentially a 'timed count' of butterflies seen in a known length of survey time. The biological and management features of the study site were recorded once during each year while the butterfly numbers and behaviour were recorded during surveys of varying lengths and frequencies, as suited the availability of the volunteer surveyors.

The details of the survey technique should be clear from instructions to recorders reproduced in tables 2.1 and 2.2. By limiting records to ten individuals of any species, the surveyor was given time to search for and record the less common species, rather than spending too much time recording hundreds of the common ones. In general the technique worked well and has provided data for the tetrad maps and flight-time graphs as well as information on butterfly behaviour (see chapter 4) and key features of the sites.

Essex Garden Butterfly Survey

For 1991-92 the Essex Wildlife Trust (EWT) co-operated in promoting a regular survey of garden butterflies to its large membership. This was extraordinarily successful in attracting over 500 EWT members to make weekly records of the butterflies in their own gardens (from 1 April to 30 September each year). The technique was especially designed for this survey as it had to take account of the fact that many of the participants were not butterfly experts and that the time spent counting the butterflies in gardens was likely to vary from week to week and garden to garden.

Table 2.1 The standard habitat survey form

Essex Butterfly Habitat Survey. *Use this form on your first visit to the survey area but add to the foodplant list if extra species are identified on later visits.*

Name & address

Name of survey site   **Approx size (ha.)**

Grid ref. of centre of site

Nature of main habitat management (*tick one only*)

☐ Nature reserve   Country park ☐

☐ Roadside verge   Agricultural land ☐

☐ Other use (Give details)

Habitat and land uses noted (*tick as many as are present in the survey area*)

☐ Broadleaf wood   Conifer wood ☐

☐ Mixed wood   Sunlit glades or rides ☐

☐ Pheasant rearing   Heathland ☐

☐ Scrub thickets   Hedgerows ☐

☐ Orchards   Close-mown amenity grass ☐

☐ Permanent grazing   Hay meadows ☐

☐ Sea walls   Saltmarsh ☐

☐ Open water   Chalk pit ☐

☐ Gravel pit   Steep slopes ☐

☐ Arable land in use   Set-aside ☐

☐ Cattle   Sheep ☐

☐ Horses

Foodplants noted (*tick all species noted growing within the survey area*)

☐ Oak trees (*Quercus* spp)   Elm trees (*Ulmus* spp) ☐

☐ Alder buckthorn (*Frangula alnus*)   Purging Buckthorn (*Rhamnus cathartica*) ☐

☐ Holly (*Ilex* spp)   Ivy (*Hedera helix*) ☐

☐ Blackthorn (*Prunus spinosa*)   Honeysuckle (*Lonicera periclymenum*) ☐

☐ Violets (*Viola* spp)   Nettles (*Urtica dioica*) ☐

☐ Sorrels (*Rumex acetosa/acetosella*)   Cow-wheat (*Melampyrum pratense*) ☐

☐ Lady's smock (*Cardamine pratensis*)   Garlic Mustard (*Alliaria petiolata*) ☐

☐ Hedge mustard (*Sisymbrium officinale*)   Birdsfoot Trefoil (*Lotus corniculatus*) ☐

☐ Wild strawberry (*Fragaria vesca*)   Creeping cinquefoil (*Potentilla repens*) ☐

Please take habitat photographs if possible or add other notes

Every member of the Essex Wildlife Trust received a full-colour wall chart of Essex butterflies which was intended to aid identification as well as promoting conservation of garden butterflies. Recorders were also encouraged to use a standard identification text (Thomas, 1986) and to record uncertainties as 'whites', 'skippers' etc. rather than to guess. The standard recording instructions are given in table 2.3.

Problems of identification by inexperienced recorders were not completely eliminated by these methods, but overall the standard of recording was excellent. Records from those reporting two or more extremely unlikely species in their gardens or several species at 'impossible' times of the year were eliminated from the detailed analysis and mapping of the data.

Table 2.2 The recording form for the timed butterfly counts

Your Name		**Survey site name**			
Date of visit				**Time survey started (hrs/mins)**	
Sun	☐ sunny	☐ warm	☐ average	☐ cool	☐ cold
Wind	☐ still	☐ breeze	☐ light wind	☐ moderate	

Do not start the survey in the rain, very cold or windy conditions. Stop surveying if the weather gets bad during the survey.

Butterfly Species ....Time 1st.......Behaviour codes.................Time 10th

..../...... ☐ ☐ ☐ ☐ ☐ ☐ ☐ ☐ ☐ ☐...../......

..../...... ☐ ☐ ☐ ☐ ☐ ☐ ☐ ☐ ☐ ☐...../......

..../...... ☐ ☐ ☐ ☐ ☐ ☐ ☐ ☐ ☐ ☐...../......

etc. (real form had more species spaces)
Nectar plants noted

Flower species	Butterfly sp 1	Butterfly sp 2	Butterfly sp 3
....	....	....	....

Behaviour codes - use the first non-flying behaviour observed.:
[R]esting - sitting, not feeding, wings closed
[B]asking, wings open, not-feeding
[N]ectaring - from a flower
[E]gg-laying (only if egg observed being laid)
[C]opulation (i.e. mating pair)
[T]erritorial, courtship or other behaviour involving another butterfly (same sp or not)
[M]ud-puddling, drinking from damp soil, pond-edge or dung
[H]oneydewing - drinking something from surface of living leaf
[F]lying - for the whole period observed

Note time of first and tenth sighting of each species and ignore sightings from 11 onwards.

In that the maximum number of a species seen at one time in each week was recorded, the survey resembles the BTO Garden Bird Survey. This method helps reduce the variations resulting from different amounts of time spent in the gardens. A few people misinterpreted these results and clearly recorded total counts for each week: producing figures that could not possibly have been seen at one time. These records were used for the tetrad dot maps but excluded from the analyses of butterfly abundance.

This garden survey produced very high levels of enthusiasm amongst previously inexperienced students of butterflies and it is intended to repeat the survey soon. It is recommended to groups in other counties, not only as a way of studying garden butterflies, but of increasing Butterfly Conservation membership at the same time.

The National Garden Butterfly Survey

The national run by Butterfly Conservation since 1990 provides an interesting contrast with the Essex survey. The main difference in methodology is that

Table 2.3 The standard instructions for weekly recording in the Essex garden butterfly survey.
Type of garden: 1. Normal small gardens in town or village next to other gardens 2. Larger gardens surrounding houses in countryside settings (¼ acre or more) **Nectar plants**: the form gives a list of likely species. Please tick any which flower in your garden this year and add a tick in the second column if you see butterflies visiting the flowers. **Caterpillar foodplants**: tick each species which you have in your garden and tick the second column if you notice caterpillars feeding. **Butterfly records**: keep a note of which butterflies you see in your garden each week. It doesn't matter how long you spend watching in the garden. Note on the form, for each species and for each week, the highest number of butterflies you see in your garden *at any one time*.

butterflies are recorded on a presence or absence basis only, so there can be no measure of abundance. On the other hand the habitat information was recorded in more detail, noting the proximity of a range of other habitats to the garden and which species of butterfly visited which species of nectar plant. The national survey, being restricted almost entirely to Butterfly Conservation members, benefits from a higher level of identification expertise amongst its surveyors but may suffer even more than the Essex survey from the 'self-selection effect'. Gardens belonging to butterfly enthusiasts are likely to be specifically managed to attract butterflies and thus record more species and individuals than is typical of gardens in general.

Details for Essex gardens in the National Garden Butterfly Survey for the years 1994-96 were generously made available by Dr Margaret Vickery. The results of the national survey are available (Vickery, 1995 & 1997) and there are some comparisons with the Essex survey in chapter 3.

Chapter 3   GARDEN BUTTERFLIES

There are some 526,000 gardens in Essex plus another 292,000 in the London boroughs north of the Thames and east of the Lea (once part of Essex and traditionally included in the Essex for biological survey purposes) (Office of Population Census, 1993). For Essex alone these total about 21,000 ha and cover almost six percent of the land surface: slightly more than all the woodland in Essex. For 'Essex in London', gardens are the largest area of land not covered in tarmac. Thus gardens are potentially very important butterfly habitats and were the subject of an intensive survey in 1991-92 (see chapter 2 for the methodology).

Gardens fall into two very distinct types: those surrounding country properties: usually fairly large and close to other habitats, and those in urban and suburban areas which are smaller and usually close only to other gardens, roads and buildings. The national survey showed that the numbers of butterflies seen was linked to the number of other habitats close by (Vickery, 1995). The Essex garden survey was conducted by self-selected volunteers mainly from the membership of the Essex Wildlife Trust. Surveyors categorised their gardens into one of the two broad categories and, unsurprisingly, the larger rural gardens had more species (average 13–16) and individual butterflies seen than the suburban ones (average 10–13 species). In the survey 26% of gardens were classified as larger, rural ones: a much greater percentage than the proportion in Essex as a whole. This is because Essex Wildlife Trust members represent a higher proportion of the population in country than in town areas. Thus our survey overstates the importance of gardens for butterflies somewhat: this bias is also clear in the data for Butterfly Conservation's national study.

The most certain way of seeing more butterflies in your garden is to move to a country house with a larger garden. Obviously this is not a very helpful conclusion and the survey data were subjected to multivariate analysis to tease out the effects of size of garden from those factors under the control of the gardener: the types of nectar plants and the available foodplants for caterpillars. A scientific paper is in preparation which will give full details of the analytical method and results; here it is sufficient to summarise the key results.

Nectar plants

Allowing for garden size, the number of most of the commoner species seen was greater in gardens with certain popular nectar plants than those without. Table 3.1 lists the 'popular' nectar plants in terms of those gardeners reporting seeing butterflies on them. The only nectar source whose presence was associated with greater numbers of several species of butterflies, was *Buddleia* (Table 3.2). Because the Essex survey was the first to use actual counts of butterflies seen and systematic reporting of the use of nectar plants this is the first survey able to prove the importance of *Buddleia*, although it is far from unexpected.

An important point to note is that the nectar plants visited most are all late flowering and attract the late summer butterflies: the abundant second generations of whites and the pre-hibernation vanessids. Butterfly gardeners should also grow early season nectar sources even though, numerically, few butterflies use them. They are used by spring species like the orange-tip.

The national survey recorded which butterflies preferred which flowers, something not done in the Essex survey. This study has just been published (Vickery, 1997) and favoured plants are given in the species accounts (chapter 8).

Table 3.1 The percentage of surveyed Essex gardens which grew each nectar plant (columns 1 and 2) and the percentage of those where butterflies (of any species) were observed making use of them (columns 3 and 4).

%	Flowers Planted	%	Flowers used
85	Buddleia	89	Buddleia
74	Lavender	63	Ice Plant
69	Ice Plant	60	Red Valerian
67	Aubretia	60	Michaelmas Daisy
62	Michaelmas Daisy	59	Lavender
60	Wallflower	55	Marjoram
59	Honesty	51	Scabious
42	Golden Rod	48	Hyssop
36	Rockrose	43	Aubretia
34	Candytuft	41	Teasel
33	Yellow Alyssum	41	Hawkbit
32	Scabious	38	Oxeye Daisy
30	Red Valerian	37	Centaurea
28	Bugle	37	Golden Rod
28	Oxeye Daisy	35	Candytuft
18	Centaurea	33	Salvia
18	Teasel	33	Honesty
16	Salvia	30	Rockrose
15	Hyssop	29	Wallflower
15	Red Clover	29	Betony
15	Marjoram	27	Yellow Alyssum
6	Hawkbit	27	Red Clover
4	Betony	13	Bugle

Larval foodplants

The survey asked for reports of larval foodplants present but the reports of grasses have not been used in the analysis because of variable accuracy of identification. Records were also requested for sightings of caterpillars on the plants, but these are likely to include moth larvae as well as those of butterflies: these data have not been used.

Table 3.2 indicates those species where the presence of the larval foodplant made a significant difference in the numbers of butterfly seen. The message is fairly clear: the common garden butterflies are mobile species that visit gardens for nectar and mostly breed elsewhere. These common species certainly can and do breed in gardens but the hatching adults then become part of the mobile population and do not add to the numbers seen in their home garden. It is also instructive to look at the flight-time graphs for the individual species in chapter 8. Nearly all species peak later in gardens than in the countryside; suggesting they visit gardens late in life having bred elsewhere.

Table 3.2 Those plants significantly associated with seeing higher numbers of butterfly species in the Essex garden survey.

Butterfly	Nectar Plant	Larval foodplant	Habitat plant
Small Tortoiseshell	Buddleia		
Peacock	Buddleia		
Comma	Buddleia		
Comma	Valerian		
Red Admiral	Buddleia		
Orange-tip	Betony		
Small Heath	Red Clover		Sorrels
Brimstone		Buckthorns	
Small Copper		Sorrels	
Common Blue		Birds'-foot Trefoil	

Two of the rarer garden species show a clear increase in numbers seen if their foodplant is present: the brimstone (alder buckthorn, *Frangula alnus* or purging buckthorn *Rhamnus cathartica*) and the small copper (sheep's sorrel, *Rumex acetosella* or common sorrel, *Rumex acetosa*). The caterpillars of both species are well camouflaged and unlikely to be spotted; it is not even certain that the extra butterflies bred on the garden foodplants, they may simply have been attracted to the garden by the presence of possible egg-laying sites but then did not successfully breed there. Either way, the implication is that you will be more likely to see these two species in your garden if you grow their foodplants.

Hibernating butterflies

For those species which hibernate as adult butterflies (which includes all the most beautiful, common garden species) there is a clear indication that they use gardens most in the late summer. After hibernation the proportion in non-garden habitats is higher. (See the flight-time graphs for small tortoiseshell, peacock, comma and brimstone in chapter 8).

The most obvious interpretation of this is that the butterflies are using garden nectar to fatten-up for hibernation and disperse to seek egg-laying sites outside gardens in the spring. Several detailed scientific studies have shown how important nectar feeding in autumn is in increasing winter survival (see review in Corke, 1991) Gardens may thus make a major contribution to the survival of these common but attractive species. The extent to which garden buildings and woodpiles are important as actual hibernation sites has not been investigated but small tortoiseshells and peacocks frequently use outbuildings and these may be their main hibernation site. There is room for further investigation of this and experiments with special butterfly hibernation boxes would be worthwhile as these could avoid the high mortality of butterflies in garages when they are disturbed in mid-winter or get trapped on awakening in spring.

Localised butterflies

At the start of the Essex Butterfly Action study ten Essex species were identified as needing special surveys to locate their habitats and assess their conservation needs (the

Table 3.4 The percentage of total sightings in the Essex garden and non-garden surveys. Those species shown in italics occur mainly in non-garden habitats. An asterisk indicates 'rare and localised' species as defined by Pollard & Eversham, (1993)

Species	Gardens	Non-gardens
Large White	21.1	8.2
Small Tortoiseshell	19.5	4.9
Small White	17.6	6.3
Peacock	11.4	3.9
Gatekeeper	6.5	12.3
Red Admiral	4.3	0.9
Holly Blue	3.7	1.0
Meadow Brown	3.6	17.2
Orange-tip	2.3	2.4
Comma	2.3	1.3
Green-veined White	1.6	5.0
Brimstone	1.2	0.9
Common Blue	1.0	6.8
Speckled Wood	0.7	6.2
Wall	0.7	0.5
Painted Lady	0.7	0.2
Small Skipper	0.6	3.8
Small Heath	0.5	4.4
Essex Skipper	0.5	3.9
Small Copper	0.4	1.0
Large Skipper	0.3	2.9
Ringlet	0.3	1.8
*White-letter Hairstreak	<0.1	0.7
*Purple Hairstreak	<0.1	0.6
*Brown Argus	<0.1	0.4
*Green Hairstreak	<0.1	0.3
*Marbled White	<0.1	0.3
Clouded Yellow	<0.1	<0.1
*Pearl-bordered	0.0	0.5
*Heath Fritillary	0.0	1.4
*Grizzled Skipper	0.0	0.1
*White Admiral	0.0	0.0
*Grayling	0.0	0.0

nationally rare and localised species indicated in table 3.4). It is clear that these species are essentially not garden species and cannot benefit from garden butterfly conservation. Their survival will only be assured by conservation management in the countryside and especially in nature reserves.

Conclusions

Gardens are important in keeping common species common and bringing them in close contact with humans who enjoy seeing them. The results of this survey suggest that specific 'butterfly gardening' activities do provide a measurable increase in the numbers and variety of butterflies using gardens.

The future of butterfly gardening

All existing butterfly gardening books concentrate on the provision of nectar sources and larval foodplants. It is possible that hibernation site provision could also be important.

Perhaps it is worth drawing a lesson from what has happened with flower gardening: most garden flowers are non-native species and many are of specially bred varieties, large-flowered, unusual colours and often sterile, certainly unknown in the wild. Butterfly gardening has helped increase the proportion of native flowers grown in gardens (even though some of the best nectar plants are non-native).

A different sort of butterfly gardening is beginning: the rise of the 'butterfly house': a greenhouse zoo to breed and display exotic species. This became a multimillion pound industry in Britain (Collins, 1987). There were three such commercial houses in Essex in 1987 (now only one remains) and some private ones created by enthusiasts in garden greenhouses. These do nothing, positive or negative, for butterfly conservation but create popular displays. Could they indicate that butterfly-gardening might go the way flower-gardening went a century ago, with artificial breeding of unusual specimens?

It is important that butterfly gardening remains what it is: a means of attracting *wild* butterflies to visit or breed in managed gardens.

Chapter 4   BUTTERFLY BEHAVIOUR

Introduction

The surveys of non-garden butterfly habitats from 1991-93 produced a great deal of information on the behaviour of butterflies. The relative abundance of each species and the flight times (for comparison with the equivalent data from the garden survey) are included in the species accounts in chapter 8. In addition to this information, the activity that each butterfly was engaged in was noted. Where this activity was nectar-feeding then the species of flower being used was also recorded.

Activity

Very often, when a butterfly was first seen, it was flying. In this case, surveyors were asked to watch it and record the first thing it did when it stopped flying. Only if it continued to fly for more than 30 seconds, or disappeared from view, was its activity recorded as flying.

The proportion of observations which were simply 'flying' varied greatly from species to species but this seems to have more to do with the method of observation than any real differences in the time spent in flight. Some species (e.g. brown argus and the skippers) are nearly impossible to identify until they stop flying: thus few were recorded as being in flight. Conversely, brimstones and male orange-tips are easily recognised at a distance in flight and a high proportion of these species were recorded as in flight.

It is the differences in the time spent on non-flying activities that are interesting and reflect real differences in the behaviour of the species. These data are summarised in table 4.1. Records of the activities of over 18,000 individual butterflies must make this one of the largest ever such studies. Butterflies were classed at rest when they were sitting with their wings together and not feeding. Some butterflies will warm themselves while in the sun in this position (e.g. the small heath) and almost never bask with wings apart. Others (the vanessids for example) spend a lot of their time basking.

The amount of time spent nectaring varied greatly. Of those that spend little time feeding from flowers, some (e.g. the small heath) seem to take little food of any sort, while others, make up for it by drinking honeydew (e.g. the purple and white-letter hairstreaks).

Table 4.1 *Rest*ing is with wings closed, *Bask*ing with wings open, *Nect*aring feeding from flowers, *Egg* laying, *Mat*ing includes only observations of paired butterflies not courtship behaviour, *Territ*orial behaviour includes any form of interaction with another butterfly, *Mud*-puddling is drinking liquids from damp soil and *Honey*dew feeding is taking aphid excrement from leaf surfaces. *N* is number of observations.

Species	rest	bask	nect	egg	mat	territ	mud	honey	N
Small Skipper	15.0	21.7	56.3	0.1	1.4	5.4	0.2	0.0	1025
Essex Skipper	19.0	21.8	56.0	0.3	1.2	1.5	0.3	0.0	1028
Large Skipper	10.8	43.8	35.8	0.0	0.3	9.4	0.0	0.0	758
Grizzled Skipper	2.2	69.6	23.9	0.0	0.0	4.3	0.0	0.0	46
Clouded Yellow	33.3	0.0	0.0	0.0	0.0	66.6	0.0	0.0	3
Brimstone	24.0	4.0	51.0	0.0	0.0	20.0	1.0	0.0	100
Large White	14.2	10.6	57.5	0.4	0.4	16.4	0.4	0.0	925
Small White	21.2	15.1	50.7	0.1	2.0	10.0	1.0	0.0	1133
Green-veined White	21.1	17.7	46.3	0.4	4.4	8.8	1.4	0.0	1125
Orange-tip	14.0	17.1	38.4	2.7	1.6	25.6	0.8	0.0	258
Green Hairstreak	62.2	11.1	8.9	13.3	0.0	4.4	0.0	0.0	45
Purple Hairstreak	38.3	14.8	0.0	0.0	1.2	24.7	0.0	21.0	81
White-letter Hrstk	29.2	0.9	21.2	0.0	0.0	11.5	0.0	37.2	113
Small Copper	8.4	38.6	48.1	0.0	0.5	4.3	0.0	0.0	391
Brown Argus	7.4	56.8	34.7	0.0	0.0	1.1	0.0	0.0	95
Common Blue	13.3	29.7	41.7	0.2	2.5	12.6	0.0	0.1	1089
Holly Blue	28.4	22.9	21.6	1.8	0.9	15.6	8.3	0.5	218
Red Admiral	13.7	45.0	34.3	0.4	0.0	5.5	0.7	0.4	271
Painted Lady	7.8	19.6	56.9	0.0	0.0	15.7	0.0	0.0	51
Small Tortoiseshell	5.7	34.1	52.0	0.4	0.2	6.7	0.7	0.2	1365
Peacock	7.7	39.8	45.5	0.2	0.0	6.4	0.4	0.0	1126
Comma	9.7	52.9	28.1	0.4	0.0	8.0	0.2	0.7	537
Pearl-brd Fritillary	10.2	13.6	72.9	3.4	0.0	0.0	0.0	0.0	59
Heath Fritillary	11.6	56.3	25.0	0.0	0.0	5.4	1.8	0.0	112
Speckled Wood	15.3	62.2	3.1	0.1	0.5	18.4	0.4	0.1	1271
Wall	10.2	48.5	30.1	0.5	0.0	9.2	1.5	0.0	206
Marbled White	10.3	20.5	46.2	0.0	5.1	12.8	5.1	0.0	39
Gatekeeper	23.0	29.2	39.3	0.1	0.9	6.7	0.5	0.4	1738
Meadow Brown	36.8	17.0	34.6	0.3	1.1	9.8	0.3	0.1	2183
Small Heath	61.2	6.9	16.4	0.0	0.8	14.6	0.1	0.0	988
Ringlet	32.8	34.7	22.1	0.0	1.1	8.8	0.0	0.4	262

The low numbers of observations of mating pairs of butterflies and of egg-laying is probably partly a result of butterflies being less easy to see when engaged in these activities.

Most species spent a small proportion of their time drinking liquid from damp soil (mud puddling) but this seems an important aspect of the behaviour of holly blues and marbled whites. The sex of the butterflies engaged in mud puddling was not noted but published studies show that it is almost always the males that do this.

Perhaps, in view of the discussion of the possible links between honeydew feeding and the affects of air-pollution (see chapter 5) the data on honeydew feeding is especially interesting. It is well known that this is the main source of food for the canopy-living hairstreaks and that some other species combine nectar and honeydew feeding. Butterflies feeding in the tree canopy on honeydew are much less easily observed than those at nectar, so the figures in the table probably understate the importance of this activity.

Those species already known to make use of honeydew were observed to do so in this survey plus a few casual uses of this food by those that are normally nectar specialists.

The feeding records of the ringlet are especially interesting, very little has been written about the behaviour of ringlets and it is generally assumed that they are nectar-feeders. This is despite the fact that they have the very short tongues characteristic of those species that use honeydew. This study is the first record of honeydew feeding by ringlets although Rob Souter in Hertfordshire (personal communication) has observed that they spend a lot of time in the canopy. Combined with the few observations of ringlets nectaring, I believe this indicates that the ringlet is a true honeydew feeder, combined with nectar-feeding, in the same way that gatekeepers do.

Nectar sources

Although there are many publications that have noted 'favourite' nectar sources few of these have been quantified outside of the garden environment. A total of 3253 butterflies from 29 species were observed at nectar. Between them they visited 113 species of wild flowers but the great majority of these plants had few records of visits. It is important to emphasise that this could be simply because some 'attractive' plants are rare as no measure was made of the abundance of potential nectar sources.

Although such a wide variety of flowering plants were visited the great majority of visits were to very few plants. The most popular eight species received 60% of all visits.

Name	ss	es	ls	gs	br	lw	sw	gw	ot	gh	wh	sc	ba	cb	hb	ra
Thistle, Cr.	43	35	15		4	39	43	26			2	15		24		1
Bramble	20	11	30		2	23	34	46	1		9	9		2	14	11
Knapweed B.	34	34	14		1	34	16	21				2	1	18		
Ragwort	14	14	3			12	18	18				24	4	18		1
Fleabane	11	10				4	9	8				8	3	23		
Birds'ft Tref.	15	12	4				3	1	1				4	61		
Buttercup	3	2	4	4		6	6	8	2			2		14	2	1
Clover, Red	29	13	8	1	3	1	3	1						8		
Dandelion	1	4			4	5	6	11	4					1		
Campion, R.			1		3	12		4	10					1		
Stitchwt G.							4	8	6					1		
Bugle					2		2	1	5			2				
Bluebell					4	2		4	1						1	
Garlic Must.						1	1	3	8							
Lady's Smk							2	3	6							
Cow-wheat	1								1						1	
Groundsel																
Holly															2	
Visits to top 18 flowers	171	135	79	5	23	139	147	163	45		11	62	12	170	20	14
Visits to 113 flower spp	253	195	138	5	37	231	257	284	75	1	11	94	13	244	27	22
No. plant spp visited	33	29	34	2	18	46	50	62	25	1	2	27	5	43	12	12

Table 4.2 (above and opposite page) Plants visited for nectar by butterflies. This table includes the ten most visited plants plus those plants which featured in the top three choices of any species (except the green hairstreak where the single observation was of a visit to hawthorn). The butterflies are indicated by the initial letters of their English names, key on next page.

These popular flower species were popular with practically all the butterflies observed. It is worth noting that these important nectar sources are virtually all 'weeds' reviled not only by gardeners but also in many cases by the managers of nature reserves.

Latin Name	pl	st	pe	co	pb	hf	sd	wb	mw	gk	mb	sh	ri	visits
Cirsium arvense	4	65	30	7			5	2		72	81	7	2	522
Rubus fruticosus	2	16	8	29		11	6	4		77	95	2	12	474
Centaurea nigra	1	3	18				1	7	5	16	45	4		275
Senecio jacobaea	1	30	8				2	6		61	23	6	1	264
Pulicaria	3	13	7	1			1	2		20	12	4	2	141
Lotus corniculatus	1							3		1	1	2		109
Ranunculus spp		5	1		3		1			2	10	11	2	89
Trifolium pratense		2							2	2	7	1		81
Taraxacum		19	15	3							2	1		76
Silene dioica			1	2			1				2			36
Stellaria holostea			2	1			1					1		24
Ajuga reptans					10									22
E. non-scriptus				5			1							18
Alliaria petiolata			1											14
Cardamine				1										12
M. pratense						8								11
Senecio vulgaris						4								4
Ilex ilex														2
Visits to top 18 flowers	12	157	95	41	10	26	13	28	9	251	278	39	19	2174
Visits to 113 flower spp	18	231	149	58	10	30	18	36	12	319	375	83	27	3253
No. plant species visited	12	42	31	15	1	8	12	14	6	34	55	29	11	113

Table 4.2 Key to species codes used in column headings

ba	Brown Argus	hf	Heath Fritillary	ri	Ringlet
br	Brimstone	ls	Large Skipper	sc	Small Copper
cb	Common Blue	lw	Large White	sd	Speckled Wood
co	Comma	mb	Meadow Brown	sh	Small Heath
es	Essex Skipper	mw	Marbled White	ss	Small Skipper
gh	Green Hairstreak	ot	Orange-tip	st	Small Tortoiseshell
gk	Gatekeeper	pb	Pearl-bordered Frit.	sw	Small White
gs	Grizzled Skipper	pe	Peacock	wb	Wall Brown
gw	Green-veined White	pl	Painted Lady	wh	White-letter
hb	Holly Blue	ra	Red Admiral		

Chapter 5   THE CAUSES OF BUTTERFLY DECLINE

Habitat specific butterflies

Butterflies come in two broad groups as regards their ecology and habitat requirements. Those said to have 'open' populations are very mobile and will colonise any suitable new habitats. The extremes of this type are those (like red admirals) that migrate to and from Europe in the course of their annual cycles. These species typically depend on plants ('weeds') that grow in temporary habitats and gardens and obviously their biology requires that the adult butterflies search out new habitats as the population would be doomed if they remained in a changing habitat that would be unsuitable for them in a year or two.

The other group have 'closed' populations and rely on habitats that normally stay the same for many years if not centuries. Their strategy is to stay where they hatch on the grounds that if the habitat was good for them when they were caterpillars it will be good for their offspring too. It is not true that 'closed' population species never disperse and find new habitats but they do so more rarely. Their survival is best where a collection of small populations exist close enough together for there to be some interchange of individuals and recolonisation of a site that for some reason has lost its population. These complexes are called metapopulations and seem to be almost essential for the long-term survival of closed population species.

Lost species in and around Essex

Essex, like all the counties of eastern England and the adjoining continent of Europe, has lost a very high proportion of its butterfly species. Nearly all the lost species are in the closed population group and in the national 'rare and localised' category of Pollard & Eversham (1995).

Table 5.1 summarises the status of all those species which once bred in eastern England with the exception of the twenty species designated as nationally "common and widespread" by Pollard & Eversham (1995) These are widespread in all the regions and are indicated in table 3.1

Lost 'open population' butterflies

Two of the extinct species, the black-veined white and the large tortoiseshell are a real mystery, from what is known of their ecology in southern Europe where they remain fairly common, they seem to have fairly open populations. Not only have they become extinct in Essex and eastern England but have gone from the whole of Britain. They did so at quite different times and yet their habitats seem still to be available. I have included some theories about the cause for their decline in the individual species accounts (chapter 8) but the truth is that no-one knows enough about their ecology to say why they disappeared. I think it is probable that their larval ecology is important: they have furry caterpillars that live gregariously in webs in trees or shrubs. This is a rare strategy: no other butterfly and only three moths do the same and one of those, the small eggar, is practically extinct in Britain. This strategy must render the caterpillars especially susceptible to birds. It is noticeable that the two moths that seem to make a success of this strategy (the brown-tail and the lackey) have warningly coloured caterpillars.

Air pollution and butterflies

Two other species with fairly mobile populations also became extinct in Essex (the comma and the speckled wood) as they did from much of England. In both cases they recolonised naturally in the middle of this century after many decades of absence. I believe that the fact that these two species drink honeydew as adults may have a lot to do with this disappearance and recolonisation: this is a new theory and the more widely held explanations for the decline and re-expansion of these two species are given in the species accounts (chapter 8).

It has often been suggested that air-pollution could have been a factor in the decline of butterflies but, while calling for more research on the topic, most experts have dismissed the idea for the following reasons:

- the loss of some species near cities can be explained in other ways.
- if air-pollution is important why does it not affect all species?
- no-one has demonstrated how air-pollution might affect butterflies.

Clearly air-pollutants are deposited generally in polluted areas. Almost all butterfly caterpillars eat leaves on which pollutants must fall but tend to select the youngest, most nutritious, leaves which are likely to carry a low pollution load. Adult butterflies most usually feed on nectar which carries no air borne pollution since it is secreted in protected nectaries and consumed within a few hours of production. Some butterflies feed partly or mainly on honeydew, the sugar-rich fluids excreted by aphids, which coat the leaves of plants with a high aphid population. Most of these honeydew feeders will also take plant sap which exudes from the trunk of some trees. Both these sources of sweet liquids are consumed by the butterflies from surfaces (mature leaves, bark) that will have accumulated sooty deposits in air-polluted areas. Thus these species are at potential risk if toxins dissolve into the honeydew and sap-runs.

Epping Forest in the extreme south-west of Essex and close to London has suffered from high levels of air-pollution. The type of pollution most likely to

Table 5. 1 Status chart for butterflies which have bred in eastern England; in Essex, the surrounding counties and adjacent European states. For the Netherlands and Flanders the standard Red-data codes are used (e**X**tinct, (**S**everely) **T**hreathened, **V**ulnerable, **R**are, **A**t risk, **N**ot **T**hreatened) and for the English counties my own assessment of current status based on recent publications (e**X**tinct, **L**ocal, re-**I**ntroduced, **W**idespread). Data from local lists mentioned in Introduction plus Tax (1989), Maes & Dyck (1996) and Swaay & Plate (1996) for the Low Countries.

Latin Name	Essx	Suff.	Cam.	Hert.	Lon.	Kent	NL	Flan	English Name
C.palaemon		X					T	V	Cheq. Skipper
H.comma	X	X	X	X	L	X	V	T	Silver-sp Skipper
E.tages	X	L	L	L	L	L	ST	X	Dingy Skipper
P.malvae	L	L	L	L	L	L	T	T	Grizzled Skipper
P.machaon	X	L	X(I)		X		En		Swallowtail
L.sinapis	X	X	X	X	X	X	X	ST	Wood White
A.crataegi	X	X	X	X	X	X	X	X	Black-veined Wh.
C.rubi	L	L	L	L	L	L	V	V	Green Hairstreak
T.betulae	X	X	X	X?	X	X	T	T	Brown Hairstreak
Q.quercus	W	W	W	W	W	W	W	W	Purple Hairstreak
S.w-album	W	W	W	W	W	W	W	W	White-letter Hstk
L.dispar			XIX				ST		Large Copper
C.minimus	X	X	X?	L	L	L	X	R	Small Blue
P.argus	X	L	X		L	X	V	V	Silver-st. Blue
L.coridon	X	X	L	L	L	L	X	X	Chalk-hill Blue
L.bellargus	X	X	X	X	X	L	X	ST	Adonis Blue
C.semiargus	X	X	X	X	X	X	X	ST	Mazarine Blue
M.arion		X			X		X		Large Blue
H.lucina	X	X	X	L	L	L			Duke of Burgundy
L.camilla	L	L	L	L	L	L	V	V	White Admiral
A.iris	X	X	X	X	X	X	T	T	Purple Emperor
N.polychloros	X	X	X	X	X	X	T	T	Large Tort.
B.selene	X	X	X	X	X	X	T	ST	Sm. Pearl-brd.Frit.
B.euphrosyne	X	X	X	X	X	L	X	X	Pearl-brd. Fritillary
A.adippe	X	X	X	X	X	X	X	X	High Brown Frit.
A.aglaja	X	X	L	L	L	L	T	ST	Dark Green Frit.
A.paphia	X	X	X	L	L	L	X	ST	Silver-washed Fr.
E.aurinia	X	X	X	X	X	X	X		Marsh Fritillary
M.cinxia		X			X	X	ST		Glanville Fritillary
M.athalia	X(I)	X	X		X	L	T		Heath Fritillary
M.galathea	L	X	L	L	L	W	X?	R	Marbled White
H.semele	X(I)	L	X	X	L	L	E	V	Grayling

affect honeydew-feeding butterflies is the deposition of particles (soot) on leaves. This reached a peak in the late 19th century at the height of domestic coal burning, and when suburbia had spread along the new railway lines close to the Forest. It declined dramatically well before the smogs of the 1950s and the Clean Air Act as people switched to more convenient electric and gas heating throughout the 20th century (Brimblecome, 1987).

Table 5.2 shows convincingly I think the different patterns of extinction, survival and recolonisation of Epping Forest by honeydew and non-honeydew-feeding butterflies.

- All the honeydew feeders, except the migratory red admirals and holly blues, became extinct in the Forest at or before the time of peak air pollution.

- Five species (probably the most mobile) have already recolonised the Forest, and they did so once air-pollution levels had declined.

- Three species appear to have suitable habitats in the Forest still but have not recolonised yet. Two of these (purple emperor and brown hairstreak) have no remaining colonies outside the Forest from which they could conceivably do so naturally. The other (ringlet) is advancing slowly southwards towards the Forest and is likely to recolonise soon.

- In contrast almost half (15 of 31 species) of non-honeydew feeders have survived in the Forest.

- Non-honeydew feeders which became extinct did so at times related to fairly obvious habitat changes and in six cases this happened after 1940 in conditions of low air-pollution.

- Only one of the non-honeydew feeders has recolonised the Forest.

Some experiments with speckled woods are underway to check directly whether polluted honeydew affects survival and/or fertility but these are at a very early stage. In the meantime, the above circumstantial evidence seems quite a strong case for the importance of air pollution in the survival of honeydew feeding butterflies near London.

Climate and weather

There has been much concern and debate about the influence of climate on butterflies (e.g. Dennis, 1993). The evidence (mainly from the National Butterfly Monitoring Scheme Data (Pollard & Yates, 1993), is convincing that variations in weather can greatly influence the numbers of butterflies seen; either immediately or in the subsequent season. There is also some evidence that longer-term trends in climate can lead to expansions or contractions in the range of butterflies.

Table 5.2 The extinctions and re-colonisations of Epping Forest and adjacent woodlands by honeydew and non-honeydew feeding butterflies. The honeydew feeders are those generally recognised to feed wholly or partially on honeydew (Porter et al., 1992; Thomas & Lewington, 1991) plus the ringlet which I judge to be a honeydew feeder based on the evidence in chapter 4. The status information is given in full in Corke (1996). The extinction decades are those after which there were no acceptable reports of breeding. The recolonisation decades are based on evidence of breeding not sightings of singletons.

Honeydew feeders	Extinct.	Re-colon.	Extinct non-honeydew feeders	Extinct.	Re-colon.
Brown Hairstreak	1900s		Dingy Skipper	1950s	
Purple Hairstreak	1900s	1960s	Grizzled Skipper	1950s	
White-letter Hairstreak	1840s	1970s	Swallowtail	1820s	
Holly Blue	n/a	n/a	Wood White	1840s	
White Admiral	1840s	1940s (ext. again 1950s)	Black-veined White	1840s	
Purple Emperor	1880s		Silver-studded Blue	1900s	
Red Admiral	n/a	n/a	Brown Argus	1900s	1990s
Large Tort.	1900s	no evidence of breeding	Chalk-hill Blue	1890s	
Comma	1820s	1930s	Duke of Burgundy	early 19th C	
Silver -washed Fr.	1870s	1940s (extinct 1950s	Small Pearl-bordered Fr.	1900s	
Speckled Wood	1890s	1960s	Pearl-bordered Fr.	1940s	
Grayling	1870s		High Brown Fr.	1920s	
Gatekeeper	1900s	1960s	Marsh Frit.	1870s	
Ringlet	1890s		Heath Frit.	1840s	
			Marbled White	1890s	

As far as Essex is concerned, these long-term climate effects are unlikely to be important. All our remaining species are in the middle of their European range in Essex and are far from the northern limit of their British range. All occur abundantly in the south of France or even further south in Europe. Thus global warming (or even cooling) will have a long way to go before it eliminates our remaining butterflies directly.

Climate change might, perhaps, bring us butterflies we do not have at present: it may be that more southerly species will colonise Essex if global warming continues. The likeliest candidate is the map butterfly (*Araschnia levana*) which has spread widely in Europe over the last few decades and is now very common in the Netherlands. It would be a lovely addition to the Essex (and British) butterfly fauna but pessimists will note that no species of butterfly has ever colonised Britain in recorded history although the geranium bronze (*Cacyreus marshalli*) may be in the process of colonising Sussex.

Changing habitats

The great majority of habitat-specific butterflies have become extinct in Essex and they have done so for reasons that relate directly to changed patterns of land-use leading to changed habitats.

Table 5.3 classifies the butterflies of Essex (past and present) in terms of their main habitats. The message is horrifying: ALL Essex butterflies with specialist requirements for coppice woodlands, heather heathlands, chalklands and damp environments have become extinct! Our only survivors, apart from the extreme generalists, are those that require shady or mature woodlands, gorse heathland, coastal grasslands or hay meadows maintained in nature reserves.

Coppice and pollard woodlands

About 5.7% of Essex is woodland (20,933 ha) and this percentage has not changed all that much over the last two centuries. The 5.7% is divided as follows: 3.5% ancient broadleaved woodland, 0.2% ancient woodland converted to conifers and 2.0% secondary woods, either deliberately planted or arising from scrubbing over of heathlands and abandoned plotlands (Essex Wildlife Trust surveys). Deliberate clearing of ancient woodlands (mainly by farmers) this century amounted to 930ha and this was considerably exceeded at the end of the last century when the majority of Hainault Forest was destroyed along with many smaller areas. Even so, the amount lost is more or less balanced by the secondary woods gained. A study of the first large scale map of Essex (Chapman and André, 1777) shows that most woods present then are still here today and more or less the same size.

Table 5.3 Essex butterflies with specialist habitat requirements. In two cases the same species appears in both the heathland and chalkland categories.

Coppice woodlands	Only few hundred ha in scattered conservation woodlands
Small Pearl-bordered Fritillary	Extinct 1950s
Pearl-bordered Fritillary	Extinct 1960s
High Brown Fritillary	Extinct 1950s
Dark Green Fritillary	Extinct 1950s
Silver-washed Fritillary	Extinct 1950s
Heath Fritillary	Extinct 1890s, re-established at 3 sites
Duke of Burgundy	Extinct 1920s
Wood White	Extinct 1880s
Mature woodlands and wood edges	**Habitat increasing, and air-pollution levels lower**
Purple Hairstreak	Widespread
Brown Hairstreak	Extinct 1900s
White-letter Hairstreak	Widespread, may be expanding
Purple Emperor	Extinct 1890s
White Admiral	2 colonies (increase of 1 1996)
Speckled Wood	Greatly expanded
Ringlet	Expanding slowly
Chalk Grassland	**Only left in (threatened) chalk-pits**
Grayling	Doomed 1997
Silver-spotted Skipper	Extinct 19th C
Mazarine Blue	Extinct 19th C
Chalk-hill Blue	Extinct 19th C
Adonis Blue	Extinct 19th C
Small Blue	Extinct 19th C
Silver-studded Blue (*P.argus cretaceus*)	Extinct 1960s
Heathlands	**only 17ha left**
Grayling	Extinct 1990s
Silver-studded Blue (*P.argus.argus*)	Extinct 1940s
Coastal Grasslands	**well preserved**
Marbled White	Expanding
Fens/Marsh/Damp Grasslands	**Mostly drained**
Marsh Fritillary	Extinct 1870s
Swallowtail	Extinct early 19th C.

From the butterflies' point of view, it is not loss of woodland area that has been the problem but cessation of coppicing and pollarding.

Until the middle of the last century practically all the smaller woods were coppiced to provide the fuel wood for the surrounding villages. The larger woods, which had been part of the medieval royal forests of Epping, Hainault, Hatfield, were managed as wood-pastures and pollarded to provide firewood.

Three major changes occurred which together eliminated coppicing and pollarding almost completely:

- in the 19th century some small woods became game coverts as interest in blood sports increased. Coppicing ceased in these woods.

- late in the 19th and early in the 20th century the remaining large blocks of woodland passed to public ownership for access and conservation. Pollarding and coppicing were abolished.

- during the 20th century, but especially after the 1940s, reduced availability of farm labour and increased ease of availability of non-wood fuels meant that coppicing was abandoned in the smaller woods, where it had continued into this century.

The increasing shade in these woods eliminated most of the ground flora and all of the specialist butterflies which needed not only the flora but the warm, sunny microclimate of an open woodland structure.

All this is now well known to conservation bodies and the accepted wisdom is that conservation woodlands should have the historic pattern of management, coppice or pollarding, restored wherever possible. About a quarter of all woodland in Essex is owned by conservation charities or local authorities as access/ conservation land. Were most of this woodland to be restored to active traditional management butterflies could return.

Although there are many examples of woods being coppiced for conservation and two small experiments with pollarding (in Epping and Hatfield forests) the total area under active management is small and unknown. The Essex Wildlife Trust, the most active and enthusiastic proponent of coppicing for conservation, has so far managed to restart coppicing on only 14% of its 480 ha of woodland nature reserves, but the figure for Essex woods in general is unlikely to be over 5%.

Even with such limited amounts of coppicing, it has been possible to restore the heath fritillary to two (probably three or four when you read this) coppice nature reserves. Provided coppicing is done in a large enough area of woodland, so that species a little more mobile than the heath fritillary can set up metapopulations, conditions would again be right for the return of some other species: this is discussed further in chapter 7.

Mature woodlands

Without exception, the butterflies that specialise in the canopy of trees or in the shadier parts of woodlands are honeydew feeders. The probable influence of air-pollution on these species has already been discussed. Mature woodlands exist in plenty, some of them in very large blocks. Most of the butterflies characteristic of this habitat are widespread or spreading in Essex. Those that are not are probably absent because of their inability to recolonise from their nearest remaining habitats, than for any shortcoming in the Essex woodlands.

Heathlands

The most recent landcover statistics for Essex show that only 17 ha of heathland remains and this is classed as 'dense': only about 5 ha of true heather heathland survives.

Proper open heathland dominated by heathers and heaths, can only develop on very freely draining soil and was a product of tree clearance and intensive (common) grazing centuries ago. A study of Chapman & André's map (1777) shows that there were very large blocks of heathland:

* north of Colchester (lost to agriculture and building)

* south of Colchester (some remaining in military hands but scrubbing over)

* around Tiptree: the remaining section ploughed in the Second World War but a small area now restored and managed. The only proper heathland left in Essex

* the Danbury/Lingwood Commons: still all common land but now mainly secondary woodland and furze

* in the Mill Green (Fryerning) area (still common land but scrubbed over)

* in parts of Epping Forest (now mainly birch-dominated wood but with some restoration work started)

A total of many hundreds of hectares.

For the heathland subspecies of the silver-studded blue it is destruction of theoretically 'protected' heathlands through unchecked scrub invasion, rather than intentional conversion of heathlands to other uses, that caused its extinction.

Some (but far from all) of the gorse-dominated heathlands have good populations of the green hairstreak.

Chalklands

The extreme north-west of Essex once had chalk downs grazed by sheep much like the classic Chiltern downlands of which they were the northern extremity. These were ploughed up and converted to arable in the first half of the 19th century: an early destruction which led to an equally early disappearance of all the chalk grassland species from this part of Essex. The other tiny area of chalk was in the south, around Grays, where it was extensively quarried, the old quarries exposing much more chalk habitat than had been there naturally. A few of the chalk specialists lingered longer there, the chalk loving subspecies of the silver-studded blue being the last to go as its chalk-quarry habitat scrubbed over after quarrying ceased.

The only really immediately practical way of restoring habitats suitable for chalk grassland species is by management of abandoned chalk quarries. There are several of these in the north-west of Essex, of historical and botanical interest, but not one has yet become a nature reserve nor even been declared an SSSI. In the south, Grays Chalk Quarry is now a nature reserve and could become increasingly important in butterfly restoration projects but other quarries in this area are being destroyed for building, in one case eliminating the last known grayling colony.

Coastal grasslands

The coastal grasslands behind the sea-walls are of major ornithological and botanical significance and have suffered greatly from agricultural changes. But as butterfly habitats these grasslands are of little importance: it is the drier grasslands on the sea-walls themselves and on natural slopes close to the sea (as at Hadleigh Downs) that are important. These are the main habitat of the marbled white in Essex: a habitat very different from those in most parts of its English range. These coastal grasslands also have good numbers of less restricted species such as the common blue and may be important for the survival of the wall brown at times now it has become rare in other parts of its range.

There is some dispute about the present conservation management of many lengths of sea-wall grassland by sheep grazing. Research is needed to judge the intensity of grazing that gives a suitable balance between the needs of different species of wildlife.

Wetlands

The early drainage of river valley wetland habitats removed all the original habitats of swallowtails (fen and marshland), and the marsh fritillary (water meadows) leading to their very early extinction in the county.

Hay meadows

Until the 1950s Essex, like the rest of England, had an agriculture that was mainly horse-powered. Thus hay was needed even in arable areas (to feed the plough-horses) as well as in the stock-rearing areas. The need for hay has declined dramatically and what is grown comes from heavily 'improved' fields with minimal wildlife interest. Almost all the remaining flower-rich meadows, with their associated fauna of mainly fairly common butterflies, are in nature reserves or public access land. The sole remaining native colony of grizzled skippers in Essex is in one large complex of such meadows at Langdon Hills, an Essex Wildlife Trust reserve.

Ants

It is slowly being realised how important are ants in the ecology of many butterflies. All the British members of family Lycaenidae have caterpillars which attract ants with the aid of special organs and most have been shown to secrete special sweet liquids from honey-glands for their ants. The pupae, too, of many species, can attract ants and most have sound producing organs which seem to be involved in the complex ant/pupa interactions (Brakefield et al., 1992)

Many Lycaenids are known to have symbiotic relationships with a limited range of ant species and it is likely that this is a general phenomenon. We know little of the influence on Essex butterflies of the range and numbers of ants that are available in their habitats but the influence is likely to be great.

Ants are not just symbionts, they are potential predators: since ants of many species can kill caterpillars. In Essex, there were concerns that wood ants (*Formica rufa*), themselves an endangered species, might adversely affect the re-established heath fritillaries. Some preliminary studies by undergraduate students working with English Nature have shown that the reverse is the case:

- Wood ants seem to be very important in transporting and encouraging the germination of cow-wheat seedlings (the foodplant of heath fritillary caterpillars).

- Although wood-ants pick-up and kill moth caterpillars of many species, when young heath fritillary larvae were offered they picked them up and immediately dropped them unharmed. Presumably the caterpillars have an ant repellent taste.

- It is notable that all the Essex woods that have (or had) heath fritillary populations have high wood-ant populations. Perhaps they are a necessity rather than a threat.

Finally, wood-ants can and do kill adult butterflies. It was noticed that many grizzled skippers released in the cool of the evening and in light drizzle, settled as soon as released and were immediately attacked by wood-ants. Butterflies released when warm and active seemed able to select roosting sites where the ants did not attack.

- A great deal more research is needed on ant/butterfly interactions.

Birds and butterflies

I once published a paper that discussed the possibility that pheasant rearing and release was a significant factor in the decline of those woodland butterflies whose larvae or pupae lived at ground level (Corke, 1989). It was not a new idea, the suggestion had first been made at the end of the 19th century. Partly in reaction to my paper a study was carried out involving the release of overwintering pearl-bordered fritillary larvae into woods with and without pheasants. Caterpillar survival was no worse where there were pheasants. This means that, on the available experimental evidence, pheasants do not seem to be important in the decline of woodland butterflies.

Many insect eating birds eat butterfly caterpillars and there have been some suggestions that bird predation may harm butterfly populations. For this to be true it would require that either the birds had switched diets or become more abundant since times when the butterflies and birds coexisted. It is known that many bird populations have declined on intensively farmed land (where butterflies are few for other reasons) but to have increased where winter feeding has decreased natural winter mortality. There are no studies that I know of which have attempted to measure the effect of small bird predation on butterflies.

In conclusion

In this chapter I have attempted to summarise the state of knowledge regarding the causes of extinctions and decline of some butterflies in Essex. The use to which this knowledge might be put, in restoring lost species or preventing the loss of others, is discussed in chapter 7.

Chapter 6   **RE-ESTABLISHMENTS OF LOST SPECIES**

The deliberate release of butterflies (or some stage in their life-cycle), in the hope that a locally extinct species will be restored, is a re-establishment attempt. Release of species not once present in a region is an introduction attempt and these are not considered a valid conservation activity. Carefully planned re-establishments on the other hand are potentially an important part of restoration ecology and can sometimes be very successful.

Of the species that have been lost from the whole of Essex none has ever recolonised as a result of deliberate habitat management to favour the butterfly. As far as I know this statement holds good for species lost from any English county. Two species have recolonised naturally (comma and speckled wood) as part of a national re-expansion in their range for reasons which are not known (but see the discussion in the previous chapter). Re-establishments have a low rate of success (only one species has been restored to Essex on a long term basis as yet) but there have been few really carefully planned attempts.

The purpose of this chapter is to put on record those re-establishment attempts which have been made and also those unofficial introductions about which anything is known.

Oates and Warren (1990) produced the only national review of butterfly introductions in Britain. They detailed eight attempts covering four species for Essex although one of these species was included in error (the silver-washed fritillary) and several other attempts were omitted. In addition, there have been several attempts since 1988 (the cut-off date for their survey).

Table 6.1 summarises all the serious attempts at butterfly re-establishments in Essex.

Excluded from this table are two releases of speckled woods, one in Epping Forest in 1956 (Anon. [Corke], 1961) and the other in Friday Wood in 1986 (clandestine, Davis & Corke, 1992) which both seemed to have failed. This is interesting in that speckled woods re-colonised each area naturally a few years after the releases, as part of the species' general re-expansion across Essex.

Also excluded are two reported releases at Debden Green: of black hairstreaks (a non-native of Essex) and heath fritillary (a non-native of the north-west of Essex). These are both described by Allfrey (1975) but the late author had no recollection of them in 1991 shortly before his death. Neither species established a colony.

Table 6.1 Summary of known butterfly re-establishment attempts in Essex. See text for further information and references.

Species	Re-establish-ment site	Donor site	Year of re-lease	Stage and numbers released	Duration of colony	Under auspices of
Grizzled Skipper	Little Baddow Heath	Fairmile &, Rewel Wood, Sussex, Chattendon Woods, Kent	1994 & 1996	wild collected adults, 4f, 4m 1994; 13f 15m,1996.	extant but weak	BC/EWT
Swallow-tail	Epping Forest	?	1848-50	adults	Failed	H. Doubleday
Sm.Pearl -brd Frit.	Belfairs Great Wood	?	1937	?	to 1948	H.C. Huggins
Pearl-bord Frit..	Little Baddow Heath	Rewel Wood	1990	39 wild caught adults	to 1994	BC/EWT
Heath Frit	N E Essex Wood	?	C19th	?	"several years"	Harwood: see Fitch, (1891)
Heath Frit.	Belfairs Great Wood	"Kentish stock"	1925	?	to 1964	?
Heath Frit.	Belfairs Great Wood	captive stock	1983	66 adults	failed	M. Warren
Heath Frit.	Hockley Woods	"Kentish"	1935	?	to 1950s	?
Heath Frit.	Hockley Woods	Thrift Wood	1987	Wild caught adults: 20 f; 18m	extant	Rochford DC/ BC/EWT
Heath Frit.	Thrifit Wood	Blean Woods, Kent	1984	Adults; 31 f, 22m.	extant	M. Warren
Heath Frit.	Belfairs Great Wood	Thrift & Hockley Woods	1997	wild collected adults, c40	new	EN/ Castle Point DC
Heath Frit.	Pound Wood	Thrift/Hockley Woods	plann ed for 1998			BC/EWT

Marbled White	Martins Farm	Ashton Rowant NNR	1987	Adults, 24f, 15m	1988	ITE/ECC
Marbled White	Woodham Mortimer	Folkestone (Downland)	1989	Adults, 17f 22m	until mid 1990s	T. Filbee
Marbled White	Bradwell Brook	Bred stock	1989	About 400 eggs	until mid 1990s	EWT
Grayling	Friday Wood	Rendelsham Forest, Suffolk	1986	Adults, 19f, 33m.	failed	clandestine
Grayling	Martins Farm	Winterton Dunes NNR	1987	50 adults	failed	ITE/ECC
Grayling	Grays Chalk Quarry	Mill Wood Pit	1996 -97	Adults & turf	Some seen 1997	EWT/ Chafford Hundred

Grizzled Skipper

Little Baddow Heath had a colony of grizzled skippers that became extinct early in the 1960s. Following management to restore the wood/heathland nature of part of the habitat it was decided to test whether it was now suitable for grizzled skipper. The only remaining natural Essex colony was neither strong enough to act as a donor site neither was it ideal in terms of habitat (since populations in heathy woodlands may be genetically different from those in grassland). Therefore donor sites in Sussex and Kent were used under English Nature licence.

The first year (1994) only four females were caught and translocated (although one adult was sighted the following year) and so the attempt was repeated in 1996 using larger numbers of adults from two sites, collected and released a week apart. On both occasions light drizzle was falling when the adults were released on the evening of collection day. The butterflies quickly settled but at the time of the second release several were observed being attacked and killed by wood ants. Those butterflies which could be found were re-caught and held until the following day for release in full sun. It was feared that the ant-kill may have caused failure or the re-establishment but a small number of progeny appeared in 1997.

Time will tell if the colony survives but clearly the relationship between wood-ants and grizzled skippers needs to be investigated. Wood-ants existed in similar density at Little Baddow Heath before 1960 when grizzled skippers occurred there naturally (G.A. Pyman, personal communication).

Swallowtail

There are many casual (illegal) releases of captive-bred stock which cause confusion with sightings of natural immigration of the continental subspecies. The only foodplant of the British subspecies is extinct in Essex. Henry Doubleday (Essex Field Club, 1882) attempted to establish the species in Epping Forest between 1838 and 1840 at a time when there is evidence that the larval foodplant existed in the area. The attempt failed.

Pearl-bordered Fritillary

The last colony of this, the last violet-feeding fritillary to be resident in Essex, became extinct at Little Baddow Heath in 1968. Following the acquisition of the site as an Essex Wildlife Trust nature reserve, habitat management recreated an open heathland glade surrounded by coppiced woodland. Violets (*Viola riviniana*) and bugle (*Ajuga reptans*, an important nectar plant) became more common and a re-establishment attempt was agreed by English Nature as part of the Essex Butterfly Action Plan.

Stephen Davis undertook a detailed study of the re-established colony over its first three years of existence, this resulted in a better understanding of the preferred egg-laying habitats as well as measuring the population numbers through the flight season.

The adults collected for introduction in May 1990 were kept in a cool box and released the following day in sunny conditions. They were observed feeding and egg-laying soon after release. A total of 25 females and 14 males were released, in two groups on 3 May and 11 May: this with the intention of spreading the egg-laying season at the introduction site. The flight-time graphs for 1991 and 1992 is given in chapter 8.

Egg-laying was observed closely over these two years, a total of 53 eggs being recorded. Interestingly 18 were on the larval foodplant (*Viola riviniana*) the rest on a range of 10 substrates: grasses (9 eggs) eight species of living plants (23 eggs) and dry oak leaves (3 eggs). Quadrats containing the egg-laying sites differed from random quadrats in which *Viola riviniana* was growing in that there was a higher density of violets; the violets were, on average, shorter; there was more bare ground, less living grass but more living vegetation of other kinds (all unpublished data courtesy of Stephen Davis).

Weather conditions in spring were good during 1990-92 but a poor spring in 1993 resulted in a low population and only one adult was seen the following year. It was assumed that the area of suitable habitat was insufficient to maintain a colony through years with poor weather, so no further re-establishment is planned unless habitat management very substantially increases the area of suitable habitat.

Curiously, a single adult was seen in 1997 by a reliable observer (who had monitored the species at Little Baddow Heath in earlier years). Whether this means the species has survived undetected beyond 1994 or that the 1997 specimen was a clandestine release remains to be decided. Unfortunately the latter seems more probable since the level of observer effort between 1994 and 1997 was very great.

Heath Fritillary

This species has been the subject of more re-establishment attempts than any other Essex species and all of them have been successful in recent times. It is only as a result of these efforts that Essex boasts two strong colonies (soon likely to be four) and joins Kent as the eastern stronghold of this nationally important species.

The ecological studies that have been made by Martin Warren as part of the national conservation effort for this species, of which these re-establishments are part, are covered in several detailed scientific reports all listed in the recent national action plan for this species (Barnett & Warren, 1995g; Warren, 1991).

The yearly population estimates are given in figure 6.1. The main conclusion from these is probably that a newly established colony 'takes-off' reaching high

Figure 6.1 The yearly population estimates for the two re-established colonies of heath fritillaries in Essex. The estimates are based on a formula devised by Martin Warren that relates the maximum number seen per hour and the size of the flight area to the estimated total population for the year. Data courtesy of Ken Ulrich, Martin Warren and English Nature. Data for Hockley Woods in 1997 not available by press date.

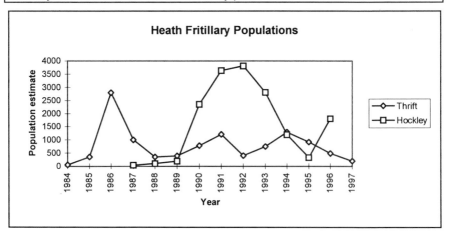

numbers after a few seasons before settling down to fluctuate around a lower average.

The continued coppice management of the woodlands, with new coppice areas being adjacent to old ones for ease of colonisation by this very sedentary butterfly, is vitally important. In all cases where Essex colonies went extinct it is known that this followed cessation of adequate coppicing.

There is every reason to hope that the two existing colonies will continue indefinitely under the current management of the woods as coppice nature reserves. The two additional establishments now under way are close to Hockley Woods and will, collectively, establish the species in a substantial area of protected, coppiced woodlands in what should become a complex of metapopulations.

Marbled White

One of the introductions was butterfly gardening on a grand scale: butterflies were released into a large garden meadow. The colony survived for several years but had already died out before the house-owner had sold his property.

Another resulted from a wish to 'do something useful' with captive-bred stock. This was technically against the policies for establishments on Essex Wildlife Trust reserves but the experiment was given retrospective approval. The colony only persisted a few years and died out at a time when the natural range of the species seems to be expanding towards the introduction site.

The marbled white is native to Essex and these native colonies have shown themselves quite capable of expanding and colonising new habitats. Introducing stock from a different habitat type (chalk downland) and outside the normal Essex range was probably a misguided venture.

The first attempt was part of a grassland restoration project on a disused landfill site (Martin's Meadow, St Osyth) and was part of a valuable scientific experiment concerned with the re-establishment of butterfly-rich grassland on an abandoned landfill site (Davis, 1989). It did not deserve to fail but it only survived a single season.

Grayling

Like the marbled whites, graylings were introduced at Martin's Meadow grassland restoration site with even less success: they did not last a single season.

There may have been several somewhat clandestine releases in and around the Friday Woods/ Berechurch Common area, although I have details of only one in table 5.1. These were close to where natural colonies had become extinct.

(Goodey & Firmin, 1992). Little habitat management had been done and the attempts failed.

The latest attempt is, a last-ditch rescue attempt. In 1994, after the species was believed to be extinct in Essex, Colin Plant and Peter Harvey found a colony remote from the lost heathland colonies of north-east Essex. This was in Mill Wood Pit: an area that proved to be one of the richest entomological habitats in Essex but this was not known until after the area had been given planning permission and surveys were done on behalf of the developer.

The developers are co-operating in conserving part of the area and are financing a translocation of the graylings to Grays Chalk Quarry nature reserve in 1996 and 1997.

This is very recent but (to my mind) the attempt is almost bound to fail: if the habitat were suitable a mobile species like the grayling would have colonised it naturally.

Chapter 7   An Action Plan for Essex Butterfly Conservation

One result of the Essex Butterfly Action project was an action plan making recommendations mainly to Butterfly Conservation and the Essex Wildlife Trust who had both sponsored the study (Davis & Corke, 1992). This was a first as a county action plan and many of its recommendations have been followed up while others have been shown to need alteration in the light of more recent studies.

Since the 1992 action plan, Butterfly Conservation has produced national species action plans for the most endangered British butterflies and is encouraging its local groups to create regional action plans for butterflies, moths and their habitats. Essex will eventually be covered by an Anglian regional plan and the Cambridge and Essex section of that plan is already well advanced (prepared by John Dawson for the Cambridge & Essex branch of Butterfly Conservation).

While it is obviously a good thing to set conservation objectives in the context of the national and regional priorities, the logic of this can sometimes go too far. There have been several criticisms of British conservation bodies for putting so much effort into (for example) the re-establishment of the large blue (*Maculinia arion*) when the species could so much more easily be saved in the rest of its European range where it still survives. British reaction is that the species should both be saved in its remaining European range AND re-established in Britain. Applying the same logic, one can have a conservation plan for Essex within the regional and national context.

The Essex Wildlife Trust has also prepared an action plan for Essex habitat conservation into the next century (Essex Wildlife Trust, 1997).

The purpose of this chapter is to link the plans of Butterfly Conservation and the Essex Wildlife Trust and, in the light of the surveys that this book summarises, to provide a personal view as to how we should focus our efforts for the conservation of Essex butterflies and their habitats.

Species conservation

It is always better to prevent a species population from becoming extinct than to have to re-establish the species once the population (and possibly its habitat) has gone. So the first question for Essex is 'what species do we still have that are in danger and what actions will help conserve them?'

We can use the changing status of butterflies in the counties that surround Essex as a guide to species which are in trouble regionally, or for which Essex has especially important populations. That was the purpose of table 5.1 (page 28). It may seem surprising that this table includes the Netherlands and Flanders (northern Belgium), our neighbours across the North Sea, as well as the English counties which abut Essex. The reasons are twofold: the high human population density, geographical nature of the countryside and pattern of farming make the low countries very similar to our part of East Anglia. We can learn from what is happening there. Also, a very active butterfly conservation organisation (die Vlinderstichting) serves the low countries and has carried out much conservation research that is relevant to Essex. It is worth noting that, although the administrative headquarters of Butterfly Conservation are in Essex, its conservation office is in Dorset: as far from Essex as Wageningen where de Vlinderstichting is based and in a countryside more different from Essex than the Low Countries.

Essex has lost almost all species of butterflies except those that have very open populations: that is the adults are very mobile and can find breeding habitats all over southern Britain. Virtually all Essex butterflies are, on a national scale, literally 'common or garden' species. The exceptions are listed in table 7.1

The priority is thus to identify those species surviving in Essex that are not doing well regionally and attempt to ensure their survival in our county.

Heath Fritillary   **Priority 1**

Although a re-establishment in Essex, the Essex colonies are doing well and are the only ones in Anglia or the Low Countries.

The required actions are:

1. Complete the programme of establishments so that Essex has four colonies, three close together and with the possibility of increasing naturally.

Table 7.1 Surviving Essex butterflies designated as of high or medium conservation priority in the draft regional action plan for Cambridge and Essex (Dawson, 1997) The Essex priority value is my opinion based on the regional list but modified by the status information included in this book.

Species	National	Local	Essex
Grizzled Skipper	M	H	1
Green Hairstreak	L	M	3
White-letter Hairstreak	M	H	3
White Admiral	L	M	2
Heath Fritillary	H	H	1
Marbled White	L	M	2
Grayling	L	H	2

2. Continue with the carefully planned coppice management of the four woodlands and try to extend this to neighbouring ones.

3. Monitor annual populations of all colonies.

4. Conduct detailed investigations on the relationship (probably symbiotic) between wood-ants (also an endangered species at the European level), common cow-wheat (the larval foodplant) and all stages in the butterfly's life-cycle.

5. Use the existing populations, which are all in public access woodlands, as a flagship species for butterfly conservation at the same time as educating visitors about the needs for habitat management.

Grizzled Skipper   Priority 1

A nationally endangered species and nearly extinct in the Low Countries. Essex has one extensive colony protected on an important EWT nature reserve (Langdon Hills) and one re-establishment attempt just underway (EWT: Little Baddow Heath).

Recommended actions are:

1. Review the ecological needs and habitat management of this species when the current study of its ecology of in Sussex is completed and available.

2. Map and monitor the Langdon Hills populations to establish whether it is a low-density single colony or a metapopulation of linked small colonies.

3. Search widely during the flight-period, especially in south-east Essex, in an attempt to locate other Essex colonies.

4. Monitor the success or failure of the re-established colony but not try again at this site if the colony fails.

5. Seek large areas of protected habitat where the current management now seems favourable to this species, with a view to further re-establishment attempts.

6. Encourage scientific study of the ecological relationship between woodland colonies of this species and the wood-ant.

Marbled White   Priority 2

This is a fairly widespread species in chalk downlands of southern England. Its Essex colonies are unusual in that they are centred on coastal grasslands in the extreme east of its English range and thus have some national interest as well as regional importance. The species is absent from most of East Anglia (except a few colonies in Cambridgeshire) and is threatened in the Low Countries.

In Essex it is currently increasing its range although it is still absent from inland sites which it occupied during the 19th century.

Conservation priorities are:

1. Maintain the one monitoring scheme transect on Leigh NNR and try to cover other colonies with new transects or other regular monitoring.

2. Attempt to discover which type of coastal grassland management is associated with the highest population levels of marbled whites in Essex.

Grayling   Priority 2

Although near extinct in Essex (the one known colony about to be destroyed and the associated rescue translocation is unlikely to succeed), graylings are not endangered in coastal Suffolk.

The discovery of this species at Mill Wood Pit just before it was due to be destroyed was a complete surprise and indicates that other colonies may await discovery in Essex.

Once strong colonies on two nature reserves (Colne Point and Fingringhoe Wick) became extinct for reasons that are not really understood: thus acquisition of sites with colonies (even if possible) would far from guarantee the species survival in Essex.

1. Promote a careful survey of possible habitats in Essex, heathlands and more especially abandoned chalk and gravel workings, to locate any surviving colonies BEFORE they are scheduled for destruction.

2. Encourage scientific studies of grayling ecology in Suffolk coastal habitats especially. There have been no detailed studies of this species.

3. Await discovery of the ecological requirements of this species before considering further establishment attempts.

White Admiral   Priority 2

Once widespread, white admirals are restricted to the extreme north-east of Essex. The recent colonisation of Friday Wood (presumably by natural means) is encouraging.

Recent research (Pollard & Cooke, 1994) suggests that browsing of honeysuckle by introduced muntjac deer may adversely affect the availability of preferred egg-laying sites. Muntjac deer are common in most parts of Essex and expanding in numbers and range.

- Continue monitoring the known sites and check sites in the Epping Forest area for possible colonisations.

- Monitor muntjac numbers in the Stour/Copperas Woods area and survey for any damage to foodplants. Depending on the results, it may be important to extend the current muntjac control programme started by the Essex Wildlife Trust in coppice woods in the north-west of Essex (for coppice protection reasons) to the north-east woodlands.

White-letter Hairstreak   Priority 3

The high conservation priority that this species has, nationally and regionally, is probably an error resulting from three factors:

- Under-recording due to its secretive habits leading to a belief that it is much less widespread than is really the case.

- An assumption that Dutch elm disease, by eliminating mature elms, will have caused the species to decline. In fact it can breed on regenerating elm suckers and planted, disease resistant, elms.

- An early error, suggesting that the species had been recorded in less than 100 ten-km squares and thus qualified for 'notable' species status in the English Nature lists.

White-letter hairstreaks are not in danger in any surrounding county and even seem to be increasing in the Low Countries. In Essex it has recolonised Epping Forest but the majority of well-recorded habitats are in the south-east of the county.

In the light of this, the only important conservation action is to continue monitoring the known colonies and surveying to gain a more complete picture of its distribution in Essex.

1. Research to discover the relative importance of its various hosts (flowering native elms, elm-suckers, non-native elms) and the nature and importance of its symbiotic relationship with ants would also be of great potential value.

Green Hairstreak   Priority 3

There are good numbers of colonies in the south-east of the county and more scattered colonies (mainly on nature conservation land) in the Danbury Ridge and Colchester/Fingringhoe region. There is no evidence of decline in these colonies but many of those in the south-east are under threat from building or landfill in the abandoned pits where they are situated. The species is also probably under-recorded.

1. Attempt to make a complete inventory of colonies in the county.

2. Identify sites where the species occurs with other valued insect species and press for these to be protected by official designation or acquisition as nature reserves.

Species but once native to Essex but now extinct

Most of the species now extinct in Essex are also lost or extremely rare in the surrounding regions. They are also mainly species with limited colonisation potential. Thus the restoration of these species requires a combination of habitat management on a large enough scale to create suitable habitats for a long-term viable metapopulation of colonies, followed by the artificial re-establishment of the species in these habitats.

For a large proportion of the lost species one or both of the following problems mean that their re-establishment in Essex can be no more than a very long-term hope:

- Too little is known of the ecology of the species in the habitat types it once occupied in Essex to know how to recreate suitable habitats.

- Recreation of a suitable large complex of habitats would be impractical given the limited resources for habitat conservation work in Essex.

The species which are 'possibles' in terms of ecological knowledge and potential habitat are considered below, grouped by habitat requirements, and prioritised for possible restoration projects.

Mature woodlands

The largest block of mature woodland with a complex of other habitats and entirely devoted to conservation/public access is Epping Forest. This was the haunt of very strong colonies of brown hairstreaks in the 19th century and there is no obvious reason for the loss of this species from the Forest except the possible effects of air-pollution in the past (see chapter 5). The cause of its decline in other parts of England, too frequent cutting of hedgerows, (Barker et al. 1996) does not apply in Epping Forest and large areas of suitable blackthorn are available: sufficient for Epping Forest to become one of the largest colonies of this species in Britain as well as restoring it to eastern England.

I believe that the only reason the species has not recolonised the Forest naturally is that there are no suitable colonies in the region from which this can occur.

The Conservators of Epping Forest have included a restoration project for the brown hairstreak in their draft management plan. Assuming the necessary permission from English Nature is granted, the project will go ahead over the next five years.

The demise of the purple emperor and its failure to recolonise Epping Forest is possibly for the same reason as the brown hairstreak. Provided the brown hairstreak restoration project succeeds (over a minimum of five years) I would recommend attempting a similar restoration of the purple emperor.

Coppice woodlands

The largest group of lost butterflies are those that require actively coppiced woodland. These butterflies vary in their size and mobility and hence the area for a long-term viable colony. The least mobile of all is the heath fritillary and this probably explains the success of its re-establishment in Essex woodlands with, as yet, quite small areas of coppice.

The re-established colony of pearl-bordered fritillaries which died out after a few years of seeming success, seems to have done so because the habitat patch was too small.

Thus, before any more attempts at restoring coppice woodland species are made there needs to be the re-creation of much larger areas of actively coppiced woodland in areas where the woodlands are in a single block or very close proximity and under the control of suitable conservation bodies.

1. At present, no statistics are available on the total number, area and location of actively coppiced woods in Essex. This needs to be remedied urgently.

2. Two woodland blocks seem strong contenders for restoration as coppice suitable for woodland butterflies: the Danbury Ridge and the woodlands in the Southend/Benfleet/Rayleigh triangle. In both cases the woodlands cover a large total area and form tight-knit blocks. They are also nearly all owned by conservation bodies or by local authorities for nature conservation reasons. Coppicing has been restarted in both areas, but on a rather piece-meal basis. A detailed historical survey is available for the south-east Essex woods (Rackham, 1986).

3. If the owning bodies could together create a management plan for the woods in each area and reinstate coppicing over more than 60% of the woodland area; conditions would be right for the restoration of at least the pearl-bordered

fritillary, small pearl-bordered fritillary, duke of burgundy and perhaps the wood-white; although the newly opened-up, de-coniferised woods of north-west Essex may be more suitable for the wood white. The larger fritillaries live at lower densities over wider areas and would be more difficult to restore (and also, being more mobile, natural recolonisation is a possibility).

Chalk pits

Abandoned chalk pits in the Grays area and the extreme north-west of Essex are excellent habitats for butterflies and localised rare plants. The pits of the north-west are old (parish pits for liming fields) and small. Many have been destroyed and none has been protected by SSSI status or acquired as a nature reserve, nor have they adequately been surveyed for butterflies.

Now that it is known that the small blue survives in Cambridgeshire a short distance from the north-west Essex pits, there is a possibility that a thorough survey could locate Essex colonies of this apparently extinct species. For the small blue the priorities are:

1. survey for undetected surviving colonies

2. acquisition for conservation of one or more small pits in the north-west

3. a restoration project into a suitably protected and managed pit.

Grays Chalk Quarry appears to have the right habitat features for the establishment of the small blue, but since the species was never known from the Grays area this is not strictly a 'restoration' project.

Grays Chalk Quarry did have the only population of the chalklands form of the silver-studded blue north of the Thames. The exact location of the original colony is now built over but the nature reserve section may be suitable. Now this form of the silver-studded blue is so rare, availability of donor stock is likely to be a problem.

1. Any restoration attempt should await further ecological studies on the butterfly and the acquisition for conservation of additional chalk pits in the Grays region.

Heathlands

The Essex Wildlife Trust's 'Essex Wildlife 2000' (1996) planning document speaks of the need to increase the 5.5 ha of heathland to 200 ha. If this is anywhere near achieved the opportunity to restore the heathland form for the silver-studded blue will surely exist.

The strongest group of colonies of this butterfly in 19th century was in Epping Forest where management to restore substantial areas of heather heathland is already underway.

- If the current management plans succeed then restoration of the silver-studded blue could well be added to Epping Forest's positive conservation plans.

The last known colony in Essex was on Mill Green Common: part of the historic Writtle Forest. This area has immense historic and ecological importance (Rackham, 1989) as a surviving medieval forest of unusual type and a mixture of ancient, once coppiced, woodlands and common (scrubbed over) heathlands.

- Not a single bit of Writtle Forest is designated as an SSSI, let alone owned or managed by a conservation body. English Nature needs to be encouraged to remedy this state of affairs and see if it is possible to restore Mill Green as real heathland.

Survey and monitoring

The needs for survey work related to particular species conservation have already been discussed. The distribution mapping of the widespread species has been well covered and will be repeated for the Millenium Atlas project. What is much more important is a site-based survey to identify areas with important communities of the more localised butterflies. Unless it is known that an important species is present there is no chance of trying to protect the habitat from loss. The Essex Wildlife Trust has completed a phase one survey of Essex identifying sites of importance for nature conservation (SINCs) which are already used by statutory bodies for planning purposes. This survey was based entirely on botanical survey.

1. Extending the survey of SINCs to cover their butterfly fauna is vitally important.

2. Surveying road-side verges (both minor rural roads and motorways) is needed to measure the importance of these habitats to butterflies. The local authorities have been most helpful in protecting verges identified as of botanical value: provided with the information they would almost certainly be able to contribute to butterfly conservation.

Site acquisition

Apart from the desirability of acquiring one or more chalk-pits, as discussed above, there is relatively little need for new purchases specifically related to butterfly conservation. Better management of the existing sites would be much more effective.

1. Thrift Wood, site of one of the heath fritillary colonies, is leased by the Essex Wildlife Trust. It may come on the market soon, in which case its purchase and long-term safeguard is of high priority.

2. A huge area of new conservation land (Thames Chase Community Forest, in total 9330 ha – it will be the largest area of conservation land in Essex) is being designated to the south of Brentwood. It is important that Butterfly Conservation tries to influence the development plans for this area.

As to the nationally extinct black-veined white, mazarine blue, and large tortoiseshell we should do nothing restoration attempts to Essex until international studies have identified the reasons for their loss from Britain. Releases of captive-bred stock are illegal as well as making study of natural immigration difficult.

Chalkland species lost to Essex

Chalk-hill blue, adonis blue, silver-spotted skipper and small blue and silver-studded blue are in this category.

These will stay absent from Essex unless changes in agricultural policy linked with the re-creation of grazed chalklands in the north-west of Essex. We must wait and see.

In the case of the small blue and silver-studded blue (form *crataegi*) re-establishment trials would be justified in a suitable large chalk-quarry under the management of a conservation body.

Possible colonisers

The map butterfly and, to a lesser extent, the Queen of Spain fritillary have become common breeding, resident species in the Low Countries. The map butterfly in particular could colonise Essex and would find many suitable habitats. Some coastal habitats could be suitable for the Queen of Spain although Suffolk dunelands are much more likely.

- Alert butterfly enthusiasts should monitor for vagrants or colonisers of these species but discourage any illegal release of captive stock.

Chapter 8   ESSEX BUTTERFLY SPECIES

Introduction to the species accounts

All the butterflies which breed, or have bred, in the wild in Essex are included, together with those which have been recorded as natural migrants to Essex without having bred in the county. They are listed in the standard systematic sequence. For the great majority of species the information given follows a standard pattern.

Name

The English and scientific name is given. The checklist of all Essex butterflies and moths (chapter 9) gives the authorship details for the scientific names and these are not repeated here. In the checklist the species are arranged in the most recently accepted taxoonomic sequence but for the butterflies in this section I have retained the sequence found in most current butterfly identification guides.

Status

This gives a short indication of the current and past status of the species (range, abundance and status as a breeding species).

Survey percentages

For the two major Essex surveys (gardens 1991-92) and rural habitats (1991-93) a percentage of sites where the species was recorded is given, together with a percentage of individual butterflies of all species representing the species under discussion. It is hoped that these figures will add some useful information to the status account, but it is important to remember that the numbers of butterflies can change dramatically from year to year. For example, had the surveys been made in 1996 the painted lady would have been one of the most widespread and abundant species.

Most of the non-garden habitats are protected environments of some sort (nature reserves or country parks) and this will have inflated the counts, compared with the farmland habitats that cover most of Essex. The garden sites were all checked weekly over the complete season but this does not apply to the non-garden survey, where some species present at a site will have been missed.

Habitats and larval foodplants

For the most part this section is based on national information from Thomas & Lewington (1991), except where it is made explicit that the reference is to Essex.

History and distribution

This section refers only to Essex and that part of London east of the Lea and north of the Thames which forms part of Essex for biological recording purposes. It compares published early information, mostly from Fitch (1891) and Harwood (1903), with the situation today. For species where changes have been great the timescale of changes is traced by reference to intervening publications.

Conservation needs

In the case of widespread and common species this section is often omitted as there are no special conservation needs. In other cases the amount of detail varies greatly depending on the level of knowledge and degree of endangerment of the species.

Biology

For those species which have been the subject of detailed ecological studies these are referred to and, in some cases, very brief summaries given. This section is intended to help conservation managers and those interested in butterfly gardening.

Butterfly gardening

A brief indication of the chances (and methods) of attracting the species to visit or breed in gardens; based mainly on the Essex garden survey but supplemented from national studies.

Distribution map

These are tetrad maps (i.e. each symbols covers 2 km by 2 km). For the commoner species only records made in the 1990s are included, garden and countryside records being distinguished. For rarer species all records are included and the map keys give details of the symbols.

Flight-time graphs

For comparability, these are based on the records from the 1991-92 garden and rural habitat surveys.

Butterfly Monitoring Scheme Data

Three sites in Essex have been monitored every year since 1983 as part of the national Butterfly Monitoring Scheme (BMS). An asterisk means that counts were missed at the normal flight-time for that species, so no estimate is possible. The figures should be used to give an indication of general trends in the abundance of each species, not as a measure of absolute numbers. These data are used courtesy of the Institute of Terrestrial Ecology. Two of the sites were used as rubbish dumps before being managed for conservation. The sites are:

1. Leigh National Nature Reserve – along and behind the seawall of Two-tree Island, previously a rubbish dump and sewage farm.

2. Stour Wood – 54 ha of diverse chestnut coppice woodland. Owned by the Woodland Trust and managed in association with the RSPB.

3. St Osyth – Martins Farm, a land-fill site restored to grassland and monitored for butterfly colonisation (Davis, 1989).

Small Skipper   *Thymelicus sylvestris*

Status

Resident, colonial but colonies are widespread; common within its colonies.

Rural sites 61%; individuals 4.2%   Gardens 23%; individuals 0.6%

Habitats and larval foodplants

Nationally Yorkshire fog (*Holcus lanatus*) the most important foodplant but some other grasses are used more rarely. The small skipper is found even in habitats with small patches of the foodplant if they are left to grow as tall clumps: roadside verges, wood edges, wild gardens and rough grasslands are important in Essex.

History

Fitch (1891) noted it "common throughout especially in marshes". Although the association with marshes and damp grasses is not particularly obvious today, it may have a slight preference for damper habitats than the Essex skipper. It is found in urban areas as well as rural ones and is probably almost as common as ever it

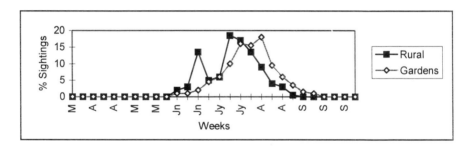

Note: this table combines data for Essex skippers and small skippers. These two species are not distinguished in the BMS.

Site/Year	83	84	85	86	87	88	89	90	91	92	93	94	95	96
St Osyth	76	38	32	71	236	386	560	84	1126	784	938	124	51	19
Stour Wood	26	38	46	26	*	10	38	33	75	81	16	54	31	66
Leigh Marshes	355	138	188	363	395	109	*	128	703	158	239	290	435	140

Small Skipper

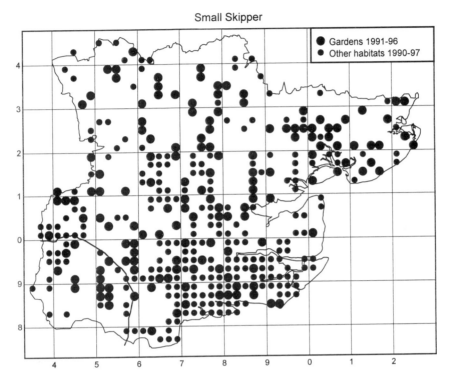

was: the lost hay meadows and pastures would not have been suitable; only the reduction in the length of hedgerows represent lost habitat.

Conservation needs

No special needs, except that management of wide roadside verges by reduced cutting would favour this species.

Butterfly gardening

Small skippers were reported from gardens, although it is not known how often this indicates breeding in the gardens and how often it means a colony near the garden. Males hold territories associated with nectar-plants often a little distance from the egg-laying sites. It should be possible to create suitable conditions in larger gardens by planting a patch of Yorkshire fog (at least 2 m^2) in sunlight and let the grass grow into tall clumps. Only cut the grass in May or June and cut it long. Leave the cut grass in situ for a few days so any caterpillars can decamp to fresh grass. This advice is based on the known ecology of the species: reports on the success or otherwise of actual experiments would be most interesting.

Essex Skipper   *Thymelicus lineola*

Status

Resident, colonial but colonies widespread; common within colonies.

Rural sites 55%; individuals 3.5%   Gardens 15%; individuals 0.5%

Habitats and larval foodplants

Nationally a variety of grasses are used, mainly cocksfoot (*Dactylis glomerata*); while, in contrast to the small skipper, Yorkshire fog (*Holcus lanatus*) is avoided. Despite using a different range of foodplants small and Essex skippers often fly

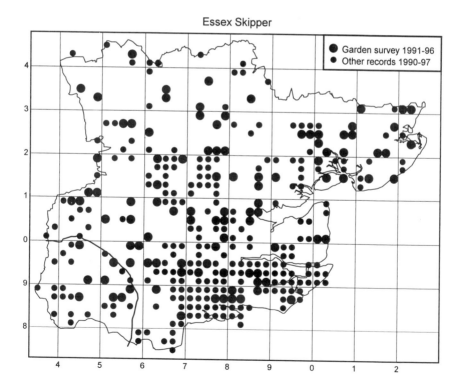

Essex Skipper

● Garden survey 1991-96
● Other records 1990-97

together in the same site, although the Essex skipper may prefer somewhat drier habitats.

History

The Essex skipper was the most recent species of butterfly to be discovered in England: from St Osyth in 1889 (Hawes, 1890). It is sometimes suggested that this species was widespread at the time of its discovery (e.g. Thomas & Lewington, 1991) and that it was its similarity to the small skipper that led an erroneous assumption that it was restricted to the Essex coastal area. As far as Essex is concerned this is not true. The discovery caused considerable excitement and there were many reports by the following year (Fitch, 1891), all of them from the coastal regions from Harwich to Southend except for specimens collected near Stansted in 1885-88 by Spiller (1890) from clover fields, in an area where the species was known to be absent in 1874-76. Its discovery was reported in the *Essex Naturalist*

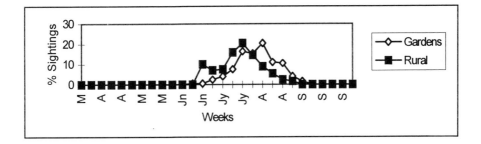

(Anon., 1890). The many lepidopterists of that time would surely have examined their specimens: but none were reported from inland areas, other than Stansted, until 1949 in the Brentwood area (de Worms, 1949).

It was not reported from Epping Forest until the 1950s (Anon. [Corke, 1961]). Publications of skipper records by Mera (1929) and Pinniger (1945) are likely to have reported this species had it been present when they were recording in the Forest. Plant (1987) quoted Buckel & Prout (1899) as reporting this species from Forest Gate in 1899: this is a misinterpretation as Buckel & Prout were referring to the large skipper by its old name of *Erynnis sylvanus* (Corke, 1996).

The records are consistent with the species being mainly coastal in its distribution at the time of discovery and having been spreading in Essex since before its official 'discovery'. There are many plausible explanations for this spread: the species may newly have colonised Britain; it may have benefitted from drier agricultural soils as land drainage increased or it may have been transported as eggs in grass-stems when hay began to be carried longer distances by road and rail. This was the case in north America, where the species was introduced and spread rapidly in this way; Scott (1986). Spiller's early records of these skippers suddenly appearing in farm fields in the east of the county at some time between 1876 and 1885 is consistent with this suggestion.

Conservation needs

None: it seems to be able to make good use of roadside verges and embankments and is more abundant and widespread than was known in the past.

Butterfly gardening

The same comments apply as for the small skipper: except that the grass species needed is different.

Silver-spotted Skipper   *Hesperia comma*

Status

Localised resident in 19th century, now extinct.

Habitats and larval foodplant

This species requires well-grazed downland with the larval foodplant, sheep's fescue (*Festuca ovina*), growing next to small patches of bare ground. A well-studied species, the ecology and detailed scientific papers being summarised in the Butterfly Conservation action plan (Barnett & Warren, 1995a).

History

The map in the Butterfly Conservation action plan erroneously indicates that this skipper was never present in Essex. The first published record for Essex (Fitch, 1888) simply lists the species as "rare, Danbury" but this was later explained as "three, Danbury, 2nd August 1884" (Fitch, 1891). Since this species is almost always associated with calcareous downland, which Danbury certainly is not, this is an improbable habitat. Emmet et al. (1985) say that Firmin et al. (1975) challenged the authenticity of this record but this is not the case: Firmin et al. give the records without comment. Fitch's record was subsequent to Raynor's (1884) report that this species was "...absent [from Maldon area], but may possibly occur at Danbury". Taken together, these reports suggest that the record may be genuine and represented a resident population in the Danbury area. Fitch was a competent and respected local naturalist based in Maldon and the author of the first detailed account of Essex butterflies. He would have known his species: although the possibility that he was defrauded by a commercial butterfly salesman giving an erroneous locality must always be considered.

The reports from north-west Essex are vague but entirely believable since they are from the Saffron Walden district which, at the time, included grazed chalk downland in the Cam drainage basin. Joseph Clarke, then trustee of the Saffron Walden Museum, reported to Fitch (1891)) "there are five specimens in the 'old collection' all caught in this neighbourhood". This collection bears no data labels and the associated accession books give no locality data. The 'old collection' was commenced in 1834 and continued until about 1880.

There is a report of an old published record from the Grays area but I cannot find the details (see Emmet et al.,1985). Again this is a chalk area and the record is entirely believable.

Finally, the only report this century is a female specimen in the H. Mace collection (Harlow Museum) labelled: "Hallingbury 29 vii 1926". Emmet et al. (1985) suggested that this might have been a vagrant from the (then) breeding colonies in Hertfordshire.

Future

Suitable chalk downland habitats have not existed for over a century and are unlikely to do so again unless a dramatic change in farming policy occurs, although conservation farming could re-create low-input grazing lands on the north-west chalk. Even then, natural colonisation is unlikely since the species is extinct in Hertfordshire, Cambridgeshire and Suffolk.

Large Skipper   *Ochlodes venata*

Status

Resident, widespread but colonial, common within colonies.

Rural sites 57%; individuals 2.5%   Gardens 13%; individuals 0.3%

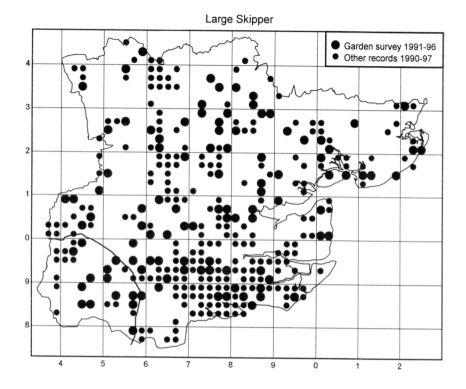

Large Skipper

Habitats and larval foodplants

Large skippers live anywhere that long, tussocky grass is allowed to grow uncut. They are found slightly more often in woodlands than the small and Essex skippers but also on rough ground and roadside verges. The main foodplant in most habitats is cocksfoot, *Dactylis glomerata*.

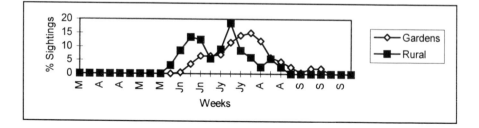

Site/Year	83	84	85	86	87	88	89	90	91	92	93	94	95	96
St Osyth	0	0	0	0	1	0	6	0	*	4	5	7	3	0
Stour Wood	9	27	3	3	50	14	26	29	17	18	18	10	26	37
Leigh Marshes	39	9	8	18	44	18	16	4	1	0	2	2	*	1

History

"Common and generally distributed in the uplands and woodlands; more common than the Small Skipper" (Fitch, 1891); "the most generally distributed species of the family and is common everywhere.." (Harwood, 1903). Today this species seems slightly less common that the small skipper but it is still just as widespread.

Conservation needs

The large skipper is not endangered and has no special conservation needs. Like the other grass-feeding skippers it has probably benefitted from the roadside verges of major roads.

Butterfly gardening

It is believed that garden sightings usually represent wanderers from nearby non-garden colonies. It is quite likely that breeding colonies can occur in larger gardens if areas of tussocky cocksfoot are permitted.

Dingy Skipper   *Erynnis tages*

Status

Recently extinct: the final Essex colony, at Berechurch, has produced no sightings since 1990 (Goodey & Firmin, 1992).

Habitats and larval foodplant

The caterpillars eat only birdsfoot trefoil (*Lotus corniculatus*) which needs to be fairly bushy since the preferred egg-laying height is 2-10 cm. The adults require patches of bare ground for basking and a supply of dead flowerheads (from the previous year) such as knapweed (*Centaurea nigra*) on which they roost.

Dingy Skipper

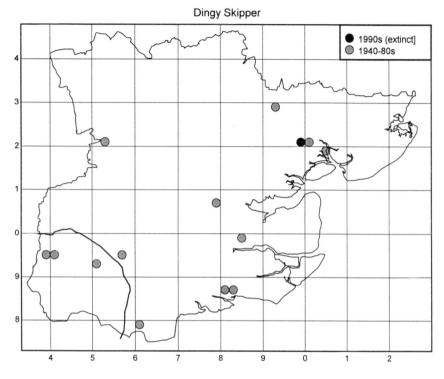

History

This has always been a localised and fairly rare species in Essex. Colonies occurred mainly on freely draining soils in grassland, heathland or sunny woodland rides. A colony at Fingringhoe Wick nature reserve became extinct in the 1960s as the open, post-gravel-pit, habitats scrubbed over. Many colonies were short-lived as they depended on the early stages of natural succession as at Fingringhoe.

Conservation needs

This is one of Britain's most rapidly declining species, at least in eastern England, and yet it is not yet included in Butterfly Conservation's national priority list. There have been no detailed studies of its ecological needs. There have been no known attempts at re-establishments anywhere in Essex and no successful ones anywhere in Britain. This species recent extinction in the Netherlands and Flanders is a warning for England: a detailed ecological study is required before any suggestions can be made about its possible restoration to Essex.

Grizzled Skipper   *Pyrgus malvae*

Status

Resident, a single surviving colony; once fairly widespread.

Habitats and larval foodplants

A wide range of foodplants are known: herbaceous and (more rarely) shrubby Rosaceae. The sole Essex colony is at Langdon Meadows NR: a large complex of meadowlands cut for hay on a freely-draining soil. When the grizzled skipper was more widespread it occurred in open woodlands (e.g. the Danbury Ridge), as well as rough grasslands.

History

Described as widespread and common in the very early 20th century (Harwood, 1903) its decline has been most rapid since the 1950s. Natural succession of open habitats to scrub, lack of sufficient coppicing in woods and loss of habitats to building are probably the main causes

Re-establishments

Two recent attempts have been made to restore this species to Little Baddow Heath NR, where it became extinct in 1960. A small number of adults, released in 1994 produced only a single adult the following year. In 1996 a larger number were released (see chapter 5) but immediate predation by wood-ants seems to have eliminated most of these butterflies very quickly. At the time of writing a few offspring hatched in 1997 but it is not known if the re-establishment will succeed in the longer term. There have been no reported re-establishment attempts (successful or not) anywhere else in Britain.

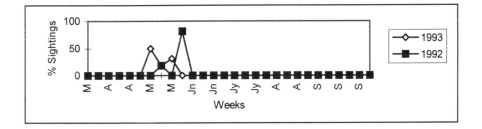

Conservation needs

Since the only Essex colony is in a large nature reserve where one of the conservation objectives is the maintenance of this butterfly, one could hope that it is fairly safe. However, it exists at very low density compared with grassland (downland) sites in Sussex and the necessary control of ragwort (*Senecio jacobaea*) at Langdon by chemical means may be a problem. This species is now recognised as nationally endangered and a detailed study of its ecology (mainly in Sussex) has just been completed. This study, when published, should give a better basis for planning habitat management and possible re-establishments than exists at present. Meanwhile, regular monitoring of the adult numbers is needed: ideally a standard butterfly-transect should be established at Langdon.

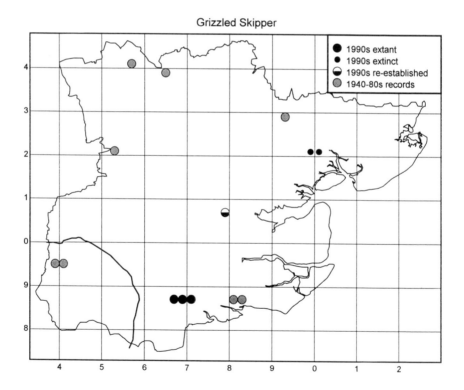

Grizzled Skipper

# Swallowtail												*Papilio machaon*

Status
Vagrant; probably a very local resident until the early 19th century.

Habitat and larval foodplant
The vagrants sighted in Essex are of the continental subspecies which inhabits a wide range of open habitats and feeds on several foodplants in the families Umbelliferae and Rutaceae: most commonly wild carrot (*Daucus carotta*) in northern Europe. There is one record of these vagrants having bred in Essex: in October 1868 F.H. Varley found five pupae on an umbelliferous plant (Essex Field Club., 1882).

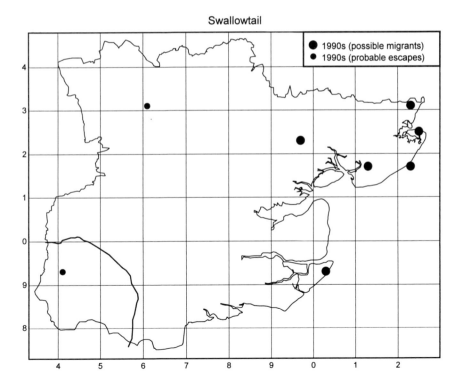

Swallowtail

The native British subspecies lives only in wetland habitats and feeds only on milk-parsley (*Peucedanum palustre*). It is not a wanderer like the continental subspecies.

History

The evidence that the British subspecies once bred in Essex, in the Lea Valley/Epping Forest area, is imperfect but fairly convincing. Stephens (1827-28) wrote "...sometimes captured close to London, in Epping Forest, at Stepney..." Newman (1871) writing of a time "about 50 years ago" reports repeatedly finding the larvae in a garden at Tottenham Green "on rue" [*Ruta* sp presumably]. At this time the Lea valley itself still contained marshland and presumably contained milk parsley since the only place this plant was known in Essex was in the Epping/Royston area in the 1850s (see Gibson, 1861). Whatever the original status, the swallowtail was absent from the Epping area by the 1860s when it was unknown in the area to Doubleday who tried, and failed, to re-establish it (see chapter 6).

The remaining rare sightings of swallowtails have been almost exclusively in coastal areas and those closely examined have been of the continental subspecies. Inland sightings in Buckhurst Hill (1991) and Thaxted (1997) were from escapes from captive stock (from a private breeder and from Mole Hall butterfly house respectively).

Future

There is no realistic chance of this species being restored to Essex. Climate change may, perhaps, allow the continental subspecies to colonise Britain. If so the south-east coastal counties like Essex are where it will happen first. In the Netherlands this is one of the species with fluctuating fortunes: certainly there is no sign of a sustained increase in range or abundance.

Biology

The many biology and conservation studies in Britain are well covered in the species action plan (Barnett & Warren, 1995b).

Wood White   *Leptidea sinapis*

Status
Extremely rare vagrant; extinct – resident very locally until early 19th century.

Habitat and larval foodplant
Woodland rides and plantations in a fairly early stage of growth. In the surviving English colonies the larvae feed on yellow meadow vetchling (*Lathyrus pratensis*) and a few other species of vetch and trefoil.

History
The late Victorian entomologists (Fitch, 1891; Harwood, 1903) were already writing of a species that had ceased to breed in Essex. Harwood believed only reports from Epping (English, 1887), when it was common in 1839, and the reports from woods near Colchester in the early 19th century, represented

Wood White

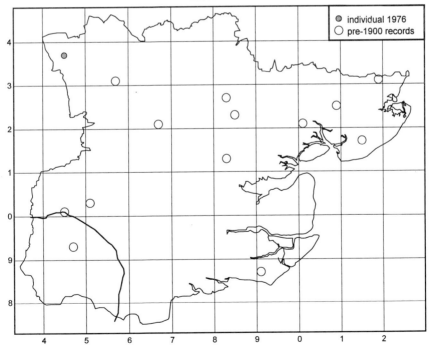

breeding colonies, although the report from Litley Wood, Debden (J. Clarke in Fitch, 1891) probably represented another. Singletons were reported from a few other sites in the 19th century and then no other record was published until one from High Wood, Duddenhoe End on 19 May 1976 by Peter Beale (published without name of recorder or locality in Emmet et al. 1985). This record was interpreted as possible evidence of recolonisation since it was "a year after one had been seen in nearby Hertfordshire." In fact 1976 was the year of the final extinction of the Hertfordshire colony at Ball Wood (Sawford, 1987).

Future

As the species has become extinct in East Anglia, Hertfordshire, Kent and across the sea in the Netherlands, there seems little chance of natural recolonisation. Warren's (1984) researches show that woodland and ride management is important for the survival of this species but this does not explain its very early disappearance from the East Anglian counties.

Pale Clouded Yellow   *Colias hyale*

Status

A very rare vagrant.

Habitat and larval foodplants

As a wandering vagrant it can be seen in any open habitat: breeding has never been confirmed in Essex, but the foodplants and breeding habitats are similar to those of the clouded yellow.

Similar species

Berger's clouded yellow (*Colias alfacariensis*) is virtually identical as an adult. It has never been confirmed from Essex and, since its preferred breeding habitat is calcareous downland (the larvae feed only on horseshoe vetch, *Hippocrepis comasa*), it is unlikely to be. Prior to 1948 (Berger, 1948) these two species were not distinguished in Britain but, in view of the ecology, old records are assumed to be pale clouded yellows, although confusions between this species and the form *helice* of the clouded yellow are quite easily made.

History

Fitch (1891) gives a long list of records from inland as well as coastal sites. He states it to be "In some years not rare, but more often quite absent..." Firmin et al. (1975) reported a seven year period ending in 1951 when it was fairly frequent on the coast. After that date, years when it was recorded are few and far between with only two sightings inland. During the last quarter century or so it has been recorded only twice: 1971 and 1983, single individuals both at Dengie.

Future

There are no conservation actions in Essex that can affect this species. It will probably remain a very rare vagrant, since it used to breed in central Europe where suitable lucerne and clover fields are being destroyed. This contrasts with the clouded yellow which has occasional mass migrations that originate in its southern European and north African strongholds.

Clouded Yellow   *Colias croceus*

Status

Migrant, sometimes breeds in Essex but never survives the winter.

Rural sites 0.01%   Gardens 0.004%

Habitat and larval foodplants

The northward migration in spring and the return one or more generations later in autumn are a regular part of the ecology of this species in Europe. Most years a few reach Essex and some years they do so in large numbers and breed in Essex. The most recent 'clouded yellow year' was 1983 after a long period when butterfly enthusiasts feared that farming changes in Britain and northern Europe had eliminated the mass migrations in the north of its range. Before then 1947 was the previous mass year with good numbers in 1959 and in 1996.

The larvae feed on clovers; once lucerne in farm fields was easily available but the 1983 breeding must mostly have been on road-side verges and commons.

Future

The numbers seen have tended to be higher in recent hot summers (although nowhere near the infux of mass years). No conservation action in Britain can influence the arrival of this species in large numbers.

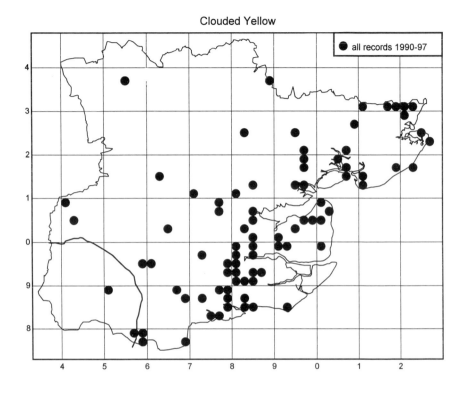

Clouded Yellow

Brimstone   *Gonepteryx rhamni*

Status

Widespread resident at fairly low density.

Rural sites 45%; individuals 0.6%   Gardens 53%; individuals 1.1%

Habitat and larval foodplants

Neither of the larval foodplants, buckthorn (*Rhamnus cathartica*) and alder
buckthorn (*Frangula alnus*), is abundant in Essex. Buckthorn is mainly found on
the chalk of the north-west and alder buckthorn on slightly acid soils. The very
long life of the adult butterfly (up to 11 months), the movements in search of
females (by males) in early spring, larval foodplants (by females) in spring,
nectaring sites in summer and hibernation sites in late summer, combined with the

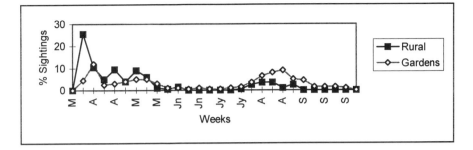

great ease of identification, mean that this species gives the appearance of being more common than it actually is.

History

Both Fitch (1891) and Harwood (1903) comment that this is a widespread species commonly seen in spring: its status has probably changed less than many other species in the course of the 20th century.

Conservation needs

Brimstones are likely to remain at their present density without any special conservation measures. Increasing the availability of the larval foodplant would probably help this species since, studied outside Essex, brimstone density was higher in areas of high buckthorn density (Pollard & Yates, 1993). Most eggs are laid on isolated juvenile trees growing in sunny exposed sites (McKay, 1991). Many of the conservation hedges and roadside plantings in Essex include buckthorns and young bushes can easily be purchased from tree nurseries. Easy availability of thistles (favoured nectar sources prior to hibernation) and spring bluebells, dandelions and primroses may help, as could the preservation of ivy covered trees and walls – although there have been no studies to measure the importance of these factors. Brimstones probably move long distances between hibernation to breeding sites (Pollard & Hall, 1980) so absence of one or more life-cycle requirement from a site does not mean the site will not be used.

Site/Year	83	84	85	86	87	88	89	90	91	92	93	94	95	96
Stour Wood	0	1	0	0	0	0	0	0	0	2	0	1	0	0
Leigh Marshes	0	0	0	0	0	0	0	0	0	0	0	0	0	2

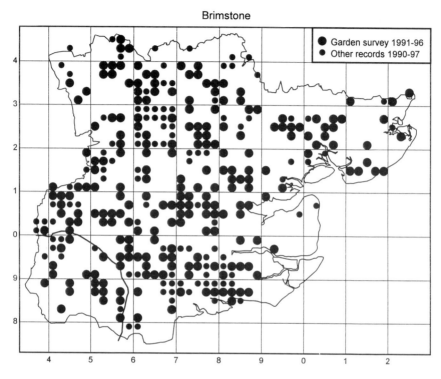

Brimstone

Butterfly gardening

The Essex garden survey showed that more brimstones were seen in gardens with buckthorns than those without and this was statistically significant even after allowing for other factors (such as size of gardens and available nectar plants). Whether this means that brimstones breed successfully in gardens or just investigate buckthorns is another matter. One large garden where the buckthorns were watched carefully had good numbers of eggs laid and the larvae survived well until they were near full-grown when all those under observation disappeared due, the garden owner believed, to bird predation. Protecting the larvae with 'sleeves' led to good survival. It should be noted that very high larval mortality is normal in all butterfly species and brimstone populations would not decline even if over 90% of larvae failed to survive. It is possible, though, that garden buckthorns are enticing brimstones to lay on bushes that are less suitable (in terms of predation and parasite level) than those in natural habitats. This needs to be investigated. Attracting summer brimstones to buddleia and runner bean flowers may help the winter survival of the butterflies.

Black-veined White   *Aporia crataegi*

Status

Extinct in Britain since 1922. Rare vagrant/escape in Essex in recent years. Status in 19th century uncertain.

Habitats and larval foodplants

The larvae fed on blackthorn (*Prunus spinosa*) or hawthorn (*Crataegus* spp) and sometimes orchard fruit trees: this is still their habit on the continent where they survive. The larvae spend the winter gregariously in a silk web.

History

In Essex the only records are from Epping Forest (1844 in Raynor, 1912) and 1850s (Stephens in de Worms, 1950). The late record from Wansted Flats (Carrington, 1879) was regarded as "very doubtful" by Fitch, (1891) and I concur. Since the species bred in all adjacent counties and regions of the continent (see Table 6.1) and became extinct very early from the London area I suspect that it was once fairly widespread in Essex but disappeared before it was recorded.

There has been one recent record on 17th May 1990 at Tollesbury (Goodey & Firmin, 1992)) which was probably a genuine vagrant from the continent. Stock from France has been reared through several generations in captivity near Woodham Mortimer in recent years and a few escapes have occurred.

Future

There have been several attempts at re-establishments in other parts of England and all have failed. Conventional wisdom has it that the species went extinct because of a series of wet autumns combined with increased bird predation (Pratt, 1983). My personal experience of this species in the French pyreneen foothills is that it is common in dry areas but rare in damper ones.

The possible significance of the larval ecology on the survival of this species is discussed in chapter 5.

Natural recolonisation is not impossible if the new dry climate of Essex persists. Artificial re-establishments should not be attempted and are illegal without an English Nature license.

Large White   *Pieris brassicae*

Status

Widespread and usually common resident, supplemented by migrants in some years

Rural sites 76%; individuals 8.0%   Gardens 97%; individuals 21%

Habitats and larval foodplants

Large whites can be seen in any open habitat but are more common in gardens than the rural countryside. They are most likely to be found as larvae on garden brassicas and garden nasturtium (*Tropaelum* spp) than on wild crucifers, although horse-radish (*Armoracia rusticana*) growing wild is used.

History

This has been a common species since records began. "Too common everywhere" (Fitch, 1891) suggests either that Fitch was an aggrieved gardener or that there may have been some decline this century as Firmin et al. (1975) and Emmet et al. (1985) suggest. There are no quantified records to support these suggestions of decline and the national monitoring since the 1970s suggests a stable population.

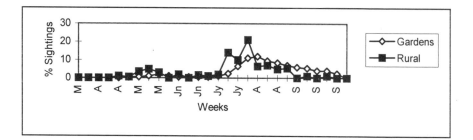

Site/Year	83	84	85	86	87	88	89	90	91	92	93	94	95	96
Stour Wood	39	24	69	217	*	*	108	49	100	632	243	100	105	17
St Osyth	*	10	73	20	*	22	*	1	4	65	7	0	1	1
Leigh Marshes	9	157	130	115	7	87	19	64	0	441	74	17	0	1

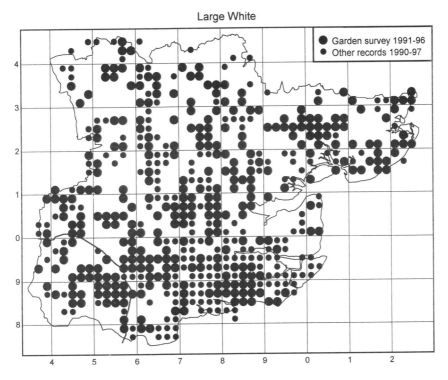

Large White

Conservation

In view of the sometimes pest status of this species specific conservation projects are not needed (at present anyway).

Butterfly gardening

Although the larvae can cause serious damage to cultivated brassicas, the adult butterflies are attractive and come easily to buddleia and other nectar sources. *Tropaeolum* planted in sunny situations will attract egg-laying females but, unfortunately, the Essex garden survey produced no evidence that this reduced the likelihood of larvae being found on cabbages as well.

Small White   *Pieris rapae*

Status

Widespread and common resident supplemented by migrants.

Rural sites 76%; individuals 6.8%   Gardens 94%; individuals 18%

Habitats and larval foodplants

Exactly the same comments apply as for the large white, although the larvae are solitary and less obvious than the gregarious hoards of the previous species.

History

"Common in every garden throughout the county" (Fitch, 1891) really still describes the situation although Firmin et al. (1975) and Emmet et al. (1985) suggest some decline in the first half of the 20th century.

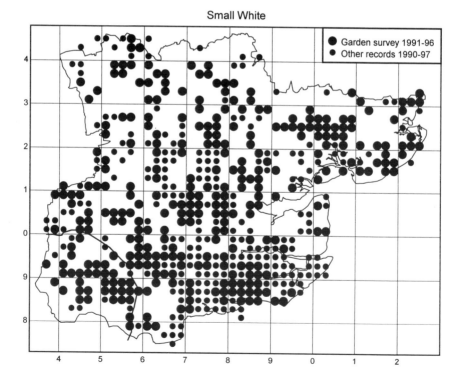

Small White

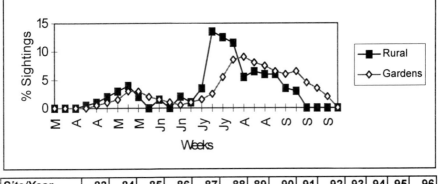

Site/Year	83	84	85	86	87	88	89	90	91	92	93	94	95	96
St Osyth	*	2	37	116	*	*	*	13	44	87	27	16	14	5
Stour Wood	1	55	38	365	*	*	27	3	15	119	6	57	*	*
Leigh Marshes	100	182	209	532	136	157	60	241	*	561	89	55	*	271

Butterfly gardening

The same comments as for the large white.

Green-veined White   *Pieris napi*

Status

A widespread and common resident especially in rural habitats.

Rural sites 67%; individuals 3.6%   Gardens 41%; individuals 1.5%

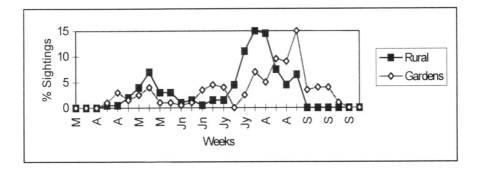

Green-veined White

Habitats and larval foodplants

Essentially a species of roadsides, hedgerows and woodland rides in rural habitats but can be seen throughout Essex including gardens and urban areas. The major foodplants in Essex are probably garlic mustard (*Alliaria petiolata*) and water-cress (*Nasturtium officinale*) but it is known to lay on small plants of a wide variety of wild crucifers. An early Essex report records it from sea-rocket, *Cakile maritima* (Harwood in Fitch, 1891).

Site/Year	83	84	85	86	87	88	89	90	91	92	93	94	95	96
St Osyth	0	0	0	0	*	*	*	6	2	4	11	11	3	0
Stour Wood	29	62	98	58	*	*	105	87	32	72	103	58	*	*
Leigh Marshes	104	104	272	498	571	492	125	297	*	811	752	847	*	167

History

As with the other two *Pieris* species, Firmin et al. (1975) and Emmet et al. (1985) report a decline from earlier abundance. For all three species records from the Netherlands suggest an increase this century and stability in Britain since the monitoring scheme began in 1976. Loss of hedgerows in Essex is likely to have reduced the amount of breeding habitat in Essex.

Conservation

No action necessary

Butterfly gardening

Can easily be attracted to nectar plants: especially the second (summer) generation of butterflies. It will probably breed in gardens if hedges have suitable wild crucifers beside them, cultivated yellow alyssum is also used..

Bath White   *Pontia daplidice*

Status

Occasional vagrant to Essex, never known to breed in the county

History

This a rare vagrant anywhere in Britain, the records being concentrated in the south-west and in certain years: 1947 was the last year in which a specimen was seen in Essex (Westcliffe-on-Sea, Common, 1947). In 1945 there was a large invasion of the south coasts of England by bath whites but none were seen in Essex that year. Fitch (1891) reported five specimens all in different years and scattered localities during the second half of the 19th century. Two other individuals were reported post-1925 both coastal in the south of the county (Firmin et al., 1975).

Future

Fairly dramatic global warming might make sighting of bath whites in Essex more frequent but don't count on it. Based on genetic differences and failure to hybridise successfully, some scientists claim that the bath whites from the east and west of the alps are different species (Geiger et al., 1988). It is not known to which of these groups the vagrants to Essex belong.

Orange-tip   *Anthocharis cardamines*

Status

A widespread and common resident

Rural sites 55%; individuals 1.5%   Gardens 83%; individuals 2.3%

Habitats and larval foodplants

Mainly a rural species, hedgerows, green lanes, wide woodland rides and large gardens being favoured habitats. The larvae feed on the developing seedpods of a wide variety of wild crucifers with garlic mustard (*Alliaria petiolata*) and charlock (*Sinapis arvensis*) being probably the most common in Essex. Lady's smock (*Cardamine pratensis*) is favoured for egg-laying in many counties and Doubleday (quoted by Firmin et al. 1975) reported this was once the case in Essex when damp meadows were common. Doubleday believed that many of the resulting larvae must have perished when the plants were cut at hay-making.

History

"Plentiful throughout the county" (Fitch, 1891). Firmin et al. (1975) reported some decline in numbers but there seems to have been a recovery since then (Emmet al., 1985).

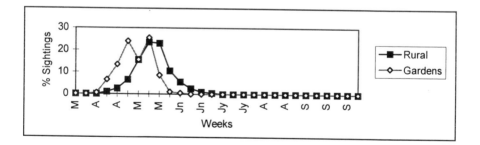

Site/Year	83	84	85	86	87	88	89	90	91	92	93	94	95	96
St Osyth	0	*	*	1	5	0	3	5	*	*	4	*	3	0
Stour Wood	5	4	14	*	*	2	2	3	*	4	12	8	4	12
Leigh Marshes	58	59	76	39	33	22	39	48	*	50	57	31	*	11

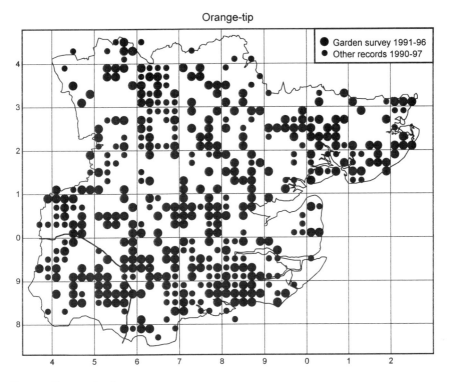

Orange-tip

Butterfly gardening

Orange tips visited a large proportion of Essex gardens but in small numbers. They are probably just passing through and are not frequently observed taking nectar. Planting lady's smock in damp ground is an effective way of encouraging egg-laying.

Green Hairstreak   *Callophrys rubi*

Status

Very localised colonies; moderately common within these colonies

Rural sites 2% individuals 0.2%   Gardens 0.002% individuals 0.001%

Habitats and larval foodplants

Open woodland, scrub or heathland habitats on very freely draining soils
(sand/gravels or chalk usually especially in old pits). In Essex chalk pits it feeds
mainly on dogwood (*Cornus sanguinea*) whereas on sand and gravel it is
associated with gorse (*Ulex* spp) or broom (*Cytisus scoparius*). There are many
gorse/broom-rich areas from which it is absent. It is probable that the pupa
overwinters in ants' nests, although the details of this and the species of ants
involved are unknown.

History

"Not common, but generally distributed" (Fitch, 1891) and "common and
generally distributed...in rough places where broom and furze grow freely"
Harwood (1903) are both unfortunately vague accounts. It seems probable that the
species is now more restricted than it once was. Both the above general reports
would suggest that green hairstreaks were known in Epping Forest (but note, Fitch
lived in Maldon and Harwood near Colchester) and yet no specific report from

Green Hairstreak

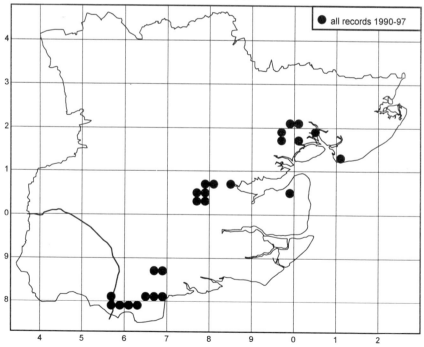

all records 1990-97

Epping Forest exists except a single specimen from the "Epping area" in the early 19th century (Doubleday, 1836).

Conservation

Several of the strongest colonies are in nature reserves (especially at Fingringhoe where it is common in some years and was especially so in 1997) and the management of Little Baddow Heath to recreate a heathland glade inside the wood led to the natural recolonisation by green hairstreaks in the early 1990s. Research is needed to understand the detailed habitat requirements of this species.

Brown Hairstreak   *Thecla betulae*

Status

Once resident, now extinct. There are no confirmed post-war records. A re-establishment experiment in Epping Forest is planned.

Habitats and larval foodplant

The eggs are laid only on sloe (*Prunus spinosa*) and in most parts of Britain these bushes are parts of hedges and thus much affected by hedgerow management. The famous Epping Forest populations were on sloe scrub and thickets in an unfarmed environment.

History

Harwood (1903) summarised the situation thus "common in some seasons in Epping Forest but scarce elsewhere." He then reported its presence before 1860 north of Colchester and at Langham and gave records from others of its occurrence near Mundon and at Hazeleigh. Fitch (1891) covers the same localities but gives a long list of publications emphasising how many people had found it easy to collect this species in Epping Forest by 'beating' larvae from sloe bushes.

Apart from some recent reports from Epping Forest, brown hairstreaks seem to have been absent from Essex for the whole of this century other than a sighting of a single adult at Shalford in "1974 or 1975" (Emmet et al., 1985) and a report of an unauthenticated sighting in 1994 mentioned by Perrin (1995). Even though this is a difficult species to detect, I believe that there are no colonies in Essex at the present time.

If this species survives in Epping Forest, as has been suggested, then it is undoubtedly the most important butterfly species in the Forest. It is a rapidly declining species and is extinct everywhere else in East Anglia and from much of eastern England.

I reviewed at length both the 19th century records and the reports of an egg found and adults sighted in 1983 and 1984 from M. Catt reported in Emmet et al. (1985), in a recent paper on Epping Forest butterflies (Corke, 1996). My conclusion was that brown hairstreaks had been lost as a breeding species from the Forest at the turn of the century having previously had a complex of populations in the central (High Beach/Fairmead) area. I suggested soot deposition selectively affecting honeydew feeding butterflies as a possible cause (see chapter 5 for further discussion of this idea). The 1980s reports I believe are most likely to have been of deliberately released insects that then failed to establish a population, perhaps through over-collecting: see Plant (1987). Thorough and repeated winter searches, by members of the Butterfly Conservation local branch, for eggs and beating sloes for larvae (under licence from the Epping Forest Conservators) in many years in

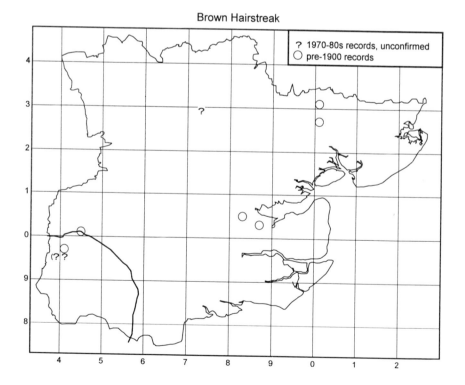

Brown Hairstreak

the 1990s has failed to detect the species and it is as certain as it can be that it is absent from the Forest.

Conservation

The Conservators of Epping Forest are actively planning a re-establishment attempt to take place before the turn of the century. The present distribution of sloe bushes has been fully surveyed and detailed consultations are taking place.

Studies elsewhere in England have shown that hedgerow management is the key factor in causing the decline of this species: overwintering eggs being destroyed by frequent mechanical hedge cutting. (Barker et al., 1996)) This problem cannot have caused the loss from Epping Forest but may have been important elsewhere in Essex.

No-one should attempt introductions elsewhere without full approval of English Nature. Survey work by egg-searching and beating should be attempted in the former habitats of this species near Maldon and around Colchester in the hope that surviving colonies may be detected.

Purple Hairstreak   *Quercusia quercus*

Status
Widespread but colonial resident, probably more common than records suggest.
Rural sites 16%; individuals 0.3%   Gardens 0.006%;individuals 0.01%

Habitats and larval foodplant
Colonies are always associated with mature oak trees: the sole larval foodplant. The adults fly around, and settle on, the tops of trees: not exclusively oaks. Their liking for ash stubs in Essex being noted by Fitch (1891). The adults feed on honeydew on tree-canopy leaves and rarely descend to nectar on bramble flowers.

History
"Common in most woods" (Fitch, 1891) "common and generally distributed...in oak woods" (Harwood, 1903). Both Firmin et al. (1975) and Emmet et al. (1985) comment on unusual abundance in hot, dry summers but lower numbers otherwise. It appears to have been absent from Epping Forest in the first half of this century (see Corke, 1996) possibly associated with soot pollution on leaves affecting honeydew-feeding butterflies (see discussion in chapter 5).

Purple Hairstreak

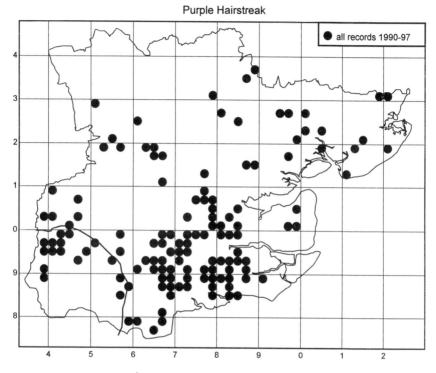

Conservation

No special measures needed except research to establish the relationships of the fully-grown larva and pupa with ants. The use of isolated oaks by colonies of this species also needs investigation.

Butterfly gardening

Records from gardens are very few and seem to be associated with butterflies from neighbouring colonies descending for nectar on rare occasions. There is no hope of attracting colonies except in large gardens with mature oaks.

Site/Year	83	84	85	86	87	88	89	90	91	92	93	94	95	96
Stour Wood	0	0	0	0	*	0	0	0	0	0	1	1	2	0

White-letter Hairstreak *Strymonidea w-album*

Status

Colonial resident, colonies widespread

Rural sites 7.6%; individuals 0.5% Gardens —

Habitats and larval foodplants

Always associated with elm trees (*Ulmus* spp), usually in hedgerows or woodland edges. The larvae often feed on the flowers of elm but this does not seem to be essential and the larvae can survive on re-grown, non-flowering elm where the main tree has died of Dutch elm disease. The adults stay in the tree tops and feed on honeydew, rarely descending for nectar.

History

Fitch (1895) describes what he called the 'black hairstreak' as "rare and very local, occurs commonly in some seasons". Although Harwood (1903) says they are found "...wherever the wych-elm grows, and is so generally distributed that it is needless to mention any special localities". All the localities mentioned by Firmin et al. (1973) are in the eastern half of the county but the map in Emmet et al. (1985) shows records from all parts of the county. There is no evidence of any current decline.

"Very rare, Epping" (Doubleday, 1836) seems to be the only report from the Epping Forest area until 1976. It is now known to be well established at Galleyhill and Gilwell Lane which are legally part of the Forest but with fewer reports from the main body of the Forest where elm is rarer. The possibility that this apparent recolonisation of the Forest is due to lowered soot-pollution is discussed in chapter 5.

Conservation

Nationally this was red-data listed as a 'notable' species, supposedly having been recorded from fewer than 100 10km-grid squares (this was an error). There was once great concern that Dutch elm disease was leading to a major decline in this species. This concern was, in part at least, a consequence of under-recording. The species is now widespread and in no danger but it still carries the 'notable' designation of English Nature.

White-letter Hairstreak

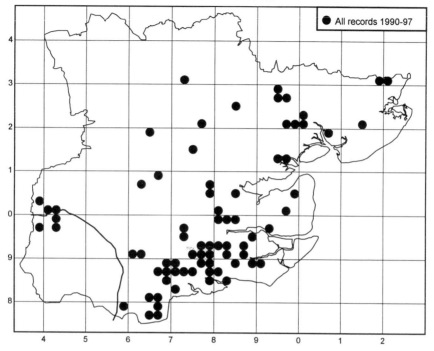

It may now breed more often on regenerating elm suckers, making it more easy to find. At Woodredon (Epping Forest buffer lands) it has been observed egg-laying on disease-resistant, planted elms. (Burman, quoted in Corke, 1996).

Continued monitoring is important but no other specific conservation action is required at present.

Small Copper   *Lycaena phlaeas*

Status

Resident, widespread but local and usually at low density.

Rural sites 52%; individuals 0.8%   Gardens 28%; individuals 0.4%

Habitats and larval foodplants

Roadside verges, woodland glades and rough ground are the main habitats in Essex. It is most common on freely draining soils and shows considerable changes in abundance from year to year. Single individuals often turn-up remote from known colonies. The two species of sorrel (*Rumex acetosa* and *R. acetosella*) are the normal foodplants.

History

"Generally distributed and common throughout the county, but by no means so abundant as was the case a few years ago" (Fitch, 1891).

"Widely distributed and still common where...rough ground or heathland provide optimum conditions" (Firmin et al., 1975). "This butterfly is still widely distributed and locally numerous..." (Emmet et al., 1985). Taken together these reports suggest over a century of decline by a butterfly that is still widely distributed: quite an achievement! The truth is, I believe, that a very large area of suitable habitat has been lost from the county so the total Essex population really has been in long-term decline. It fluctuates in numbers from year to year but probably has not declined *in density* over the long-term within the surviving colonies.

Conservation

This species could benefit from wide roadside verges not being planted-up with trees in plastic tubes but left as unfertilised grasslands cut annually. Restoration of heathlands and preventing the loss of other open areas to scrub would also help. The species seems to be in decline in Essex and the surrounding areas and needs

Site/Year	83	84	85	86	87	88	89	90	91	92	93	94	95	96
St Osyth Year	0	2	1	3	1	3	7	2	16	9	4	5	2	3
Stour Wood	2	0	3	2	0	0	10	0	15	11	5	3	9	6
Leigh Marshes	1	1	1	0	1	2	0	4	0	3	2	0	0	1

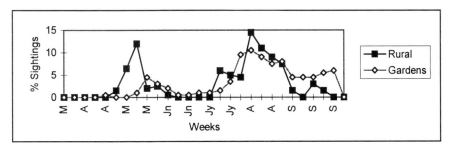

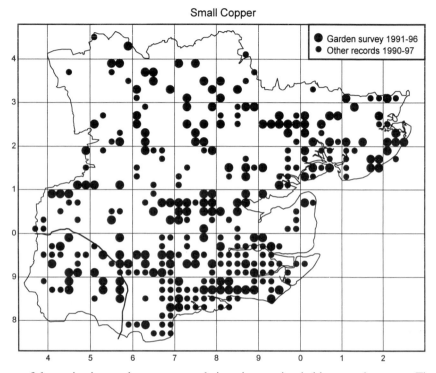

Small Copper

careful monitoring and more research into its precise habitat requirements. The
cause of the fluctuations in populations in good habitats has not been investigated
but may be a host/parasite cyclic interaction as with the holly blue. This, too, needs
research.

Butterfly gardening

This is not a common garden species, but the Essex garden survey showed clear
evidence that it was more likely to be seen in gardens where sorrel was present:
suggesting that small coppers may actually breed in these gardens and not just be
passing through. Creation of 'wildflower mini-meadows' with sorrels and where
the vegetation is allowed to grow fairly long in full sun could attract small
breeding populations. Ragwort and fleabane are favoured nectar sources.

Long-tailed Blue   *Lampides boeticus*

Status

Very rare vagrant.

History

The only two certain records (except for those known to be accidentally imported) are of one specimen in each of 1931 and 1932; both in north-east Essex.

A spot representing a single sighting for southern Essex (VC18) appears in Emmet & Heath (1989) but I have not yet discovered the origin of the record.

These blues bred in Islington, north London, not far from Essex, in 1990 (Wurzell, 1990): the first recorded breeding in the wild in Britain.

Butterfly Gardening

This will continue as a rare vagrant but might breed on occasions in gardens in Essex as it has in London. Optimists should plant bladder senna (*Colutea arborescens*) in full sun.

Small Blue   *Cupido minimus*

Status

Once resident, extinct since the late 19th century.

History

"Mr Joseph Clarke writes me, 'I caught one against the milestone on the Debden road, a mile south of Walden; but there are eight others in the Museum [Saffron Walden] old collection all caught, I believe, in this district' " (Fitch, 1891). These are the only records that I accept: the chalky district around Saffron Walden would have been suitable for this species before it was converted to arable in the 19th century. Small blues survived until recently, and may do so still, in nearby Cambridgeshire (Gog and Magog Hills).

The two 20th century guides to Essex butterflies (Firmin et al., 1974; Emmet et al. 1985) give old records from the Epping area. I quote in full my recent discussion of the status of this species in Epping Forest (Corke, 1996): An undated record 'from the Epping District' (Harwood, 1903) is attributed to Messrs J.A. Clarke and W. Machin. The fact that the foodplant (*Anthyllis vulnerata*) was not found in the Forest and that the lepidopterists working in the Epping district at the time did not locate this species, must cast doubt on this record. The record in Morris (1865) of this species from 'Amesbury' has sometimes been taken as an Epping Forest record but from the context it is obvious that Amesbury in Wiltshire is intended. The foodplant has recently been located on Bell Common in artificially seeded ground (M. Hanson, personnal communication)."

Future

Old chalk quarries provide the only possible habitat for small blues in Essex. Despite their apparent absence this century, the presence of small blues just over the border in Cambridgeshire suggests they may be rediscovered in north-west Essex.

Silver-studded Blue   *Plebejus argus*

Status

Extinct. Two subspecies once bred in the county: ssp *P. a. cretaceus* is now confined to calcicolous grassland in Dorset and was lost to Essex in 1960. *P. a. argus* was last recorded in Essex in 1949.

Habitat and larval foodplants

The typical subspecies, *P .a. argus,* lives on heathlands and the caterpillars feed on the flower and leaf buds of a variety of heathland shrubs and some non-woody plants. Often the eggs are laid on bracken but this is not a foodplant. Protection of the eggs, larvae and pupae by ants (genus *Lasius*) is probably very important for survival in the wild.

Subspecies *cretace*us is a chalkland form that feeds mainly on birdsfoot trefoil (*Lotus corniculatus*) and whose ant relationships have not been investigated but are almost certainly important.

History

Three colonies existed in the county at different times. The large Epping Forest colony was famous in the latter part of the 19th century (see Fitch, 1891) and seems to have been localised to the (then) heathland in the High Beach area. "Still very common...opposite High Beach Church" and "Very common on a piece of dry ground along the side of the road near the 'King's Oak'." are two typical reports quoted by Fitch. This colony was still known to Harwood (1903) but did not survive until 1925; in the intervening twenty years scrub encroachment of the heathlands made the habitat unsuitable.

The 1949 report of a flourishing colony "in the Brentwood area" (de Worms, 1950) was certainly 'old news' as the authority was that same year publishing a note saying "it would seem there are still some isolated and restricted localities...in the High Woods area [Writtle Forest]" and reporting a sighting of a singleton at Fryerning (Williams, 1950). Williams also referred to a colony at Kelvedon, near Brentwood [this can only refer to Kelvedon Hatch] around the turn of the century.

In 1953 a small colony of ssp. *cretaceus* was discovered in the old chalk quarry at Grays. By 1960 the quarry was under the protection of the Essex Naturalists' Trust but the butterfly had become extinct as the quarry scrubbed over.

Silver-studded Blue

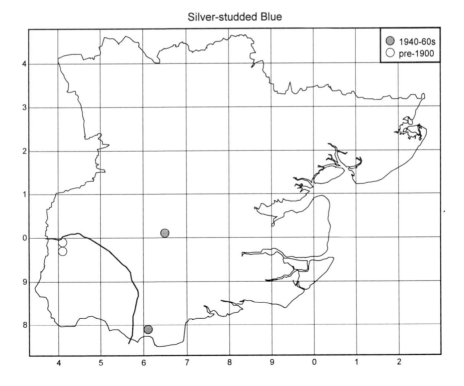

Future

Natural recolonisation seems extremely unlikely. The present attempts to recreate heathland in Epping Forest (in the exact area where the butterfly once lived) and better management of the Grays Chalk Quarry could make re-establishments a possibility. This is discussed in chapter 7.

Brown Argus   *Aricia agestis*

Status

Resident, colonial greatly increased in range and abundance during the 1990s.
Rural habitats 6.5%; individuals 0.1%   Gardens 0.004%; individuals 0.001%
[note major increase since these surveys]

Habitats and larval foodplants

The textbook habitat for this species is on downland, feeding on rock-rose (*Helianthemum chamaecistus*) . This seems never to have been the case in Essex where the butterfly has always been recorded mainly from areas with no known rock-rose. *Geranium* species have probably always been its major foodplant in Essex with *Geranium dissectum* probably the most important (Bailey, 1994).

History

"Not rare, but local" was the succinct opinion of Fitch (1891); he then listed a number of colonies and reports scattered across the county: perhaps one of the most interesting is from Harwood who had told him it was scarce in Colchester and that he (Harwood) had "not taken twenty". When Harwood wrote in 1903 he noted that "it has recently become one of our commonest butterflies. Previous to 1896 it was quite a rarity in the neighbourhood of Colchester, but in that year many thousands of specimens might have been taken; for they abounded in all directions, and the species has continued to hold its ground since, although in lesser numbers." This massive increase has happened again a hundred years later although not reaching the numbers seen by Harwood. In between, brown argus colonies seem to have survived in low numbers mainly in the south-east of the county, although the timing of the reduction of numbers is unknown. Both Firmin et al. (1975) and Emmet et al. (1985) regarded this species as very local and considered that habitat loss was the cause of its decline.

Brown Argus

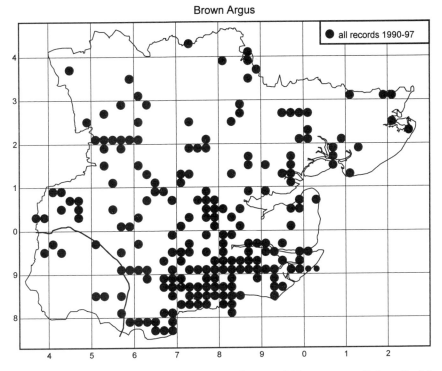

all records 1990-97

The early stages of its recovery in the south-east of Essex are well described by Bailey (1994) and by 1995/96 it was not only widespread in Essex but a similar increase was occurring in our neighbouring counties of Hertfordshire and Suffolk and elsewhere in East Anglia.

Conservation

When a rare and declining species suddenly becomes a common and expanding one it is a cause for joy: but it also suggests that some detailed research is needed as we have no convincing explanation for the change in status and thus no means of knowing if this is a short or long-term recovery and whether we can do anything to help the species maintain its new status.

Many suggestions have been made to explain the spread:

- An evolutionary switch to a more widely available foodplant? But in Essex at least *Geranium* spp seems always to have been the major foodplant.

- Greater availability of suitable habitats on set-aside fields? Possible, but most of the new colonies are not in these fields.

- Foodplant availability due to low rabbit populations following the recent myxomatosis outbreak? But there are no records of a similar expansion when rabbits suffered previous dramatic declines from this cause.

- A run of years with good weather conditions? This seems quite plausible and would explain the synchronised expansion over a very wide area. But this species is already known as a fluctuating species: past fluctuations in rockrose-feeding populations being much more localised.

My own guess is that several factors are involved probably including weather and interactions with parasitoids. There is no known habitat management to favour this species and it will probably decline again after a few years of abundance.

Common Blue   *Polyommatus icarus*

Status

Widespread resident, locally common, fluctuates in abundance.

Rural sites 58%; individuals 5.7%   Gardens 44%; individuals 1.0%

Habitats and larval foodplants

Sunny, sloping roadside verges and sea-walls, heathlands, wide rides in open woods and meadows are all used. The commonest foodplant is birdsfoot trefoil (*Lotus corniculatus*). The loss of flower-rich hay meadows must greatly have reduced the number of colonies in Essex.

History

"Abundant everywhere" (Fitch, 1891) and "abundant everywhere, especially on the coast, where vast numbers may be seen at rest on grass stems towards the close

Site/Year	83	84	85	86	87	88	89	90	91	92	93	94	95	96
St Osyth	5	47	181	162	508	*	11	2	126	179	121	139	0	2
Stour Wood	*	23	4	4	0	0	2	13	43	48	82	9	11	19
Leigh Marshes	12	27	22	37	37	16	4	13	2	27	26	82	*	17

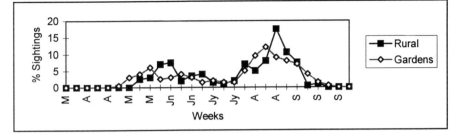

of day" (Harwood, 1903) suggest that it was then much commoner than in the second half of the 20th century, although there has been no large loss of range.

Conservation

Stopping open land developing into closed scrub and the continuation of hay-making as part of the management of nature reserves and access land is important. There have been some concern that high levels of grazing as part of the

Common Blue

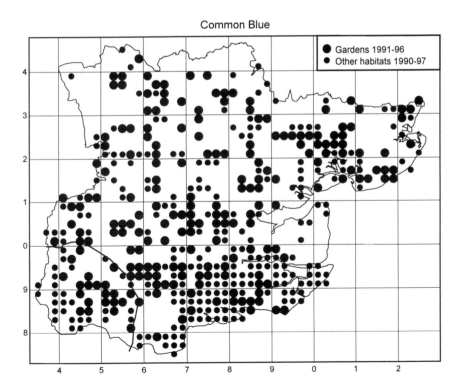

conservation management of sea-walls may be detrimental to this species: this is not certain and some research is needed.

Butterfly gardening

Gardens seem to be a secondary habitat: visited mainly in times of abundance in neighbouring areas. Large gardens with space to create mini-meadows can hope to gain breeding populations of this species.

Chalk-hill Blue   *Lysandra coridon*

Status

Extinct resident, very rare vagrant.

Habitat and larval foodplant

This species name describes its habitat well: it lives on chalk or limestone downland, well-grazed and with horseshoe vetch (*Hippocrepis comosa*) the caterpillars' only normal foodplant.

History

In the 19th century there were clearly three areas where the species bred; two just where they would be expected, the chalklands of the south-east and north-west and one which would be hard to believe if it had not been vouched for by so many eminent entomologists: Epping Forest.

Fitch (1891) said "recently observed by Mr Dale near the town of Newport in Essex". Fitch must have had a long memory: "recent" was almost two centuries before his time as Mr Dale was a friend of John Ray and his discovery was reported in *Historia Insectororum* (Ray, 1710) some years after Ray's death. The report must date from the 17th century. It was still present around Saffron Walden in Fitch's time as the then trustee of the Saffron Walden Museum (J. Clarke) confirmed. The Rev. G.H. Raynor also wrote to Fitch "Stray specimens have been taken at Childerditch, probably stragglers from Grays where the species occurs regularly". The chalk downs of Saffron Walden were ploughed up well before the end of the 19th century and the south Essex chalk suffered quarrying and building as well. These colonies were never reported as surviving into the 20th century.

The Epping colonies are a mystery. Fitch summarises the records well, drawing on observations from Henry Doubleday, Edward Newman and several others: not

Chalk-hill Blue

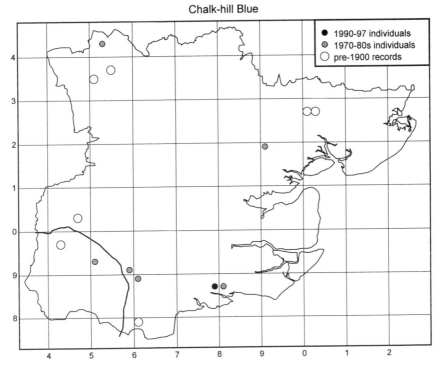

people to make a mistake. The species appeared just before 1859 and was soon common near Loughton and in clover fields near Epping. The colonies persisted until at least the mid-1860s and an odd specimen was seen in 1885 and another in 1892 (Argent, 1892). No horseshoe vetch has ever been recorded from the Epping Forest area and an alternative foodplant must have been used (it is known that several vetches and trefoils can serve as foodplants).

It may well be significant that the London to Loughton railway opened in 1856 and the Epping New Road was cut through the centre of the Forest from Woodford to Epping in 1835. The soil disturbance may have helped create suitable habitats and insects may have been accidentally helped to travel along the railways and highways. Harwood noted (1903) that "Previous to 1860 it occasionally occurred on the railway banks near Colchester".

Present and future

Odd specimens still occur: mostly on the Hadleigh Downs (vagrants from Kent presumably) and a few in the north-west of the county where the nearest colonies are a few miles over the borders in the Devil's Dyke (Cambridgeshire) and Therfield Heath (Hertfordshire). No suitable downland habitat is likely to be re-created but the motorway verges of the new roads in north-west Essex could profitably (if dangerously) be investigated for undetected natural colonies.

Adonis Blue   *Lysandra bellargus*

Status

Extinct. Probably bred in the north-west of Essex in the early 19th century.

History

Fitch (1891) reports information from Joseph Clarke (of Saffron Walden Museum) that it has been caught "once or twice in the Saffron Walden district". There are no other published records. The species survived at Therfield Heath (Hertfordshire) into the 1950s and vagrants could have reached Essex as rare chalk-hill blues still do. However, what is known of the nature of the chalk-downland in Essex, prior to its conversion to arable in the mid-1800s, suggests that the adonis blue was once a native species.

Future

No suitable habitat remains in Essex and even if it were re-created, natural colonisation would be most improbable.

Mazarine Blue   *Cyaniris semiargus*

Status

Extinct in Essex in the 19th century and in Britain since before the turn of the century.

History

Fitch (1891) accepted that it had bred in the Saffron Walden area based on reports from Joseph Clarke and its presence in the Museum 'old collection'. Fitch considered a report from Epping Forest erroneous.

Future

No one knows the reasons for the loss of this species from Britain. One theory (Chapman, 1909), that clover crops acted as a 'trap' to egg-laying females whose offspring then failed to complete their development before harvest, if true, implies that Britain should once more be suitable, since clover is now much more rarely grown as a crop.

Detailed ecological studies of this blue on the continent of Europe would be needed before any attempt to restore it to Britain and there is no logical reason why such attempts should be made in Essex.

Holly Blue   *Celastrina argiolus*

Status

Resident, often widespread but with strongly cyclic populations. It is never truly abundant but can be widespread and common.

Rural sites 47%; individuals 0.8%   Gardens: 78%; individuals 3.8%

[these surveys in years of high population levels]

Habitats and larval foodplants

Typically a butterfly of woodlands and wood edges it also commonly uses gardens. In Essex, the usual foodplants are the flower buds and developing fruit of holly (*Ilex aquifolius*) (spring) and ivy (*Hedera helix*) (summer) but in years of high populations there have been many observations of laying on other shrubs.

History

Fitch (1891) "Fairly common and generally distributed throughout the county". Harwood (1903) "widely distributed, but often scarce in some districts; but in

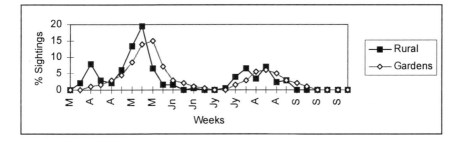

Holly Blue

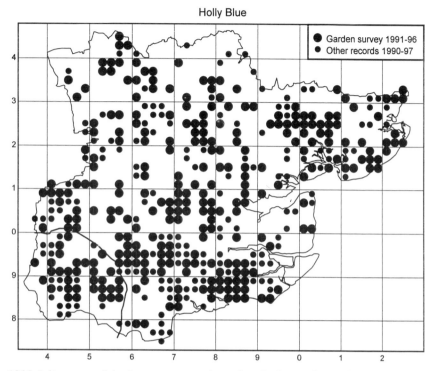

1900-1 it appeared in far greater numbers than had ever been observed before".
Emmet et al. (1985) record 1967-71, 1979 and 1985 as periods of high abundance.
It seems that the overall distribution and cyclic changes in abundance have not
changed much in the last century.

Biology

Two factors seem to be involved in the cycles of abundance. Holly blues have 'a
parasitic wasp (*Listrodromus nycthemerus*) specific to them and which is the only
important parasite of the caterpillar. It has recently been confirmed that the parasite
gets much commoner in a sequence of years when the butterfly is common:

Site/Year	83	84	85	86	87	88	89	90	91	92	93	94	95	96
St Osyth	0	2	0	0	0	0	5	16	0	0	0	0	0	1
Stour Wood	0	1	5	0	0	0	5	20	2	13	0	0	4	25
Leigh Marshes	0	1	4	1	0	3	1	28	5	17	0	0	0	8

reaching the point where 99% of larvae were killed (Revels, 1994). The butterfly then gets rare: probably many colonies becoming extinct. This must obviously cause a dramatic decline in the parasite, although this has yet to be studied, and then the caterpillars have a reduced mortality rate and the species can expand again. It also seems that warm summers coincide with expansions in this species (Pollard & Yates, 1993); probably aiding the build-up in numbers and spread of the butterflies. Thus the cycles are a natural phenomenon and we must be content with seeing holly blues commonly only in certain years.

Butterfly gardening

The Essex survey shows that most gardens will be visited by holly blues whether they contain holly, ivy, both or neither. Garden holly (flowering female bushes) and ivy allowed to flower and fruit are likely to be used for breeding.

Duke of Burgundy   *Hamearis lucina*

Status

Extinct, localised resident until 1920s.

Habitat and foodplants

The prime habitat in Essex (and much of southern England) was large blocks of coppiced woodland with primroses (*Primula vulgaris*) growing in half-shade. Although it can breed on scrubby downland, feeding on cowslips (*Primula veris*) it was never known in this habitat in Essex.

History

"Rare and very local, especially considering how common is its food-plant; always in or on the borders of woods." Fitch (1891) goes on to quote records from the Tendring area (Hartley Wood especially), and the south-east (Hall Wood, Woodham Ferrers: now called Thrift Wood, Bicknacre) and Eastwood where it was "not common". Records exist from the Saffron Walden area (undated museum specimens from the first half of 19th century) and Gaynes Park/Ongar Park Woods, near Epping in 1839-41 from which area it then "suddenly vanished never to return". Thus the species was known from localities in all four quarters of the county but was confined to the two coastal quarters by the end of the 19th century.

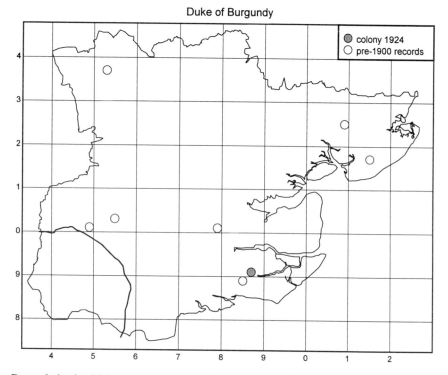

Duke of Burgundy

Records in the 20th century are a single report from Harwich (Mathew, 1912) and "abundant near Rochford, 1924" (Harvey, 1924). There were no suitable woods nearer Rochford than Hockley Woods and the other nature reserve woodlands immediately to the south. This is almost certainly the area from which Frohawk knew the species in Essex and collected a male on 9 June 1918 whose painting appears in his 'Natural History of British Butterflies' (Frohawk, 1924).

Conservation

Now that Thrift Wood, Bicknacre and the complex of woods in the Southend area are nature reserve and again under coppice management; a re-establishment programme should be considered if detailed study of the habitats now in the woods reveal them to be suitable.

White Admiral   *Ladoga camilla*

Status

Very local breeding species. Two colonies known in 1995-97, previously one.

Habitat and larval foodplant

A woodland butterfly that needs honeysuckle (*Lonicera periclymenum*) growing in partial shade for egg-laying: this is the only larval foodplant. The adults feed mainly on honeydew in the canopy but if bramble blossom (*Rubus fructicosus*) is present in a sunny position they will take nectar.

History.

The ups and downs of this species are complex. Fitch (1891) states succinctly "Rare, every year becoming more so". This tallies with what was happening nationally at that time when the range of white admirals was in the process of contracting greatly, to the point where it is often stated that in the early decades of this century they survived only in the extreme south of their former range, mainly in Hampshire and the adjoining counties (Heath et al., 1984; Emmet & Heath, 1989; Thomas, 1991: all these statements deriving from a very detailed study by Pollard, 1979). It seems that it did not quite disappear from Essex since Firmin, et al. (1975) state that it survived continuously this century in the extreme north-east woods (where it breeds today). This is supported by evidence from Suffolk (Mendel & Piotrowski, 1986) of its continuous survival in the Bentley Woods area which is just in the same 10-km square as the Essex colonies.

Fitch goes on to cite detailed records, almost all of which indicate breeding colonies in the north-east of the county or scattered records of individuals elsewhere. There seems to be a conflict between the two records quoted from Doubleday: "For the first time in my life I saw this beautiful butterfly near Colchester last July [1836], and its elegant appearance when on the wing will not soon be effaced from my mind. It is vain to try to describe it" (Doubleday, 1837)" and "One, near Park Hall, Epping" (Doubleday, 1837). Anyway, since Doubleday was an enthusiastic naturalist and grew up in Epping; to say nothing of all the other late 19th century entomologists who collected in Epping Forest and did not report white admirals, it is fairly clear that the species was not breeding there at any time after 1830, if ever in the 19th century.

The continuity of the mainly coastal Essex distribution is well attested from very early times: John Ray received a specimen on 11 July 1695 "captured by a Mr Moreton not far from the town of Tollesbury" (Ray, 1710). I would love to know

White Admiral

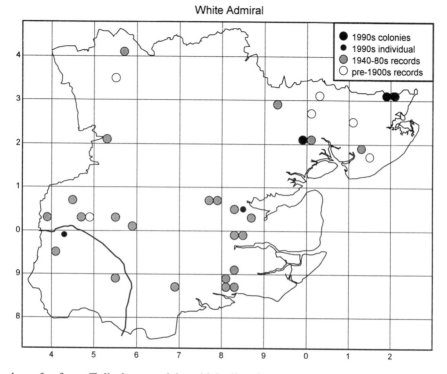

how far from Tollesbury and in which direction. It is fairly obvious that white admirals were absent from the Braintree area in the late 17th century or Ray would not have noted this provision of what, to him, was clearly an unusual species. It was reported early from Hartley Wood (Jermyn, 1827) and the woods in this area have held the butterfly ever since, although only Stour and Copperas wood do so at present. There was a short-lived colony in Riddles Wood in recent years. Douglas, (1842) was concerned that it "seems to be gradually disappearing" from woods in this area. Butterfly enthusiasts are often over pessimistic.

Nationally the white admiral spread to occupy the southern half of England in the years 1930-42. By the end of this period it was a widespread species in Essex and seems to have spread from two centres: south and towards the centre from its survival haunts in the extreme north-east of Essex and eastwards across the Lea into Epping and Hatfield Forests. The map shows the full extent of its distribution by the early 1950s.

The subsequent decline back to its permanent (?) haunts in the north-east were not well documented but seem to have occurred in the late 1950s and early 1960s.

Present situation

It looks as though the white admiral could be starting another phase of (slow) expansion. After some years when the Stour/Copperas Woods housed the only colony, white admirals reoccupied Friday woods in 1995 and are spreading. In the south-west there were several sightings in Galleyhill Woods (Plant, 1987) although there is not a breeding colony there at present, nor in Epping Forest where wanderers (presumably from the Hertfordshire colonies near Ware) have been seen. Now that Galleyhill Woods are part of the Epping Forest buffer lands it is hoped that suitable management will enable a breeding colony to establish.

Conservation and Ecology

It is interesting to note that the way the young caterpillar spends the winter hibernating in a honeysuckle leaf attached to the bush, was discovered by Dr Maclean in Colchester.

The major study of this species (Pollard, 1979) concluded that it was runs of warm years that enabled the species to expand since the caterpillar growth period was shortened and thus the predation rate by birds reduced. This was combined with an increase in un-coppiced woods or plantation woods at a suitable stage of growth where honeysuckle was available in suitable (shaded) conditions for the caterpillars.

More recent researches have shown that the relationship with weather conditions is not so clear cut (Pollard & Yates, 1993) and that muntjac deer may have an

Site/Year	83	84	85	86	87	88	89	90	91	92	93	94	95	96
Stour Wood	4	3	1	1	*	0	0	0	2	0	6	3	7	24

adverse effect by removing low-level honeysuckle leaves: the preferred egg-laying sites (Pollard & Cooke, 1994). These deer are now very widespread and common in Essex.

My own suggestion that, as one of the butterflies that feeds on honeydew, white admirals may have been adversely affected by pollution deposits at times of high smoke pollution, is discussed in chapter 5.

Although we are still far from certain about the complete reasons behind the expansions and contractions in range, it is clear that white admirals are mobile and can colonise habitats when the local conditions and regional climate are right. Thus artificial re-establishments are unlikely to be necessary or successful.

Habitat management to increase the number of woods with honeysuckle growing in abundance in partially shaded conditions, combined with nearby rides or glades providing bramble flowers as nectar sources, may help.

Purple Emperor   *Apatura iris*

Status

Extinct as a breeding species since before the First World War but with very rare vagrants.

Habitat and larval foodplant

Requires large tracts of woodland with sallow (*Salix* spp: the larval foodplant) growing in full sun at the edge of rides or glades and mature (often oak) trees (master trees) around which the adults congregate for mating. Adults feed mainly on honeydew in the canopy, combined with mud-puddling, carcass and excrement feeding by the males. Neither sex feeds on nectar.

History

It is probable that the first collected specimen to be described came from Essex, collected at Hedingham Castle in 1695 and described by John Ray (1710). The first caterpillars to be described in Britain also came from Essex: beaten from sallow bushes in Brentwood on 26 May 1758 by Dru Drury, he gave one to Moses Harris who described its appearance and rearing to adulthood in *The Aurelian* (1766).

Its main centre of distribution by the mid to late 19th century seems to have been the same north-east Essex woods favoured by the white admiral, although it was known from Epping Forest, sometimes quite commonly, until the end of the 19th century and there are a few records from the Saffron Walden area at that time.

The decline seems to have gone unnoticed but no records exist after the First World War other than of occasional individuals which seem to have been vagrants. The most recent record is of a specimen inside a house in Wivenhoe on 20 August 1983 (Firmin & Goodey, 1992) and two sightings by M. Catt in Epping Forest in 1983 (Emmet et al., 1985). The latter I regard as unconfirmed or possibly the result of a clandestine release.

Purple Emperor

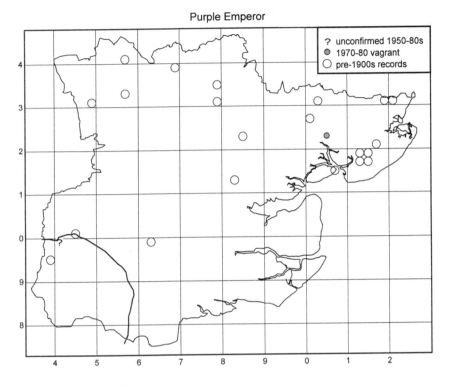

Conservation and ecology

Normally purple emperors live at low density and a single colony can cover several small woods. The reduction in the total number of woods and the limited suitability of those that remain (sallow in sun and some large 'master' trees are required) is probably the reason for the final loss from Essex in the north-east. This does not apply to Epping Forest where a very large area of mature woodland with reasonable areas of sallow exist. Possibly lack of enough sallow may have been a problem in the past but this does not seem to be the case now. The possibility that, close to London, feeding on polluted honeydew and sap-runs was the problem is considered in chapter 5. See chapter 7 for a discussion of the possibility of attempting a re-establishment in Epping Forest.

Red Admiral   *Vanessa atalanta*

Status

Widespread migrant, common in some years and very rarely overwintering in Britain.

Rural sites 47%; individuals 0.9%   Gardens 92%; individuals 4.3%

Habitats and larval foodplant

Nettle (*Urtica dioica*) is the only foodplant recorded from Essex. The eggs are laid singly and the larvae live in silk-sewn leaves, usually the stalk being partially bitten through so that the leaves wilt. The sewn leaves are very characteristic in appearance. The nettles used are always in full sun but not necessarily within a large patch. A thin row of nettles growing against the sunny side of a wall or fence are often selected for egg-laying. The adults may be seen anywhere.

Red Admiral

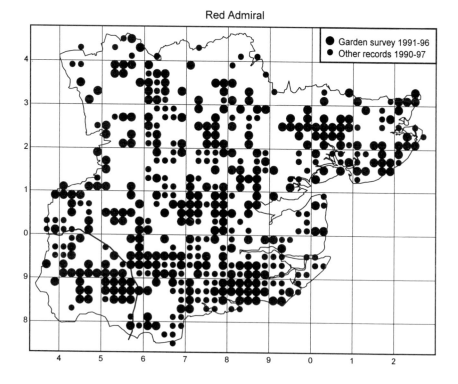

● Garden survey 1991-96
● Other records 1990-97

Site/Year	83	84	85	86	87	88	89	90	91	92	93	94	95	96
St Osyth	3	2	4	1	13	7	1	0	*	4	1	0	3	3
Stour Wood	6	3	7	11	*	*	7	21	16	80	32	16	27	29
Leigh Marshes	5	1	2	2	10	8	*	2	11	8	5	7	*	5

History

Fitch's comment (1891) "Apparently by no means so common in the county now as formerly, though generally distributed" may perhaps reflect a run of poor immigration years in the 1880s. Nationally it has been stable in the period 1976-91 (Pollard & Yates, 1993) but individual years vary dramatically.

Conservation

Since the British population is entirely dependent on annual immigrations from southern Europe, no conservation actions are needed in Britain. Establishment releases are totally unnecessary although releases of surplus captive reared stock do no harm.

Butterfly gardening

Red admirals are attracted to the same nectar plants as peacocks and small tortoiseshells. They also enjoy rotting fruit (apples or plums). Quite small nettle patches, if sheltered but sunny, can attract egg-laying females.

Biology

Red admirals are continuously brooded: the adults moving into Britain and north in the spring and early summer switching to a largely southward migration in late summer and autumn. They rarely hibernate successfully but adults can be seen in

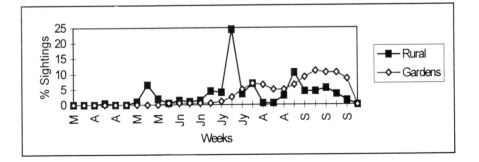

any month of the year given a spell of warm weather. There are two colour forms
of the larvae (light or dark) for reasons unknown.

Painted Lady   *Cynthia cardui*

Status

Migrant, breeding frequently in Essex but never overwintering. Great variation
from year to year in numbers of migrants.

Rural sites 49%; individuals 0.2%   Gardens 49%; individuals 0.7%

Habitat and larval foodplant

This is essentially a non-woodland butterfly although sunny clearings are used. In
open habitats it can be seen almost anywhere. Nectar plants in gardens are visited
frequently. Disturbed land with thistles (*Cirsium* spp and *Carduus* spp) in full sun

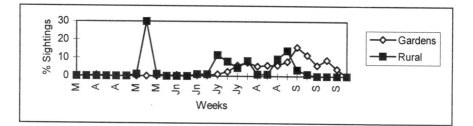

are the main breeding sites but plants other than thistles e.g. mallow, (*Malva* spp)
and stinging nettles (*Urtica dioica*) are used more rarely. This species is
continuously brooded and cannot hibernate. A southern migration occurs in late
summer and autumn.

History and Distribution

"Uncertain and irregular in appearance, but generally distributed. Some years...

Site/Year	83	84	85	86	87	88	89	90	91	92	93	94	95	96
St Osyth	2	0	2	0	3	17	1	0	*	1	0	0	2	32
Stour Wood	0	0	4	3	*	*	0	1	1	3	2	0	0	53
Leigh Marshes	2	0	3	1	0	13	0	0	2	11	0	0	*	20

Painted Lady

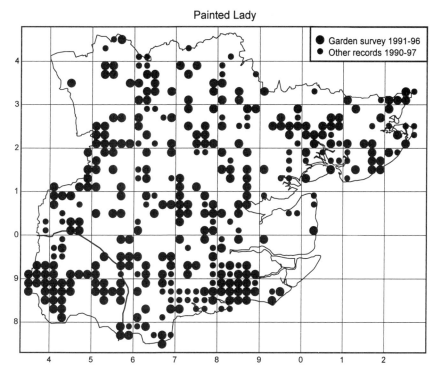

abundant, in others quite absent" (Fitch, 1891). This is still a perfect description of the situation today.

Years when it is exceptionally abundant are fewer than good red admiral years and are not synchronised with that species.

The year of maximum numbers in living memory was 1996 when, at Curry Farm a hectare or so of thistles was completely covered in eggs and a few weeks later with an estimated half million larvae. (Perrin, 1996). The chrysalids all shimmering as they emerged in immense numbers were watched by Stephen and Bob Dewick. In 1996 it was probably the commonest butterfly in most habitats: contrast that with the 1991-93 survey results where it was quite a rarity.

The fluctuations in the numbers arriving as immigrants depend on conditions in the extreme south of Spain and north Africa in very early spring. If numbers build up rapidly the northward migration starts early, the butterflies breeding as they go. Early establishment in Britain means that one or two generations bred in Essex will further increase the numbers by late summer.

Peak post-war years recorded in Essex were 1945, 1947, 1948, 1966, 1969 1980, 1985, 1988, 1996.

Butterfly gardening

Grow buddleias and wait for a good year. Alternatively grow an acre of thistles!

Small Tortoiseshell   *Aglais urticae*

Status

Widespread and common resident re-inforced by large-scale immigrations in some years.

Rural sites 71%; individuals 4.0%   Gardens 99%; individuals 19.5%

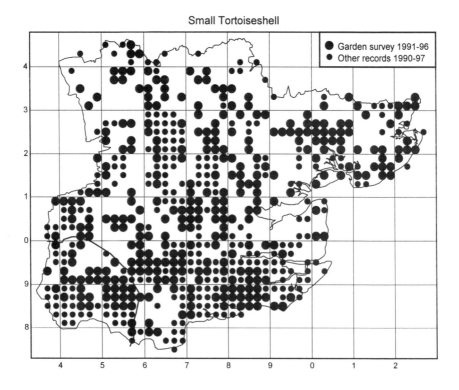

Small Tortoiseshell

Site/Year	83	84	85	86	87	88	89	90	91	92	93	94	95	96
St Osyth	4	13	48	68	382	48	28	21	*	97	34	18	34	*
Stour Wood	22	49	29	34	*	*	7	8	12	62	11	13	32	13
Leigh Marshes	27	116	134	119	294	125	*	60	121	211	67	90	*	42

Habitat and larval foodplant

Nettle (*Urtica dioica*) is the only foodplant reported in Essex. The nettle-patches selected for egg-laying are always in full sun. Habitats providing nitrogen-enriched soils are especially favoured (e.g. agricultural land, river banks, sewage farms) and large patches growing in gardens close to manure heaps are sometimes used. The larvae live gregariously in batches of 60 – 100 and are easily seen. The adults are common in gardens and other habitats with nectar plants.

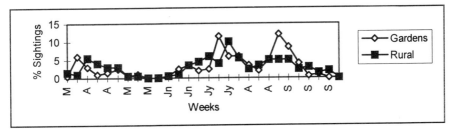

Ecology and biology

Small tortoiseshells are a classic example of a butterfly with an 'open' population: the adults are very mobile and migrate freely within Britain as well as crossing the channel. In Essex they are normally double-brooded (see flight-time graph) but in cold summers they may become single-brooded. The detailed studies on the life-cycle strategies of this and other nettle-feeding vanessids are summarised in Corke (1991).

It is not known what factors regulate the population density of small tortoiseshells but it is probable that most of the variation in density from one year to the next is explained by weather variations during the caterpillar season and in the numbers of immigrants from abroad. Thus 'bad' tortoiseshell years are nothing to worry about in conservation terms.

History

This has always been known as one of the commonest and most widespread butterflies in the county: "Particularly abundant throughout the county." (Fitch, 1891).

Conservation

Small tortoiseshells will continue to be widespread without any special conservation efforts, their abundance varying from year to year reflecting the (linked) climate variations and level of immigrations.

Establishments

Small tortoiseshells are easy to rear in captivity from wild collected larvae: this is a species that is ideal for use in schools since the time from first generation caterpillar to adult falls within the summer school term. Such butterflies reared for educational purposes are, and should be, released after hatching. For such a widespread and mobile species this does no harm but it is entirely unnecessary for the survival of the species.

Butterfly gardening

One of the most attractive garden butterflies, small tortoiseshells visit gardens primarily for nectar: especially the second generation butterflies prior to hibernation. The flight time graphs for gardens show a distinctly greater peak than in country habitats. Ice-plant, Michaelmas daisy and buddleia are the best nectar plants to provide.

Providing larval foodplants will not increase the number of adult butterflies in your garden but, with luck, you may attract the butterflies to breed. Nettle-patches should be big (2m² at least) in full sun, sheltered from strong winds and close to your manure-heap or rubbish dump. Eggs are only laid on young leaves so the second generation adults seek regrowth nettles: thus your nettle patch should be cut (in part at least) to encourage regrowth.

Providing hibernation sites may assist in retaining butterflies in autumn and helping them survive the winter. Cool sheds containing stored wood that will not be disturbed through the winter are ideal. The door must be slightly ajar to allow entry and the window (if there is one) left open in spring or obscured so that the butterflies escape through the door.

Large Tortoiseshell   *Nymphalis polychloros*

Status

Extinct as a breeding species, as it almost certainly is in Britain. Very rare vagrants from across the channel can be confused with clandestine releases of captive stock.

Habitat and larval foodplant

Typically a woodland and woodland edge species that needs abundant nectar sources (especially sallow bloom) in early spring after hibernation of the adults. The adults go into hibernation early and, in France where the species survives, are much more frequently seen in spring than in summer. The larvae are gregarious on elms (*Ulmus* spp.), sallows (*Salix* spp.) and sometimes poplars (*Populus* spp.) or trees in the family Rosaceae: the records from Essex being "never...feeding on anything but elm, generally on stubs" [Maldon area] (Fitch, 1891); low-branch of

Large Tortoiseshell

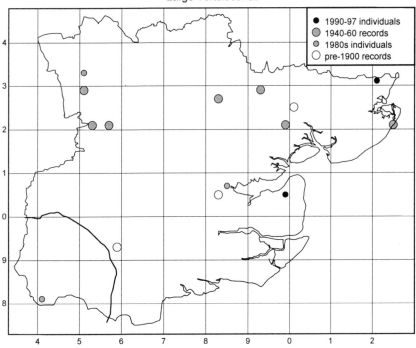

cherry-tree in Brentwood garden (Raynor, 1888); feeding on elm, sallow, and osier ([Colchester area] Harwood (1871); broad and round-leaved sallow (Ray, 1710).

History

"Fairly common and distributed throughout the county" Fitch (1891) and "so excessively abundant in north Essex and on the southern side of the Stour that I could have take hundreds of broods if I required them" (Harwood, quoted by Thomas & Lewington, 1991) was the happy state of affairs at the end of the last century. "virtually absent from the county" was the situation in 1975 (Firmin et al.). In between it had remained widespread until about 1910 and then survived mainly in the woods in the north-east of Essex but with scattered sightings elsewhere. It spread temporarily in the late 1940s and seems to have been breeding in Hatfield Forest, the Maldon area and perhaps Epping Forest; although there migrants or introductions are a possibility and there are no records of breeding, (Plant, 1987).

The decline in the early 1950s was dramatic, disappearing from its last breeding haunts in north-east Essex by 1954. Since then all reports have been of individuals, no larvae have been found and most of the reports have been from coastal areas: strong evidence that the species is now an occasional vagrant from the continent and has been lost as a breeding species since the 1950s. This is probably the case in Britain as a whole, but clandestine releases of bred stock combined with an unwillingness to declare the species extinct, has meant that large tortoiseshells have only recently been added to the list of extinct British species.

Conservation ecology

So far there have been no detailed studies of the ecology of this species in Europe nor any very convincing suggestions as to why it was lost from Britain. The decline pre-dated Dutch elm disease so that is not the problem. Despite many releases none have succeeded in re-establishing the species anywhere, so whatever the problem was in the 1950s it still applies. The periodic outbreaks and high levels of larval parasitism suggest some interaction with a parasite may be important. Basically we do not know and will only find out by research on colonies on the other side of the North Sea.

Camberwell Beauty   *Nymphalis antiopa*

Status

Occasional vagrant, sometimes in large numbers, has never bred in Essex (or England)

Ecology

On the continent this species has an ecology similar to the large tortoiseshell, the same larval foodplants, the same early hibernation and the same fluctuations in abundance. The main difference is that in Britain it has never established breeding colonies nor even have the larvae ever been found in the wild.

The most recent year of a large influx of Camberwell beauties was 1995 when there were many reports from all over Essex and eastern England generally. More individuals were reported than in all previous years together. Sightings in the spring of 1996 give pretty clear evidence of successful hibernation here and this is

Camberwell Beauty

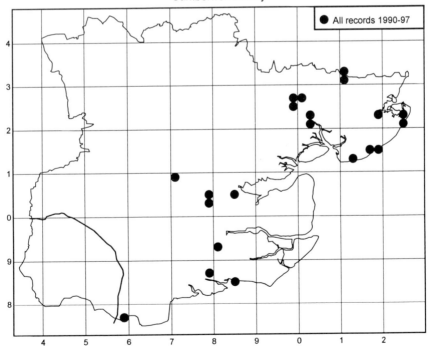

All records 1990-97

certain in Cambridgeshire where one was observed throughout the winter
hibernating in a garage.

Peacock   *Inachis io*

Status

A widespread and common species throughout the county.

Rural sites 68%; individuals 3.9%   Gardens 96%; individuals 11%

Habitat and larval foodplant

As for the small tortoiseshell, the stinging nettle (*Urtica dioica*) is the only
recorded foodplant in Essex. The type of nettle-patches selected for egg-laying are
very similar to those favoured by the small tortoisehell but the larval webs are most

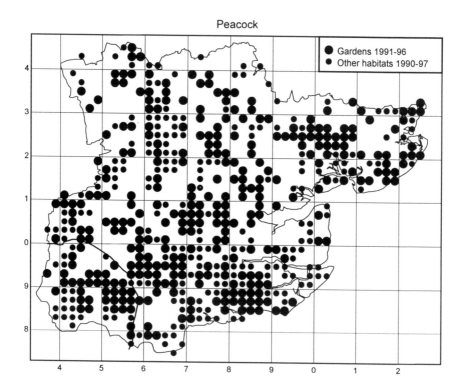

Peacock

● Gardens 1991-96
● Other habitats 1990-97

Site/Year	83	84	85	86	87	88	89	90	91	92	93	94	95	96
St Osyth	3	3	2	2	12	3	2	6	13	11	3	3	9	5
Stour Wood	36	38	91	51	9	0	4	17	23	107	36	27	82	107
Leigh Marshes	4	14	14	21	21	16	8	12	37	50	29	7	14	38

often in the centre of very large nettle patches. In spring the adults often fly in woodland rides but they do not lay eggs on woodland nettle patches.

History

A hundred years ago it was "Common everywhere, but apparently less so in Essex now than formerly"(Fitch, 1891). 'Good' peacock years are separated by years of lower abundance but there has been no indication of a long-term decline during the present century: nationally the reverse applies (Pollard & Yates, 1993).

Conservation

None required, except perhaps some research to establish the population regulation factors. If lack of safe hibernation sites is a limiting factor, provision of artificial hibernacula might increase the abundance of this very attractive butterfly.

Ecologyy and biology

Very similar to the small tortoiseshell except that it is single brooded in Essex in all but the hottest and sunniest summers. Because the summer adults go into hibernation as soon as they have an adequate store of fat (laid down by nectaring) they cease activity earlier in summer than the small tortoiseshell (see flight-time graphs)

Butterfly gardening

Peacocks visit gardens mainly in summer, nectaring prior to hibernation. The best nectar plants are buddleia, ice plant (*Sedum spectabile*) and Michaelmas daisy

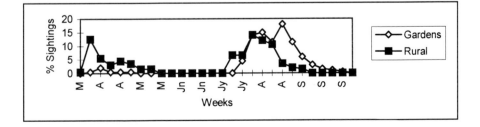

(*Aster novi-belgii*). Large woodpiles, especially those containing hollow logs, are excellent for hibernation. Peacocks also use sheds and other outbuildings (beware of them becoming trapped against closed windows on waking in spring) and sometimes enter houses. There is a high mortality rate in houses because of the low humidity and winter heating: it is probably best to move them early in autumn into suitable outbuildings.

Comma   *Polygonia c–album*

Status

Resident, widespread and fairly common

Rural sites 54%; individuals 1.3%   Gardens 79%; individuals 2.3%

Habitats and larval foodplants

Most commonly a woodland ride and woodland edge species, the comma can be seen as an adult in a wide variety of habitats including gardens. It is not an open meadow butterfly. The larvae feed mainly on stinging nettle (*Urtica dioica*) and, unlike the other nettle feeders, use nettles in light or partial shade as well as sunlit patches. There are also several cases of them feeding on regenerating elm-suckers in Essex.

History

"Very rare, if not now extinct in the county, like the hop industry" was how Fitch (1891) summarised the situation. An important statement since, to Fitch and others of his time, the comma's normal larval foodplant was cultivated hop (*Humulus* spp.) which reminds us that there was once a hop-growing industry in Essex.

Specifically for Epping, Doubleday (1836) wrote "Many years since it used to occur in profusion at Epping; I cannot give any date but it was when I was a mere

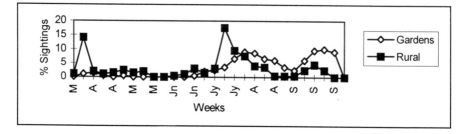

Comma

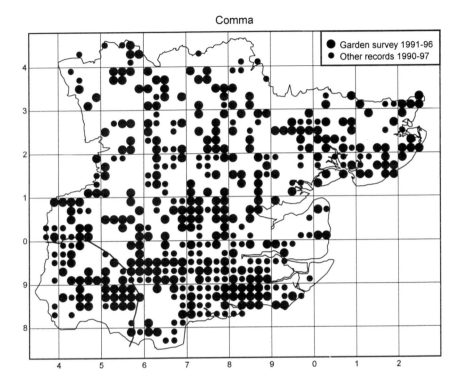

child – I should judge about 1817 or 1818....Since those times I have never met with the insect here." Fitch could give a few isolated records of individual Essex specimens all in areas remote from London and that is all. It was extinct as a breeding species and so it remained until the 1930s when it rapidly recolonised the county and was countywide by the mid-1940s (Firmin et al., 1975) and so it remains today.

In Britain it survived the 'gap' only in the west-Midlands and Welsh Marches. The decline and recovery happened on an almost identical timescale in the Netherlands (Tax, 1989).

Site/Year	83	84	85	86	87	88	89	90	91	92	93	94	95	96
St Osyth	0	0	0	0	0	0	0	0	*	0	0	1	3	*
Stour Wood	12	7	2	9	*	*	16	4	24	14	0	7	16	8
Leigh Marshes	1	6	0	7	1	7	*	1	9	15	6	4	*	7

Conservation and ecology

It seems that early in the 19th century, throughout its English range, this really was a hop-feeding species. Also it seems to have been very much more abundant though with no greater a range than at present. The theory that commas made use of commercial hop-fields and laid for preference, if not exclusively, in this habitat, is plausible. The hop industry collapsed in the 1870s except in the west Midlands (where the comma survived) and Kent, where it did not. Perhaps the arrival of early insecticides, used on hops from 1883 may have suddenly affected the remaining commas. Only after some decades did a minor evolutionary change occur so that commas laid for preference on nettle: then they expanded in range again. (Pratt, in Emmet & Heath, 1989).

The above is such a plausible theory that I hesitate to point out that the comma is also one of the honeydew and sap-run feeders that could have been affected by pollution deposits on trees in the east of England – see discussion in chapter 5.

Butterfly gardening

Commas selectively visit Essex gardens with buddleia and valerian. They do not seem to hibernate in garden buildings, as small tortoiseshells and peacocks do, but may breed on partially shaded nettles (pre-flowering stage) in larger gardens.

Small Pearl-bordered Fritillary   *Boloria selene*

Status

Extinct since the mid-1950s

Habitat and larval foodplants

In Essex this was a species of open, coppiced or pollarded woodland on gravel or acid soils. The larvae feed on violets: mainly the dog violet (*Viola riviniana*) and prefers areas two years after they have been opened up.

History

"In open places in woods. Common in Epping Forest and in many other restricted localities throughout the county." (Fitch, 1891). That is not a selective quotation from Fitch it is the entirety of his entry: some other species got a page or more. Open woodlands, coppiced or pollarded, growing on gravel or sandy ridges, were common in Essex and so was the small pearl-bordered fritillary. What was there to worry about? The lack of precise records means that the map is almost devoid of pre-1900s records!

After the 1930s it seems to have been on the way out. H.C. Huggins introduced it at Belfairs Wood in 1937 and 1940. The colony survived until 1948. Elsewhere the only real colony(ies) reported were in the Brentwood area where "Pearl-bordered Fritillary and Small Pearl-bordered Fritillary were very common in their usual haunts [in the Brentwood area]" (Williams, 1953). If only the excellent Fred Williams had been a little more precise: that was the last ever report of this species breeding in Essex. Although Fred Williams was the Lepidoptera recorder for the Essex Field Club, his records do not seem to have survived him. Perhaps he was referring to Norsey Wood where another observer reported the pearl-bordered fritillaries in 1952: seen from the train on the 20th of May (Friedlein, 1953).

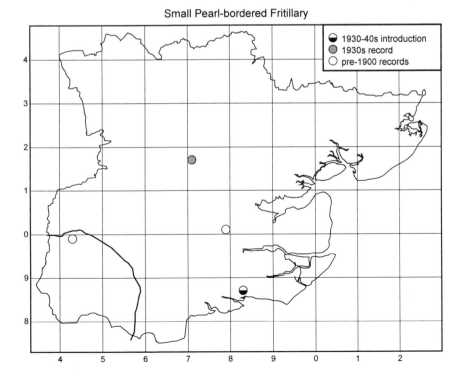

Small Pearl-bordered Fritillary

Conservation and ecology

All the existing ecological and national distribution knowledge is summarised in the recent Butterfly Conservation Species Action Plan for this species (Barnett & Warren, 1995c). Almost all the long list of recommendations concentrate on monitoring and safeguarding the species in the west and north of Britain where it still exists. For us in the Anglian region the only relevant recommendation is the one concerning re-introductions (into networks of suitable habitats it is emphasised): see the discussion in chapter 7.

Pearl-bordered Fritillary   *Boloria euphrosyne*

Status

Extinct as a native since the late 1960s. Re-established for a few years in the 1990s. Probably now extinct.

Habitat and larval ecology

In Essex, and south-eastern England generally, the habitat was almost identical with that of the small pearl-bordered fritillary and the two species once occurred together in many well-drained open woodlands on gravel or acid soils. The larval foodplant is also dog violet (*Viola riviniana*). The subtle difference was in preferred micro-climate for egg-laying (this species liking drier soils and the warmest conditions immediately after coppicing).

History

"Common in open places in woods, more so than [the small pearl-bordered fritillary] and earlier in appearance; generally distributed. Abounds in Epping Forest and in most large woods of the county." Fitch (1891). The pattern of decline began later than with the previous species and strong colonies survived well into the 1960s although the Epping Forest "abundance" had been reduced to a few scattered and unconfirmed reports in the 1940s and none since 1949.

The final colony was at Little Baddow Heath (now part of the Essex Wildlife Trust complex of Danbury woodland and heathland reserves). This colony became extinct in 1968 and was re-established for a few years in 1991. The detailed story of this re-establishment experiment is given in chapter 6.

Pearl-bordered Fritillary

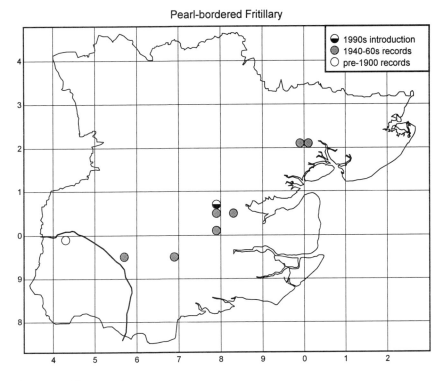

Conservation ecology

Butterfly Conservation's Species Action Plan (Barnett & Warren, 1995d) for this species gives a detailed summary of what is known of the ecology and requirements of this species and, as befits one of the most endangered species in Britain, it has been subject of some detailed studies.

It is clear that suitable woodland management, in woods that once held the species, is all that is required for re-establishment of the species. But for the re-established colony to stand a good chance of survival it needs to be part of a complex of

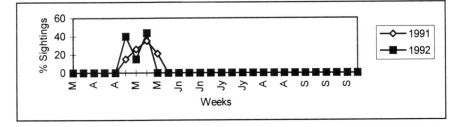

colonies on a large area where the rotating management is constantly making new clearings. The opportunities for further re-establishment trials in Essex is discussed in chapter 7.

Queen of Spain Fritillary   *Argynnis lathonia*

Status

A rare vagrant: no record since 1918 until recent years.

Habitat

The pattern of sightings of this rare migrant to Britain (mainly along the south coast) suggest it arrives from France and from populations of this species where short to medium length migrations are part of the normal biology. This would explain the very rare arrivals in Essex.

It has been suggested that this species cannot survive the English winter (Thomas & Lewington, 1991) but this seems unlikely to be the case with the other ecological race of this species: those that inhabit the dunelands of the Netherlands and form resident populations in a climate similar to the East Anglian one. These duneland butterflies feed, as larvae, on field pansies (*Viola arvensis* and *V.tricolor*). It is firmly established in the Dutch and Danish dunelands and is doing well (but is extinct in Flanders). Presumably this race is less mobile than the southern European ones (butterflies resident in fairly small habitat systems undergo natural selection for low mobility).

In Essex the foodplants of the duneland race grow only on arable land where ploughing would make it difficult for the butterfly to complete its life-cycle.

History

Fitch (1891) summarises records for the 19th century: most near Colchester and all the others near the coast except for one in Braintree. A few years (e.g. 1818) produced several records but the average was well under one report per three years.

The only 20th century record was of two in Colchester in 1918 until 1995 when there were four reports of individuals from various parts of Essex at the same time as the arrival of many Camberwell beauties. These records were: Bradwell-on-Sea (TM0282) in July, Lanermere (TM1822), Thorrinton (TM0818) and Kelvedon

(TL8618), these three August. These migrants are likely to have come from the Netherlands and Danish duneland populations in my opinion.

High Brown Fritillary   *Argynnis adippe*

Status
Extinct since 1960 but with occasional vagrants.

Habitat and larval foodplant
Until it became extinct in eastern England everyone thought it lived mainly in coppice woodlands. Now research elsewhere in England has shown the importance of bracken-dominated habitats. In either habitat the larvae feed on dog violets growing in a warm, dry microclimate ideal for their development. Whether the

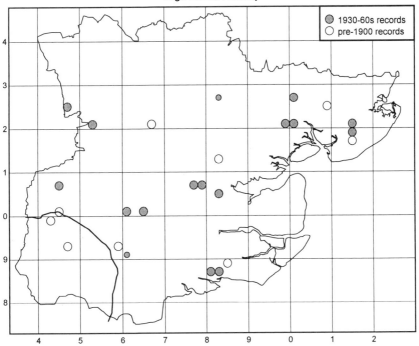

High Brown Fritillary

stands of bracken in Epping Forest or elsewhere were ever important Essex habitats for this butterfly is not known, but it seems probable they were.

History

"Not common, but probably generally distributed in our larger woods. Apparently rarer now than formerly" is how Fitch (1891) summarised the late 19th century situation. It is clear from the list of records Fitch gives that the species had been present in the Epping Forest and Hainault area but was then gone, it remained more common in the Colchester and north-east Essex areas and in the Brentwood region.

By the late 1930s it was spreading, reaching Hatfield Forest at that time and the Maldon area by 1947. It was present in south-east Essex at this time although the beginnings of a decline were noted in 1948. The last records in that region were in 1960 (Hadleigh Down) (Firmin et al., 1975).

It is probably significant that the areas where it was reported "abundant" up to the 1950s were the Brentwood, Fryerning, and Blackmore district and the Doneyland, Berechurch and High Woods area south of Colchester: both areas which, at that time, had plenty of bracken-dominated heathland but which have now scrubbed over and mostly become woodland.

Occasional records, of individual specimens continued, mostly in hot summers, since the extinction as a breeding species and into the mid-1980s.

Conservation and ecology

The Species Action Plan for this species (Barnett & Warren, 1995e) rightly concentrates on work in the west and north of England where the few viable colonies of this species persist. As a large, mobile species, which lives at fairly low density, re-establishment into small nature reserves is not an option. Appropriate habitat re-creation in large areas such as Epping Forest might be possible but this would probably conflict with other management objectives.

Dark Green Fritillary   *Argynnis aglaja*

Status

Extinct (as resident) since the late 1950s or early 1960s. Vagrants still occur.

Habitat and larval foodplant

The main habitat types for this species are chalk and limestone downlands and coastal dunes or grasslands: but not in Essex of course. At the peak of its abundance in Essex it became a woodland species as it did elsewhere in south-east England, living in open coppiced woods or wide woodland rides. The caterpillars feed on violets, mainly dog violet (*Viola riviniana*).

History

"Rare; on commons, heaths and rough hillsides. Local and apparently disappearing from the county" (Fitch, 1891) followed this summary with very few records

Dark Green Fritillary

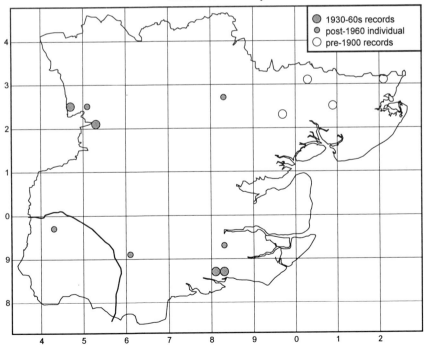

indeed, some of which he noted as doubtful. In Hadleigh it survived until 1934 when the locality was destroyed by building (Firmin et al. 1975). It occurred in small to moderate numbers on Danbury Ridge 1936-38 and for several years to 1947 in Hatfield Forest. The main centre seems to have been the (now) country parks near Brentwood.

It is fairly clear that this was the rarest of the large Fritillaries in Essex and yet it is the only one still to breed in some of our surrounding counties. Today it is the least infrequent vagrant to Essex of all the extinct Fritillaries.

Conservation

Nationally this is the least endangered of the large fritillaries. Essex has always been short of classic habitats for this species and it is unlikely that it will return as a breeding species, either naturally or through deliberate re-establishment.

Silver-washed Fritillary   *Argynnis paphia*

Status

Extinct as a breeding species since the late 1950s. Occasional vagrants since.

Habitat and larval foodplant

This is very much a species of open, coppiced, woodland. The larvae feed on various violets but most commonly the dog violet (*Viola riviniana*).

History

"Formerly abundant in most of our larger woods, now rare and local" Fitch (1891). Like the other two large fritillaries, it increased its range dramatically during the 1930s and 1940s. By 1947 it was quite abundant in Hatfield Forest in the west and well established in the Maldon and North Fambridge areas to the east of the county and had strongholds in the Colchester area (Firmin et al., 1975). It did not recolonise Epping Forest but otherwise became quite widespread. The decline in the 1950s was rapid ending with the sudden disappearance in 1958 from its haunts at Berechurch. Vagrants still occur, the most recent being at Jaywick in 1997.

Silver-washed Fritillary

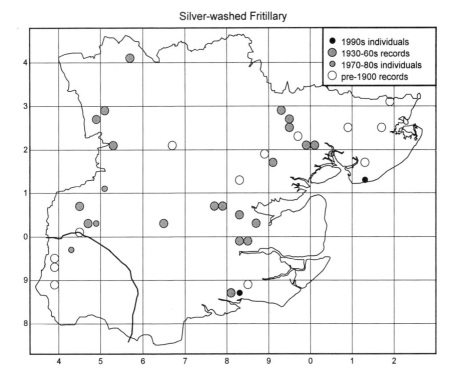

Conservation

As a strictly woodland species (a requirement built in by the need for the females to lay their eggs on tree-trunks close to violets) it might be possible to manage a large area of woodland through short-rotation coppicing and attempt a re-establishment of the species. This has yet to be done in any of the eastern counties, from which the species has been lost. A plan to re-introduce the species to Hatfield Forest in the early 1990s was abandoned following a change of mind by the National Trust.

Marsh Fritillary   *Eurodryas aurinia*

Status
Extinct since the middle of the 19th century.

Habitat and larval foodplant
The very localised colonies occur in damp meadows or dry downland where the larval foodplant: devil's bit scabious (*Succisa pratensis*) grows in abundance.

History
"Rare and very local, in damp meadows" (Fitch, 1891). From the records he gives and what other information exists, Fitch seems to have been guilty of wishful thinking. It was not rare but extinct when he wrote. The only colonies known ever to have existed in Essex were in the Roding Valley water catchment and the

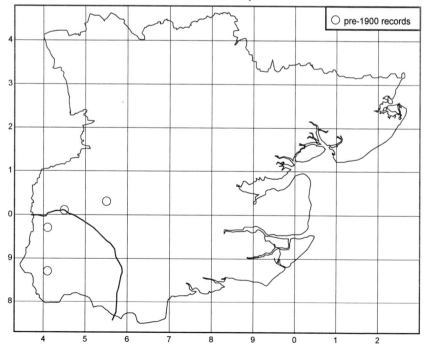

Marsh Fritillary

Saffron Walden region and none since four were reported from Epping Forest in 1857 (Tyssen, 1857).

Conservation

The Species Action Plan (Barnett & Warren, 1995f) gives a detailed summary of the ecology or this species. All the recommendations in this plan are concerned with maintaining the species in the west of its range in Britain, not with restoring it to regions from which it was lost over 100 years ago. Colonies of this species can survive in quite small areas and are very easy to introduce into habitats with the larval foodplant. A significant proportion of the known colonies were created in this way.

Heath Fritillary   *Mellicta athalia*

Status

Extinct but [re-]established at two sites.

Habitat and Larval Foodplant

In Essex, the only larval foodplant is common cow-wheat (*Melampyrum pratense*) growing in coppiced woodlands on slightly acidic soils.

History

The nineteenth century records show that the main colonies were in the woods around Colchester and it was in this region that the species survived longest (until after 1870 but not beyond the turn of the century). It has been suggested (Stovin in Stokoe, 1944) that it was the darkening of these woods as coppicing gave way to game preservation that caused the extinction: a suggestion made by others for several parts of Britain). The Colchester area woodlands still exist and still contain

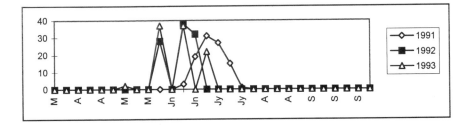

the larval foodplant (Tarpey & Heath, 1990). The records from the Epping area are of few individuals and pre-date 1850. Cow-wheat also survives in these habitats (Jermyn, 1974).

Establishments

All the recorded establishment attempts of this species have been in habitats from which the species was never recorded as a native. With the one exception, of a habitat from which the foodplant is absent, all have worked and produced colonies that have survived several years. Where these introduced colonies have become extinct it is clear that cessation of suitable coppice management was the cause (except for the early introduction by Harwood where the site is unknown).

The two extant Essex colonies have survived since the mid-1980s and are in SSSI nature reserves specially managed to maintain good populations of the larval foodplant and the butterfly. In 1997 English Nature established a third Essex colony (in Belfairs Wood) now that a suitable management regime is in place and

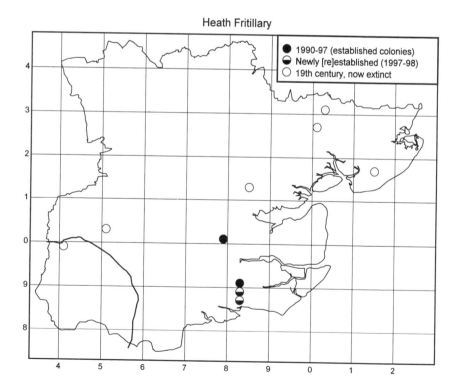

Heath Fritillary

the Essex Wildlife Trust plans a fourth in nearby Pound Wood (which has a good cow-wheat population).

Conservation needs

In the national context, this is the most important Essex butterfly. Heath fritillaries have been rescued from the verge of extinction by positive conservation (Warren, 1991) and the Essex colonies are the only places in which it survives in East Anglia and one of only two regions in eastern England.

The two current colonies seem likely to survive provided the present management regime is continued and an attempt to increase the number of colonies to four in underway. This is being done using donor stock (adult butterflies, as has succeeded before) from Essex colonies (which are now strong and where the species may already have undergone micro-evolution adjusting it to conditions in Essex).

Despite current views that pheasants have little effect on fritillary butterflies (see chapter 5) it is noticeable that the two Essex sites have no pheasant rearing. In the Kent (Blean Woods complex) pheasant-rearing has continued even on nature reserves and the heath fritillary colonies are at low levels despite best-practice coppice management. No doubt it is just a coincidence. This species has full legal protection under the Wildlife & Countryside Act and any investigations involving capture of any stage require a licence from English Nature.

The two Essex sites are nature reserves with public access at all times. Visitors wishing to see the butterflies are welcome provided they take care not to damage the habitat (in particular by treading on the foodplants) or disturb egg-laying females. Any sightings of people capturing specimens should be reported to the police and the Essex Wildlife Trust immediately.

Ecology and biology

This species has been the subject of very detailed research (summarised in Barnett & Warren, 1995g) as part of the national conservation campaign. Of its three habitat types only coppice woodland with cow-wheat is used in eastern England.

Little is known of parasitoids attacking the larvae: there are no known species-specific parasitoids and no parasitised stock was introduced when the species was re-established in the county. In 1992 Stephen Davis and Tony Filbee (personal. communication) reared a batch of larvae collected in spring in Thrift Wood: none were parasitised. The hatched adults were returned to Thrift Wood on the day of emergence: a condition of the English Nature licence for this study.

Spotted Fritillary   *Melitaea didyma*

Status

Single colony established for one year only; source unknown

History

This is a species from mainland Europe and the short-lived colony in Essex is its only occurrence as a breeding species in Britain. The following account is verbatim from Pyman (1987):

"TQ78 Fobbing Marshes, six, 6th August 1986 (per C.H.S. Hodder). This remarkable record represents the second British occurrence (the first being regarded as suspect) of this fritillary which, on the continent, extends northwards to Belgium. The 'colony' was discovered by two schoolboys who collected two of the insects and gave them to C.H.S. Hodder (their biology master). In view of the remoteness and unsuitable nature of the site it is felt unlikely that the insects had been released there. The possibility that they were the progeny of an impregnated female blown across the North Sea cannot be discounted, but it is perhaps more likely that their parent had arrived on a tanker (the Mobil oil terminal is only 1.25 miles away) or other vessel berthing on Thames-side."

Colin Plant (personal communication) examined these two specimens when they were exhibited at a London Natural History Society meeting soon after capture. They were of the subspecies *M .d. didyma* which occurs widely in central Europe. This subspecies was exceptionally abundant in parts of France in 1986.

Monarch   *Danaeus plexipus*

Status

A very rare vagrant to Britain from America, mainly to the south-western regions. Emmet et al. (1985) give only four records for Essex the most recent of these was in July 1982, at Loughton. One was seen in Chelmsford by Colin Penney in 1985. Another at Jaywick in 1995, seen by Jon Young, is the most recent record, in a year of large numbers of reports in southern England.

Speckled Wood   *Pararge aegeria*

Status

Widespread and common in woodlands having recolonised Essex completely since 1955.

Rural sites 61%; individuals 6.2%   Gardens 29%; individuals 0.7%

Habitat and larval foodplants

Woodlands with dappled shade and other partly shaded habitats (which can include larger gardens) are the sole haunt of the speckled wood. Both sexes feed on honeydew in the tree canopy. The eggs are laid on a wide variety of grasses growing in warm sheltered spots in these habitats.

Speckled Wood

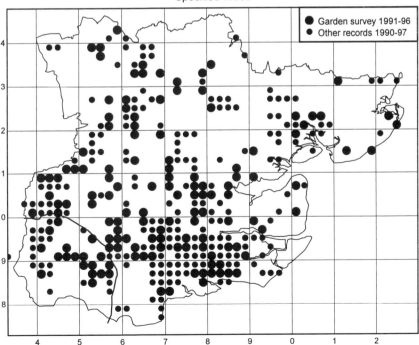

History

"Common in most woods in the county and in shady lanes and about hedgerows on the outskirts; generally distributed, but not everywhere, mostly local. Quite absent now in the Colchester district where it was formerly common" (Fitch, 1891). I have quoted Fitch's assessment at length because it helps date the start of the decline of this species which seems to have occurred throughout the county in the mid-19th century. B.G. Cole added an editor's note "Still very common in Monks Wood, Epping Forest" – again important as much for the implication that it had been lost from the southern parts of the Forest as for the dated report from the central region. Writing of the period 1869-74 Meldola (1891) said "...was never seen at Leyton, but commonly in the Forest" [implying most or all of the Forest].

Only 12 years later Harwood (1903) could write "...was common in the eastern counties in the middle of the last century, but ere its close had vanished completely from nearly all its former haunts...Why it disappeared is a mystery, for it was common in nearly every copse and shady place, and abounded in some woods where it was quite unmolested by collectors."

Apart from scattered reports of odd individuals, some perhaps resulting from clandestine and admitted releases see chapter 5, speckled woods seem to have remained extinct as a breeding species until 1955 when they recolonised Langdon Hills (Firmin et al., 1975). From then on the pattern was a spread northwards and westwards, reaching the extreme north-west by the early 1990s and recolonising Epping Forest from the north. It has now reached further into London than Meldola would have believed possible.

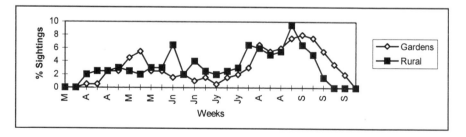

Site/Year	83	84	85	86	87	88	89	90	91	92	93	94	95	96
Stour Wood	0	0	1	0	0	0	0	0	0	0	7	14	48	24

Butterfly Gardening

Some larger gardens with shady corners have reported small colonies of speckled woods. They are usually uninterested in nectar plants. Males hold territories in sunspots and their interactions with other individuals makes for enjoyable butterfly watching.

Wall   *Lasiommata megera*

Status

Recent very rapid decline to the point of absence from most inland sites. Previously a widespread species subject to large fluctuations in abundance.

Rural sites 38%; individuals 0.5%   Gardens 34%; individuals 0.5%

[note these surveys pre-date the recent steep decline]

Habitat and larval foodplants

According to Thomas & Lewington (1991) "...areas of dry, unfertilized grassland with a ...broken terrain, and an abundance of bare patches" are the main habitat from which it spreads into other full-sun grassland habitats in years of abundance. The larvae feed on a variety of grasses which naturally grow as tussocks (*Dactylis glomerata* and *Deschampsia flexuosa*) or grow as walls of grass against fences or hedges (*Agrostis* spp and *Holcus lanatus*).

History

"Abundant; flying along every hedge in the county in the summer" was how Fitch (1891) described the status of the wall: it seems that walls have declined even faster than hedges. This decline is recent; "generally distributed and common" described the situation in 1974 (Firmin et al., 1975) but "Following the drought summer of 1976 it suffered a spectacular decline but it staged a full recovery by 1979" was added to the "generally distributed and, as a rule, common" in Emmet

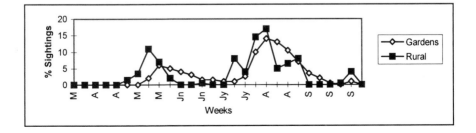

Site/Year	83	84	85	86	87	88	89	90	91	92	93	94	95	96
St Osyth	0	1	1	0	3	0	3	4	0	0	4	1	0	0
Stour Wood	40	14	0	4	0	0	45	54	8	14	19	25	6	0
Leigh Marshes	62	12	5	0	0	6	0	32	3	0	2	0	0	1

et al. (1985). My own experience in part of Epping Forest from the 1950s to mid 1960s (Corke, 1968) is that it was very common and declined sharply in the years 1962-67. It seems to have been more common in the coastal regions and the freely draining soils of the centre of the county; this equates well with its known habitat preferences at the national level (Thomas & Lewington, 1991).

It has declined in the 1990s to the point were it is practically absent from the county. There were 30 known sites in 1995, 25 in 1996 and only 5 sites reported for 1997 at the time of going to press. Joe Firmin reports that it is still present in the north-east coastal zone; always one of its strongholds.

Wall Brown

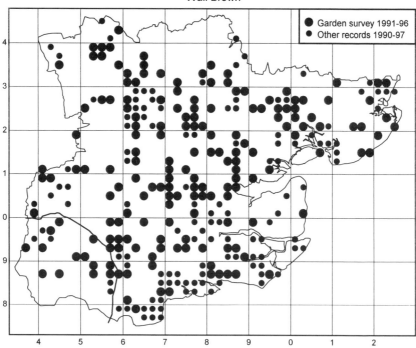

Fluctuations and decline

Common butterflies usually get less full reports than the rare ones and this seems to have been the case in Essex for the wall. At a national level it suffered dramatic declines in range in the 1860s which it has largely regained. Locally, colonisations of secondary habitats occur in good years; helped by the two or three generations a year. It seems probable that Essex walls also showed fluctuations in abundance before those reported for the 1960s and 1970s but that these were not noticed by recorders who were mainly based in the east and centre of the county, in areas which have a high density of the butterfly's primary habitat.

The dramatic and prolonged decline in the second half of the 1990s has occurred in all our surrounding counties and also in the Low Countries. It has not occurred in northern England and seems to be associated with the arable and urban areas. Variations in climate have been the first explanation for many, but these seem contradictory. Thomas & Lewington (1991) report the ill effects of a series of wet summers in the 1980s at the national level, in Essex a decline in the 1970s was blamed on a hot, dry summer. Analysis of the national butterfly monitoring survey data (Pollard & Yates, 1993) showed that warm summers were associated with higher counts that summer but lower than normal the next. Since the species is fairly common in habitats from the southern shores of the mediterranean to southern scandinavia, it seems that it can be fairly tolerant of climatic variations.

Fluctuations such as the wall has shown are, in some other species, known to result from interactions with parasites. This has been suggested as a possible cause for the recent decline in the wall (Murray, 1997).

The ecology and population dynamics of walls have never been studied in any detail and such a study is an urgent priority. At present it is impossible to say whether the reduced fortunes of the wall in and around Essex is a prelude to extinction or a mere low in the normal pattern of fluctuations.

Butterfly gardening

Walls visit gardens, nectar from buddleia and may breed in larger gardens with wild grass in full sun. Most gardens are likely to be secondary habitats occupied only in periods of reasonable abundance.

Marbled White   *Melanargia galathea*

Status

Well-established on coastal grassland habitats in the south-east of Essex. Currently increasing in range and abundance.

Rural sites 8.7%; individuals 0.3%   Gardens 0.004%; individuals 0.001%

Habitats and larval foodplants

The caterpillars can eat a variety of grasses but it is believed that red fescue (*Festuca rubra*) is essential for the young caterpillars: the eggs are dropped amongst grasses not attached to a foodplant chosen by the female butterfly. In Essex it is largely restricted to coastal grasslands in the south-east but with a recent colonisation of an old chalk quarry.

Marbled White

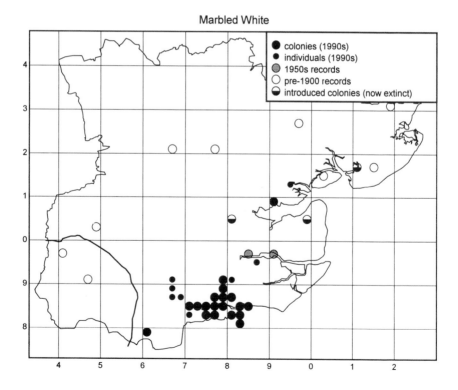

Site/Year	83	84	85	86	87	88	89	90	91	92	93	94	95	96
St Osyth	0	0	0	0	0	1	0	0	0	0	0	0	0	0
Leigh Marshes	3	2	9	10	1	4	0	2	15	1	2	2	8	1

History

"It is most frequent with us round Braintree" (Ray, 1710). "Very local; it has disappeared from many of its old localities and is rapidly becoming rare in others" (Fitch, 1895). The inland colonies disappeared early, for example the last reports from Epping Forest were in the 1830s, Hainault Forest in the 1850s and woodland localities in the Colchester area did not survive into the latter half of the 19th century.

Survival through the low point of the late 1950s was on Canvey Island and the coastal grassland slopes of the adjacent mainland.

The range and numbers of reports have increased during the 1990s although it is still restricted to the extreme south-eastern part of the county. A pair seen mating at North Fambridge in 1997 by Joe Firmin, this is the first recent indication of a spread back north of the river Crouch.

Conservation

Little is known of the population biology of this butterfly nor of its exact habitat requirements. Its habitats in Essex are atypical: in most parts of England it is a downland species. Recent attempts at establishing the species slightly outside its natural range in Essex produced colonies that survived only for a few years: see chapter 6.

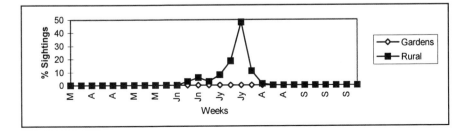

Grayling   *Hipparchia semele*

Status

Probably extinct as a native species but colonies may remain undiscovered.

Larval foodplants and habitats

From what is known of its foodplant preferences nationally (Thomas & Lewington, 1991) the Essex populations are likely to have fed mainly on the grasses *Festuca ovina* or *Agrostis setacea*. Essex colonies have always been on very dry, free-draining soils: mainly the sands and gravels near Colchester and on the coast but also known from chalk quarries.

History

"Very rare and local; on dry hill-sides, but generally confined to chalk or limestone soils." (Fitch, 1891). The comment on its habitat preference is odd since

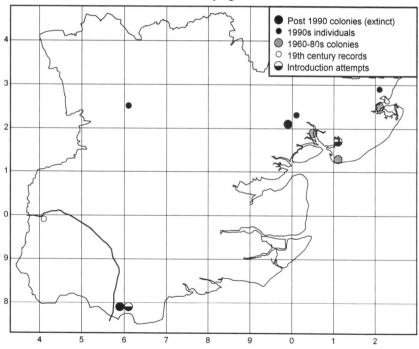

Grayling

the Essex habitats listed are all flat, sandy heaths except for the Saffron Walden area where some specimens in the local museum were believed to have come from that area. Harwood (1903) also regarded it as very rare and local, reports being of odd 'stragglers' even in the Colchester district where he believed it had once been common on "some of the extensive heaths and moors that surrounded Colchester in past times."

The 19th century heathlands in Epping Forest (at a time when the silver-studded blue was common there) would have seemed a likely habitat for graylings and yet the only record from this well-studied area was a single specimen collected by Meldola in 1869 and listed by de Worms (1959). The specimen is now in the Hope Entomological Collections at Oxford University and I am grateful to Dr G. C. McGavin for checking it for me. The data label says "Epping Forest Sept 8/69" plus an acquisitions label giving its origin from the Meldola collection. The specimen is a male, looking somewhat washed-out and rather smaller than the norm. Graylings wander: for example the 1995 record of one photographed in a garden near Dunmow a long way from any known colony. The Epping Forest record may represent a colony lost early from the Forest or a single wanderer.

The fact that graylings were well established on two nature reserves (Colne Point and Fingringhoe Wick) in the 1960s and were reported common in and around Colchester (especially the Berechurch area) at the same time, suggests that a considerable increase in abundance had taken place in the intervening 50 or 60 years, perhaps involving colonisation from the strong Suffolk colonies.

The nature reserve colonies died out in the late 1960s (Fingringhoe) and early 1970s. The Berechurch (Middlewick ranges) colony was the sole known Essex colony from then until 1992 when it became extinct.

In 1996 a colony was discovered in an old chalk quarry just as the site was about to be developed for housing. An attempt is under way to translocate this colony but success seems improbable.

Introductions

Unsuccessful introductions were made at St Martins Farm, St Osyth (a restored grassland site); at sites in the Berechurch region from which the species had become extinct and a recent translocation from Mill Wood pit to Grays Chalk Quarry nature reserve. There are more details in chapter 6.

Site/Year	83	84	85	86	87	88	89	90	91	92	93	94	95	96
St Osyth	0	0	0	0	2	0	0	0	0	0	0	0	0	0

Butterfly gardening

Wanderers are occasionally seen in gardens although graylings have never been known to breed there. Since it is possible that undetected colonies survive somewhere in Essex, it is worth watching for garden sightings and then searching likely habitats (such as chalk pits) in the area.

Gatekeeper   *Pyronia tithonus*

Status

Widespread and abundant. Has increased in range by re-colonisation of the urban regions of south-west Essex and north-east London.

Rural sites 74%; Individuals 12.3%   Gardens 84%; Individuals 6.5%

Larval foodplant and habitats

Essentially this is a hedgerow species: or any other habitat where longish grass grows in the lee of shrubs and trees but still in the sun. A wide-range of fine and medium-leaved grasses are known as larval foodplants: there have been no detailed ecological studies of its foodplant preferences but the micro-habitat of the grass (tallish plant in sunny, sheltered spot) may be more important than the grass species (Thomas & Lewington, 1991).

History

"Abundant everywhere in the county" (Fitch, 1891). This is still true today, although the actual numbers in the county will have declined in proportion to the length of hedgerows since Fitch was writing.

A curious change occurred in the range of gatekeepers near London: they were completely absent from London and Epping Forest in the first half of this century

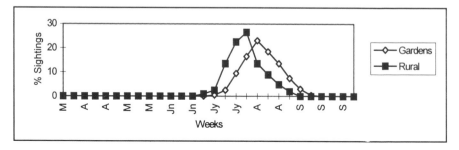

Site/Year	83	84	85	86	87	88	89	90	91	92	93	94	95	96
St Osyth	5	5	13	21	48	41	126	55	173	190	114	44	31	11
Stour Wood	401	386	205	377	*	129	237	236	322	246	211	199	272	189
Leigh Marshes	373	623	411	380	300	162	*	459	580	374	204	231	348	337

but spread back into Epping Forest from the northern end between the early 1960s and mid-1980s and is now the commonest species in many parts of the Forest. This happened at a time of national extension of range northwards which has been ascribed to climatic factors (Pollard & Yates, 1993) but this seems unlikely to be the explanation for a southern extension of range into the city. I have suggested that this was due to a recovery from the effects of air-pollution which seem to have affected most butterflies that feed on honeydew as adults (see discussion in chapter 5 and Corke, 1996).

Gatekeeper

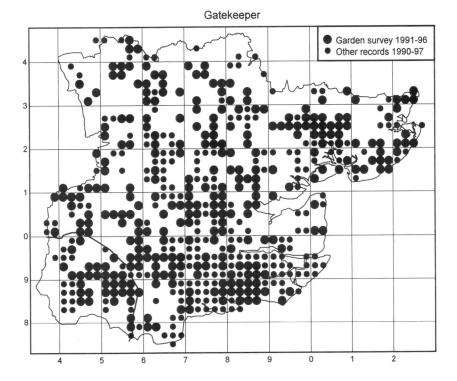

Butterfly gardening

Gatekeepers can be encouraged to breed in larger gardens where it is possible to grow hedges (of native shrubs ideally) with unkempt grass on the sunny side of the hedge. Bramble flowers are excellent nectar sources.

Meadow Brown   *Maniola jurtina*

Status

Widespread and common in colonies in open, long grass habitats.
Rural sites 87%; Individuals 17.2%   Gardens 65%; Individuals 3.6%

Larval foodplant and habitats

Most typically found in open, fairly long grassland but also in wide woodland rides and glades. A wide variety of fine or medium leaved grasses are used as foodplants *Poa*, *Lolium* and *Agrostis* species being the favourites quoted in national studies (Thomas & Lewington, 1991).

History

"Very abundant in all meadows, as everywhere" (Fitch, 1891). Although meadow browns are still common in the right habitat, suitable meadows are rare. When Fitch was writing, and for 50 years thereafter, Essex agriculture was horse-powered and cattle rearing was widespread so hay meadows were common. Now this is a butterfly of wide roadside verges, woodland glades, public open spaces and nature reserves together with large gardens. It still appears to be the commonest Essex butterfly from the surveys in rural sites although these surveys were done mainly in nature reserves. The land occupied by meadow browns is probably only about 5% of that where they lived at the turn of the century.

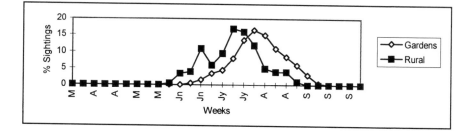

Site/Year	83	84	85	86	87	88	89	90	91	92	93	94	95	96
St Osyth	144	98	283	214	960	821	819	175	518	235	242	203	99	24
Stour Wood	155	116	48	110	*	112	162	335	293	335	388	456	392	358
Leigh Marshes	105	107	118	176	144	99	*	47	84	62	61	80	95	30

Conservation needs

Very large colonies exist on many Essex nature reserves (e.g. Roding Valley and Langdon) where sensitive management by cutting hay-meadows over a period of days and encouraging flower-rich sward favours this species. This form of management could also be used more widely for the management of grasslands in country parks.

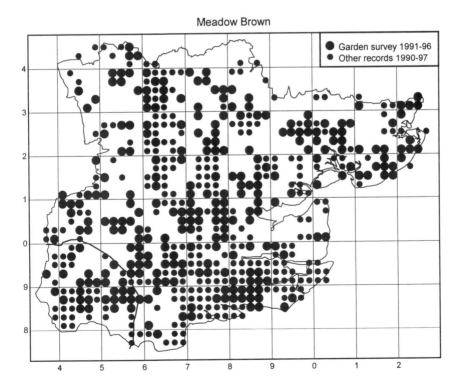

Meadow Brown

Butterfly gardening

The garden survey recorded meadow browns as widespread but far from abundant in most gardens. In large gardens 'mini-meadows' in full sun are likely to be suitable for meadow browns if left to grow until mid-July before cutting. Meadow browns occur right into the London part of Essex although those seen in smaller gardens are probably wanderers rather than members of a breeding colony.

Small Heath   *Coenonympha pamphilus*

Status

Widespread and fairly common in open, short grass habitats.

Rural sites 61%; Individuals 4.4%   Gardens 19%; Individuals 0.5%

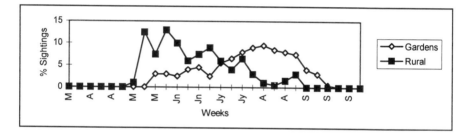

Larval foodplant and habitats

Open grassy habitats, ideally with grass shorter than that preferred by meadow browns. Freely draining soils seem to have higher populations and set-aside fields put down to grass can acquire large populations very quickly. A wide variety of grasses are used as larval foodplants in England with a possible preference for *Festuca* spp (Thomas & Lewington, 1991)

Site/Year	83	84	85	86	87	88	89	90	91	92	93	94	95	96
St Osyth	55	140	514	635	623	*	299	175	*	165	80	43	4	1
Stour Wood	8	5	2	0	*	0	0	0	1	2	0	0	0	1
Leigh Marshes	39	77	37	51	30	18	*	225	89	67	41	*	*	52

History

"Very common everywhere throughout summer" (Fitch, 1891). This is no longer the case and much of the loss has been ascribed to the scrub encroachment on ungrazed land that followed the reduced rabbit population after myxomatosis (Firmin et al. 1975). This is still a very widespread butterfly and the multiple generations each year allow rapid population increases when conditions are good. Over much of the county, roadside verges are probably the most important habitat.

Small Heath

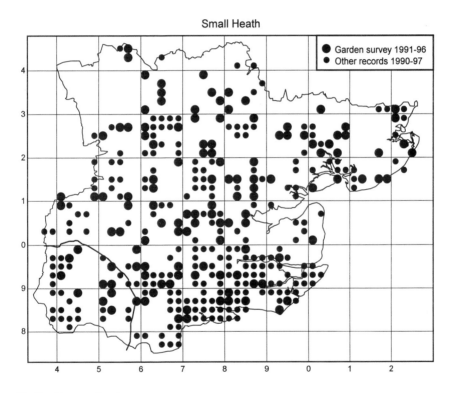

Garden survey 1991-96
Other records 1990-97

Butterfly gardening

Small heaths are relatively rare garden butterflies. They are known to like buttercups as nectar plants on the rather rare occasions when they take nectar. Cultivation of mini-meadows may attract this species to breed if the grass is fairly short.

Ringlet   *Aphantopus hyperantus*

Status

Widespread and common in colonies associated with long grass in woodlands or near tall hedgerows. Absent from habitats on the London side of the M25 but expanding its range in this direction.

Rural sites 29%; Individuals 1.8%   Gardens 9.6%; Individuals 0.3%

Larval foodplants and habitats

Colonies are usually associated with woodlands: in wide rides and glades, at the edges of woods or in damp, long grassland with thick hedgerows close by. Tussock grasses are used as foodplants: usually only one species at any given colony with cocksfoot (*Dactylis glomerata*) and slender false brome (*Brachypodium sylvaticum*) being the favoured species in England.

Ringlet

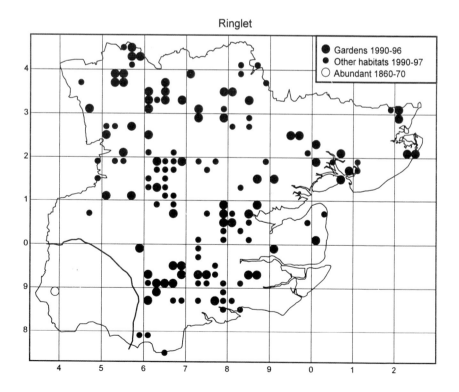

● Gardens 1990-96
● Other habitats 1990-97
○ Abundant 1860-70

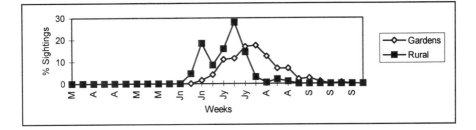

History

"This very lazy-flying woodland butterfly is common throughout the county." (Fitch, 1891). A note was added to Fitch's account by the editor that the species had been "extremely abundant in the Forest, near Walthamstow, in the wet summer of 1860...". This is an interesting record as the species was last recorded from Epping Forest in the 1890s and is not known on the London side of the M25 at the present time. It seems to be spreading towards London on the outside of the M25 and many parts of Epping Forest appear to be ideal habitats for it. It may have been lost from Epping Forest due to air-pollution (see chapter 5) and its colonial habits and limited dispersal have, as yet, prevented it from recolonising the Forest now that conditions are suitable.

Conservation

No detailed ecological studies have been published for this species but two are under way at present (one in Hertfordshire) so the requirements of this species may soon be known more precisely. Ringlets seem to be in no danger and it is preferable to monitor their natural spread towards London rather than try artificial re-introductions at present.

Butterfly gardening

Large country gardens often have this species and, since ringlets are not very mobile, this presumably means they breed in the garden or close by. Bramble is a clear favourite amongst nectar plants.

Site/Year	83	84	85	86	87	88	89	90	91	92	93	94	95	96
Stour Wood	34	101	102	295	*	158	80	41	84	127	98	137	205	43

Chapter 9   A CHECKLIST OF ESSEX LEPIDOPTERA

There are 1840 species of moths and butterflies on the current Essex list (approximately 72% of the British total) but 232 of these have not been recorded since 1980 and may be extinct in the county, and a further 162 are regarded as being migrants or vagrants or where insufficient data is available for determining their status. This leaves 1446 species which are likely to be true residents and able to survive in Essex all year round. Another 42 species have been mentioned in the literature but have been rejected by the Essex Lepidoptera Panel (see appendix).

The order of the following list broadly follows that as given in Emmet (1996), the numbers are those used in the older checklist (Bradley & Fletcher, 1979) and thus the sequence of species is not always the same as the sequence of numbers..

Legend to Systematic List

Guide reference: Gives the appropriate page number of the principal Essex guides:

S#   The smaller moths of Essex (SME), by A. M. Emmet. 1981. Essex Field
           Club. ISBN 0 905637 11 7.
L#   The larger moths and butterflies of Essex (LMBE), by A.M.Emmet,
           G.A.Pyman and D.Corke. 1985. Essex Field Club. ISBN 0 905637 13 5.
*   New Essex records made after the publication of the above guides.
           Both SME and LMBE are still available from the Essex Field Club.

Resident Species: Status/Occurrence/Density

Non-resident species: Status/Frequency

Status

Res.	Resident	Able to survive in Essex continuously
Vag.	Vagrant	Wanderers from another county, where they may be resident continuously
Mig.	Migrant	Species from another country, unable to survive our climate long-term
Acc.	Accidental	Imported species, unable to survive our climate outside
Int.	Introduced	Species deliberately introduced
Unc.	Uncertain	Uncertain of validity of record or information regarding status
NRR	No recent record	(no records after 1980)

Occurrence

WS	Widespread	Of general occurrence. Found everywhere there is suitable habitat
LC	Local	Rather restricted. Distribution of foodplant may be a factor, for example
VL	Very Local	Found in only three 10km squares or fewer

Density

HD	High Density	Large numbers encountered annually
MD	Medium Density	Smaller numbers recorded, usually (but not always) annually
LD	Low Density	Recorded rarely or seldom seen unless searched for

Non-resident frequency

C	Common	Good numbers encountered usually annually
F	Frequent	Fair numbers recorded sporadically
O	Occasional	Small numbers recorded sporadically
R	Rare	Has appeared only a few times

Priority species

Species listed as of national or local priority in the Species Action Plan (Dawson, 1997) are shown in **bold italic type**.

Micropterigidae

0001	Micropterx tunbergella Fabr.		S26	Res.	VLLD
0004	Micropterix aruncella Scop.		S26	Res.	LCLD
0005	Micropterix calthella Linn.		S26	Res.	LCMD

Eriocraniidae

0006	Eriocrania subpurpurella Haw.		S26	Res.	WSHD
0007	Eriocrania chrysolepidella Zell.		S26	Res.	LCLD
0008	Eriocrania unimaculella Zett.		S26	Res.	LCLD
0009	Eriocrania sparrmannella Bosc.		S27	Res.	LCMD
0010	Eriocrania salopiella Stt.		S27	Res.	LCLD
0011	Eriocrania haworthi Bradl.		S27	Res.	LCMD
0012	Eriocrania sangii Wood		S27	Res.	LCMD
0013	Eriocrania semipurpurella Steph.		S27	Res.	WSHD

Hepialidae

0014	Hepialus humuli Linn.	Ghost Moth	L38	Res	WSMD
0015	Hepialus sylvina Linn.	Orange Swift	L38	Res.	WSMD
0016	Hepialus hecta Linn.	Gold Swift	L38	Res.	LCLD
0017	Hepialus lupulinus Linn.	Common Swift	L38	Res.	WSHD
0018	Hepialus fusconebulosa DeG.	Map-winged Swift	L38	Vag.	R

Nepticulidae

0019	Bohemannia quadrimaculella Boh.		S28	Res.	VLLD
0040	Bohemannia pulverosella Stt		S29	Res	WSHD
0020	Etainia decentella H.-S.		S30	Res.	LCMD

0021	Etainia sericopeza Zell.	S30	Res.	VLMD
0022	Etainia louisella Sirc. (*sphendamni* Her.)	S30	Res.	LCMD
0041	Ectoedemia atrifrontella Stt.	S29	Res.	VLLD
0023	Ectoedemia argyropeza Zell.	S28	Res.	WSHD
0024	Ectoedemia turbidella Zell.	S28	Res.	VLHD
0025	Ectoedemia intimella Zell.	S28	Res.	LCMD
0026	Ectoedemia agrimoniae Frey	S28	Res.	LCMD
0027	Ectoedemia spinosella Joann.	S28	Res.	LCHD
0028	Ectoedemia angulifasciella Stt.	S28	Res.	WSMD
0029	Ectoedemia atricollis Stt.	S28	Res.	WSHD
0030	Ectoedemia arcuatella H.-S.	S28	Res.	VLLD
0031	Ectoedemia rubivora Wocke	S28	Res.	LCMD
0032	Ectoedemia erythrogenella Joann.	S29	Res.	LCMD
0034	Ectoedemia occultella Linn. (*argentipedella* Zell.)	S29	Res.	SHD
0035	Ectoedemia minimella Zett. (*mediofasciella* Haw.)	S29	Res.	LCLD
0036	Ectoedemia quinquella Bedell	S29	Res.	LCHD
0037	Ectoedemia albifasciella Hein.	S29	Res.	WSHD
0038	Ectoedemia subbimaculella Haw.	S29	Res.	WSHD
0039	Ectoedemia heringi Toll	S29	Res.	WSHD
0042	Fomoria septembrella Stt.	S29	Res.	WSMD
0046	Trifurcula immundella Zell.	S30	Res.	WSHD
0048	Trifurcula cryptella Stt.	S30	Res.	LCLD
0050	Stigmella aurella Fabr.	S30	Res.	WSHD
0053	Stigmella splendidissimella H.-S.	S30	Res.	LCLD
0055	Stigmella aeneofasciella H.-S.	S30	Res.	LCLD
0058	Stigmella ulmariae Wocke	S30	Res.	VLLD
0063	Stigmella lemniscella Zell. (*marginicolella* Stt.)	S30	Res.	WSHD
0064	Stigmella continuella Stt.	S30	Res.	LCMD
0065	Stigmella speciosa Frey	S31	Res.	LCLD
0066	Stigmella sorbi Stt.	S31	Res.	VLLD
0067	Stigmella plagicolella Stt.	S31	Res.	WSHD
0068	Stigmella salicis Stt.	S31	Res.	WSHD
0070	Stigmella obliquella Hein.	S31	Res.	WSLD
0073	Stigmella trimaculella Haw.	S31	Res.	WSHD
0074	Stigmella assimilella Zell.	S31	Res.	LCLD
0075	Stigmella floslactella Haw.	S31	Res.	WSMD
0076	Stigmella carpinella Hein.	S31	Res.	VLLD
0077	Stigmella tityrella Stt.	S31	Res	WSHD
0078	Stigmella incognitella H. - S. (*pomella* Vaugh.)	S31	Res.	LCMD
0079	Stigmella perpygmaeella Doubl.	S32	Res.	WSHD
0080	Stigmella ulmivora Fol.	S32	Res.	WSMD
0081	Stigmella hemargyrella Koll	S32	Res.	WSMD
0082	Stigmella paradoxa Fre	S32	Res	VLHD
0083	Stigmella atricapitella Haw	S32	Res.	WSHD
0084	Stigmella ruficapitella Haw	S32	Res.	WSHD
0085	Stigmella suberivora Stt	S32	Res.	WSHD
0086	Stigmella roborella Johan	S32	Res.	LCMD
0087	Stigmella svenssoni Johan	S32	Res.	VLLD
0088	Stigmella samiatella Zell	S32	Res.	LCMD
0089	Stigmella basiguttella Hein	S32	Res.	WSHD
0090	Stigmella tiliae Frey	S33	Res.	LCMD
0091	Stigmella minusculella H.-S	S33	Res.	VLLD

0092	Stigmella anomalella Goeze	S33	Res.	WSHD
0093	Stigmella centifoliella Zell	S33	Res.	LCMD
0095	Stigmella viscerella Stt	S33	Res.	WSHD
0097	Stigmella malella Stt.	S33	Res.	WSHD
0098	Stigmella catharticella Stt.	S33	Res.	LCMD
0099	Stigmella hybnerella Hb.	S33	Res.	WSHD
0100	Stigmella oxyacanthella Stt.	S33	Res.	WSHD
0103	Stigmella nylandriella Tengst.	S33	Res.	LCMD
0107	Stigmella regiella H.-S.	S33	Res.	LCMD
0108	Stigmella crataegella Klim.	S34	Res.	WSHD
0110	Stigmella betulicola Stt.	S34	Res.	LCLD
0111	Stigmella microtheriella Stt.	S34	Res.	WSHD
0112	Stigmella luteella Stt.	S34	Res.	WSHD
0113	Stigmella sakhalinella Pupl. (*distinguenda* Hein.)	S34	Res.	LCLD
0114	Stigmella glutinosae Stt.	S34	Res.	LCMD
0115	Stigmella alnetella Stt.	S34	Res.	LCMD
0116	Stigmella lapponica Wocke	S34	Res.	WSHD
0117	Stigmella confusella Wood	S34	Res.	WSHD
0118	Enteucha acetosae Stt.	S34	NRR	

Opostegidae

0119	Opostega salaciella Treit.	S35	Res.	LCMD
0121	Opostega crepusculella Zell.	S35	Res.	VLLD
0122	Opostega spatulella H.-S.	S35	NRR	

Heliozelidae

0154	Heliozela sericiella Haw.	S38	Res.	WSMD
0156	Heliozela resplendella Stt.	S39	Res.	WSMD
0157	Heliozela hammoniella Sorh.	S39	Res.	LCMD
0158	Antispila metallella D.& S. (*pfeifferella* Hb.)	S39	Res.	WSMD
0159	Antispila petryi Mart.	S39	Res.	LCLD

Adelidae

0140	Nematopogon swammerdamella Linn.	S37	Res.	WSMD
0141	Nematopogon schwarziellus Zell.	S37	Res.	WSMD
0143	Nematopogon metaxella Hb.	S37	Res.	VLLD
0144	Nemophora fasciella Fabr.	S38	Res.	LCLD
0146	Nemophora cupriacella Hb.	S38	Res.	VLMD
0148	Nemophora degeerella Linn.	S38	Res.	WSMD
0149	Adela cuprella D.& S.	S38	NRR	
0150	Adela reaumurella Linn.	S38	Res.	WSHD
0151	Adela croesella Scop.	S38	Res.	VLLD
0152	Adela rufimitrella Scop.	S38	Res.	LCMD
0153	Adela fibulella D.& S.	S38	Res.	LCMD

Incurvariidae

0128	Phylloporia bistrigella Haw.	S37	Res.	LCMD
0129	Incurvaria pectinea Haw.	S37	Res.	LCLD
0130	Incurvaria masculella D.& S.	S37	Res.	WSMD
0131	Incurvaria oehlmanniella Hb.	S37	Res.	LCLD
0132	Incurvaria praelatella D.& S.	S37	NRR	

Prodoxidae

0133	Lampronia capitella Cl.		S37	Res.	VLLD
0135	Lampronia luzella Hb.		S37	Res.	VLLD
0136	Lampronia rubiella Bjerk.		S37	Res.	VLLD
0137	Lampronia morosa Zell.		S37	Res.	VLLD
0138	Lampronia fuscatella Tengst.		L37	Res.	VLLD

Tischeriidae

0123	Tischeria ekebladella Bjerk.		S35	Res.	WSHD
0124	Tischeria dodonaea Stt.		S36	NRR	
0125	Emmetia marginea Haw. (*Tischeria* Zell.)		S36	Res.	WSHD
0126	Emmetia gaunacella Dup. (*Tischeria* Zell.)		S36	NRR	
0127	Emmetia angusticollella Dup. (*Tischeria* Zell.)		S36	Res.	LCMD

Tineidae

0203	Infurcitinea argentimaculella Stt.		S41	NRR	
0196	Morophaga choragella D.& S.		S41	Res.	LCLD
0215	Nemapogon granella Linn.		S42	Res.	VLLD
0216	Nemapogon cloacella Haw.		S42	Res.	WSHD
0217	Nemapogon wolffiella K.& N.		S42	Res.	LCMD
0218	Nemapogon variatella Clem.		L119	NRR	
0219	Nemapogon ruricolella Stt.		L119	Res.	VLLD
0220	Nemapogon clematella Fabr.		S42	Res.	VLMD
0223	Nemaxera betulinella Fabr.		S42	Res.	VLMD
0224	Triaxomera parasitella Hb.		S42	Res.	LCMD
0226	Triaxomasia caprimulgella Stt.		S42	NRR	
0227	Monopis laevigella D.& S. (*rusticella* Hb.)	Skin Moth	S42	Res.	WSMD
0228	Monopis weaverella Scott.		S42	Res.	LCMD
0229	Monopis obviella D.& S. (*ferruginella* Hb.)		S42	Res.	WSMD
0230	Monopis crocicapitella Clem.		S43	Res.	LCMD
0231	Monopis imella Hb.		L119	Res.	VLLD
0234	Trichophaga tapetzella Linn.	Tapestry Moth	S43	NRR	
0236	Tineola bisselliella Hum.	Common Clothes Moth	S43	Res.	VLLD
0237	Niditinea fuscella Linn. (*fuscipunctella* Haw.)				
		Brown-dotted Clothes Moth	S43	Res.	LCLD
0238	Niditinea piercella Bent.		S43	Res.	LCLD
0239	Tinea columbariella Wocke		L119	Res.	VLLD
0240	Tinea pellionella Linn.	Case-bearing Clothes Moth	S43	Res.	LCMD
0242	Tinea translucens Meyr.		S43	NRR	
0243	Tinea dubiella Stt.		S43	NRR	
0245	Tinea pallescentella Stt.		S43	Res.	VLLD
0246	Tinea semifulvella Haw.		S43	Res.	LCMD
0247	Tinea trinotella Thunb.		S43	Res.	WSHD
0212	Haplotinea insectella Fabr.		S42	Res.	VLLD

Psychidae

0180	Diplodoma herminata Geoff.		S40	Res.	LCLD
0175	Narycia monilifera Geoff.		S39	Res.	WSMD
0176	*Dahlica triquetrella Hb. (Solenobia Dup.)*		*S39*	*Res.*	*VLLD*
0177	Dahlica inconspicuella Stt.	Lesser Lichen Case-bearer	S40	NRR	
0181	Taleporia tubulosa Retz.		S40	Res.	WSMD
0183	Bacotia sepium Speyer		S40	NRR	

0184	Luffia lapidella Goeze		S40	Res.	VLLD
0185	Luffia ferchaultella Steph.		S40	Res.	WSHD
0188	Proutia betulina Zell. (*Psyche* Schr.)		S40	Res.	VLLD
0186	Psyche casta Pall.		S40	Res.	WSMD
0187	Psyche crassiorella Bru.		S40	NRR	
0189	Epichnopterix plumella D.& S.		S41	Res.	WSMD
0190	Whittleia retiella Newm.		S41	Res.	LCLD

Roeslerstammiidae

0447	Roeslerstammia erxlebella Fabr.		S58	Res.	LCMD

Bucculatricidae

0265	Bucculatrix cristatella Zell.		S45	Res.	LCMD
0266	Bucculatrix nigricomella Zell.		S45	Res.	LCMD
0267	Bucculatrix maritima Stt.		S45	Res.	LCMD
0270	Bucculatrix frangutella Goeze		S45	Res.	LCLD
0271	Bucculatrix albedinella Zell.		S45	Res.	WSMD
0272	Bucculatrix cidarella Zell.		S45	Res.	LCMD
0273	Bucculatrix thoracella Thunb.		S46	Res.	LCMD
0274	Bucculatrix ulmella Zell.		S46	Res.	WSHD
0275	Bucculatrix bechsteinella B&S (*crataegi* Zell		S46	Res.	WSMD
0276	Bucculatrix demaryella Dup.		S46	Res.	VLLD

Douglasiidae

0398	Tinagma ocnerostomella Stt.		S55	Res.	VLLD

Gracillariidae

0280	Caloptilia cuculipennella Hb.		S47	NRR	
0282	Caloptilia elongella Linn.		S47	Res.	LCMD
0283	Caloptilia betulicola Her.		S47	Res.	WSMD
0284	Caloptilia rufipennella Hb.		S47	Res.	LCMD
	Recorded by SME from four 10km squares but has now extended its range to ten 10km squares.				
0285	Caloptilia azaleella Brants	Azalea Leaf Miner	*	Res.	VLLD
0286	Caloptilia alchimiella Scop.		S47	Res.	LCMD
0287	Caloptilia robustella Jäckh		S47	Res.	WSMD
0288	Caloptilia stigmatella Fabr.		S47	Res.	WSMD
0290	Caloptilia semifascia Haw.		S47	NRR	
0293	Caloptilia syringella Fabr.		S47	Res.	WSHD
0294	Aspilapteryx tringipennella Zell.		S47	Res.	WSMD
0297	Calybites auroguttella Steph.		S48	Res.	WSMD
0299	Parectopa ononidis Zell.		L120	Res.	LCMD
0301	Parornix betulae Stt.		S48	Res.	WSHD
0302	Parornix fagivora Frey		S48	Res.	VLLD
0302a	Parornix carpinella Frey		*	Res.	VLLD
0303	Parornix anglicella Stt.		S48	Res.	WSHD
0304	Parornix devoniella Stt.		S48	Res.	WSHD
0305	Parornix scoticella Stt.		S48	Res.	LCMD
0308	Parornix finitimella Zell.		S48	Res.	WSHD
0309	Parornix torquillella Zell.		S48	Res.	WSHD
0310	Callisto denticulella Thunb.		S48	Res.	WSHD
0313	Acrocercops brongniardella Fabr.		S49	Res.	LCLD

Following the capture of a specimen in Colchester during 1991, the first in Essex since 1903, this species has spread rapidly and has now been recorded from thirty-five 10km squares.

0314	Leucospilapteryx omissella Stt.	S49	Res.	WSMD
0315	Phyllonorycter harrisella Linn.	S49	Res.	WSHD
0316	Phyllonorycter roboris Zell.	*	Res.	VLLD
0317	Phyllonorycter heegeriella Zell.	S49	Res.	WSMD
0318	Phyllonorycter tenerella Joann.	S49	Res.	WSMD
0319	Phyllonorycter saportella Dup.	S49	NRR	
0320	Phyllonorycter quercifoliella Zell.	S49	Res.	WSHD
0321	Phyllonorycter messaniella Zell.	S50	Res.	WSHD
0323	Phyllonorycter oxyacanthae Frey	S50	Res.	WSHD
0324	Phyllonorycter sorbi Frey	S50	Res.	LCMD
0325	Phyllonorycter mespilella Hb.	S50	Res.	LCMD
0326	Phyllonorycter blancardella Fabr.	S50	Res.	WSHD
0327	Phyllonorycter cydoniella D.& S.	S50	Res.	LCMD
0329	Phyllonorycter spinicolella Zell. (*pomonella* Zell.)	S50	Res.	WSHD
0330	Phyllonorycter cerasicolella H.-S	S50	Res.	LCMD
0331	Phyllonorycter lantanella Schr.	S50	Res.	LCLD
0332	Phyllonorycter corylifoliella Hb.	S50	Res.	WSHD
0332a	Phyllonorycter leucographella Zell.	*	Res.	WSMD

First recognized in Britain in 1989 at Wickford, Essex. Has since spread to other parts of the country.

0333	Phyllonorycter viminiella Sirc.	S51	Res.	LCLD
0334	Phyllonorycter viminetorum Stt.	S51	Res.	VLLD
0335	Phyllonorycter salicicolella Sirc.	S51	Res.	WSMD
0336	Phyllonorycter dubitella H.-S.	S51	Res.	LCMD
0337	Phyllonorycter hilarella Zett. (*spinolella* Dup.)	S51	Res.	LCMD
0338	Phyllonorycter cavella Zell.	S51	Res.	VLLD
0339	Phyllonorycter ulicicolella Stt.	S51	Res.	LCLD
0340	Phyllonorycter scopariella Zell.	S51	Res.	LCLD
0341	Phyllonorycter maestingella Müll.	S51	Res.	WSHD
0342	Phyllonorycter coryli Nic.	S51	Res.	WSHD
0343	Phyllonorycter quinnata Geoff.	S52	Res.	WSHD
0345	Phyllonorycter rajella Linn.	S52	Res.	WSMD
0347	Phyllonorycter anderidae Fletch.	*	Res.	VLLD
0351	Phyllonorycter lautella Zell.	S52	Res.	WSMD
0352	Phyllonorycter schreberella Fabr.	S52	Res.	WSHD
0353	Phyllonorycter ulmifoliella Hb.	S52	Res.	WSHD
0354	Phyllonorycter emberizaepenella Bouché	S52	Res.	VLLD
0356	Phyllonorycter tristrigella Haw.	S52	Res.	WSMD
0357	Phyllonorycter stettinensis Nic.	S52	Res.	LCMD
0358	Phyllonorycter froelichiella Zell.	S52	Res.	LCLD
0359	Phyllonorycter nicellii Stt.	S52	Res.	WSMD
0360	Phyllonorycter kleemannella Fabr.	S52	Res.	LCMD
0361	Phyllonorycter trifasciella Haw.	S52	Res.	WSMD
0362	Phyllonorycter acerifoliella Zell. (*sylvella* Haw.)	S53	Res.	WSMD
0363	Phyllonorycter platanoidella Joann.	S53	Res.	LCLD
0364	Phyllonorycter geniculella Rag.	S53	Res.	WSMD
0365a	Phyllonorycter platani Stdgr	*	Res.	LCLD
0368	Phyllocnistis unipunctella Steph.	S53	Res.	WSMD

Yponomeutidae

0450	Scythropia crataegella Linn.	Hawthorn Moth	S59	Res.	WSMD
0424	Yponomeuta evonymella Linn.	Bird-cherry Ermine	S57	Mig.	O

Has appeared in small numbers during most recent years, culminating with a spectacular invasion during 1989.

0425	Yponomeuta padella Linn.	Orchard Ermine	S57	Res.	WSMD
0426	Yponomeuta malinellus Zell.	Apple Ermine	S57	Res.	LCMD
0427	Yponomeuta cagnagella Hb.	Spindle Ermine	S57	Res.	LCMD
0428	Yponomeuta rorrella Hb.	Willow Ermine	*	Mig.	O
0430	Yponomeuta plumbella D.& S.		S57	Res.	LCMD
0431	Yponomeuta sedella Treit. (virginipunctata Retz.)		S58	Vag.	R
0435	Zelleria hepariella Stt.		L121	Res.	VLLD
0436	Pseudoswammerdamia combinella Hb.		S58	Res.	LCLD
0437	Swammerdamia caesiella Hb.		S58	Res.	WSHD
0438	Swammerdamia pyrella Vill.		S58	Res.	WSHD
0440	Paraswammerdamia albicapitella Scharf. (spiniella Hb.)		S58	Res.	WSMD
0441	Paraswammerdamia lutarea Haw.		S58	Res.	WSHD
0442	Cedestis gysseleniella Zell.		S58	Res.	LCMD
0443	Cedestis subfasciella Steph.		S58	Res.	WSMD
0444	Ocnerostoma piniariella Zell.		S58	Res.	LCLD
0445	Ocnerosoma friesei Svens.		S58	Res.	LCMD
0449	Prays fraxinella Bjerk.	Ash Bud Moth	S59	Res.	WSMD

Argyresthiidae

0401	Argyresthia laevigatella H.-S.		S56	Res.	LCMD
0403	Argyresthia glabratella Zell.		S56	Res.	VLMD
0407	Argyresthia dilectella Zell.		S56	Res.	VLLD
0409	Argyresthia ivella Haw.		S56	Res.	VLLD
0410	Argyresthia brockeella Hb.		S56	Res.	WSHD
0411	Argyresthia goedartella Linn.		S56	Res.	WSHD
0412	Argyresthia pygmaeella D.& S.		S56	Res.	WSMD
0414	Argyresthia curvella Linn. (arcella Fabr.)		S56	Res.	LCMD
0415	Argyresthia retinella Zell.		S56	Res.	WSHD
0416	Argyresthia glaucinella Zell.		S56	Res.	LCLD
0417	Argyresthia spinosella Stt. (mendica Haw.)		S56	Res.	WSHD
0418	Argyresthia conjugella Zell.		S57	Res.	VLLD
0419	Argyresthia semifusca Haw.		S57	Res.	LCMD
0420	Argyresthia pruniella Cl.	Cherry Fruit Moth	S57	Res.	LCHD
0421	Argyresthia bonnetella Linn. (curvella Linn.)		S57	Res.	WSHD
0422	Argyresthia albistria Haw.		S57	Res.	WSHD
0423	Argyresthia semitestacella Curt.		S57	Res.	LCMD

Ypsolophidae

0451	Ypsolopha mucronella Scop.		S59	Res.	LCLD
0452	Ypsolopha nemorella Linn.		S59	Res.	LCLD
0453	Ypsolopha dentella Fabr.	Honeysuckle Moth	S59	Res.	WSMD
0455	Ypsolopha scabrella Linn.		S59	Res.	WSMD
0456	Ypsolopha horridella Treit.		S59	Res.	LCMD
0457	Ypsolopha lucella Fabr.		S59	Res.	VLLD
0458	Ypsolopha alpella D.& S.		S59	Res.	LCLD
0459	Ypsolopha sylvella Linn.		S59	Res.	LCMD
0460	Ypsolopha parenthesella Linn.		S60	Res.	WSMD

0461	Ypsolopha ustella Cl.		S60	Res.	WSHD
0462	Ypsolopha sequella Cl.		S60	Res.	LCMD
0463	Ypsolopha vittella Linn.		S60	Res.	LCMD
0251	Ochsenheimeria mediopectinellus Haw.		S44	Res.	VLLD
0252	Ochsenheimeria urella F.v.R. (*bisontella* L.& Z.)		S44	NRR	
0253	Ochsenheimeria vacculella F.v.R.		S44	Res.	VLLD

Plutellidae

0464	Plutella xylostella Linn.	Diamond-back Moth	S60	Res.	WSHD
0465	Plutella porrectella Linn.		S60	Res.	LCMD
0469	Eidophasia messingiella F.v.R.		S60	Res.	LCMD
0471	Digitivalva perlepidella Stt.		S60	Res.	VLMD
0472	Digitivalva pulicariae Klim.		S60	NRR	
0473	Acrolepiopsis assectella Zell.	Leek Moth	*	Res.	VLLD
0474	Acrolepiopsis betulella Curt.		S61	Unc.	
0475	Acrolepiopsis marcidella Curt.		S61	NRR	
0476	Acrolepia autumnitella Curt. (*pygmeana* Haw.)		S61	Res.	WSMD

Glyphipterigidae

0470	Orthotaelia sparganella Thunb.		S60	Res.	LCLD
0391	Glyphipterix simpliciella Steph.	Cocksfoot Moth	S54	Res.	WSHD
0393	Glyphipterix equitella Scop. (*minorella* Snell.)	S54	NRR		
0396	Glyphipterix fuscoviridella Haw.		S54	Res.	LCMD
0397	Glyphipterix thrasonella Scop.		S54	Res.	VLMD

Lyonetiidae

0254	Leucoptera laburnella Stt.		S45	Res.	WSMD
0256	Leucoptera spartifoliella Hb.		S45	Res.	WSHD
0259	Leucoptera lotella Stt.		S45	NRR	
0260	Leucoptera malifoliella Costa (*scitella* Zell.)		S45	Res.	WSMD
0264	Bedellia somnulentella Zell.		S45	Res.	VLMD
0263	Lyonetia clerkella Linn.		S45	Res.	WSHD

Oecophoridae

0637	Schiffermuelleria tinctella Hb.		S76	NRR	
0638	Denisia albimaculea Haw. (*augustella* sensu auctt.)		S76	NRR	
0640	Batia lunaris Haw.		S76	Res.	WSMD
0641	Batia lambdella Don.		S76	Res.	VLLD
0642	Batia unitella Hb.		S76	Res.	WSHD
0643	Dafa formosella D.& S.		S76	NRR	
0644	Borkhausenia fuscescens Haw.		S76	Res.	WSHD
0645	Borkhausenia minutella Linn.		S77	NRR	
0646	Telechrysis tripuncta Haw.		S77	Res.	LCLD
0647	Hofmannophila pseudospretella Stt.	Brown House-moth	S77	Res.	WSHD
0648	Endrosis sarcitrella Linn.	White-shouldered House-moth	S77	Res.	WSHD
0649	Esperia sulphurella Fabr.		S77	Res.	WSMD
0650	Esperia olivella Fabr		S77	Res.	VLLD
0652	Alabonia geoffrella Linn.		S77	Res.	WSMD
0653	Aplota palpella Haw.		S77	NRR	
0654	Pleurota bicostella Cl.		S77	NRR	
0657	Hypercallia citrinalis Scop.		S77	NRR	
0658	Carcina quercana Fabr.		S77	Res.	WSHD

0660	Pseudatemelia josephinae Toll		S77	Res.	LCLD
0661	Pseudatemelia flavifrontella D.& S.		S78	NRR	
0662	Pseudatemelia subochreella Doubl.		S78	Res.	LCLD
0877	Stathmopoda pedella Linn.		S94	Res.	VLLD
0663	Diurnea fagella D.& S.		S78	Res.	WSHD
0664	Diurnea phryganella Hb.		S78	Res.	WSMD
0665	Dasystoma salicella Hb. (*Cheimophila* Hb.)		S78	Res.	VLLD

Batrachedridae

0878	Batrachedra praeangusta Haw.		S95	Res.	WSMD
0879	Batrachedra pinicolella Zell.		S95	Res.	VLMD

Coleophoridae

0486	Augasma aeratella Zell.		S63	NRR	
0487	Metriotes lutarea Haw.		S63	Res.	VLMD
0488	Goniodoma limoniella Stt.		S63	Res.	LCMD
0490	Coleophora lutipennella Zell.		S64	Res.	WSHD
0491	Coleophora gryphipennella Hb.		S64	Res.	WSMD
0492	Coleophora flavipennella Dup.		S64	Res.	WSHD
0493	Coleophora serratella Linn.		S64	Res.	WSHD
0494	Coleophora coracipennella Hb.		S64	Res.	LCLD
0494a	Coleophora prunifoliae Doets		S64	Res.	LCLD
0495	Coleophora spinella Schr. (*cerasivorella* Pack.)		S64	Res.	WSHD
0496	Coleophora milvipennis Zell.		S64	Res.	LCMD
0496a	Coleophora adjectella H.-S.		S64	Res.	VLMD
0497	Coleophora badiipennella Dup.		S65	Res.	LCMD
0499	Coleophora limosipennella Dup.		S65	Res.	LCMD
0501	Coleophora siccifolia Stt.		S65	Res.	WSLD
0503	Coleophora fuscocuprella H.-S.		S65	Res.	VLLD
0504	Coleophora lusciniaepennella Treit. (*viminetella* Zell.)		S65	Res.	WSMD
0509	Coleophora violacea Ström		S65	Res.	LCMD
0510	Coleophora juncicolella Stt.		S66	Res.	VLMD
0511	Coleophora orbitella Zell.		S66	NRR	
0512	Coleophora binderella Koll.		S66	Res.	LCLD
0513	Coleophora potentillae Elisha		S66	Res.	LCMD
0502	Coleophora trigeminella Fuchs		S65	Res.	VLLD
0515	Coleophora albitarsella Zell.		S66	Res.	LCLD
0516	Coleophora trifolii Curt.		S66	Res.	LCMD
0517	Coleophora frischella Linn.	Clover Case-bearer	L121	Res.	LCMD
0518	Coleophora mayrella Hb. (*spissicornis* Haw.)	S66	Res.	LCMD	
0519	Coleophora deauratella L.& Z.		S66	Res.	LCMD
0520	Coleophora fuscicornis Zell.		S67	Res.	VLMD
0521	Coleophora conyzae Zell.		S67	Res.	VLLD
0522	Coleophora lineolea Haw.		S67	Res.	WSMD
0523	Coleophora hemerobiella Scop.		S67	Res.	WSMD
0524	Coleophora lithargyrinella Zell.		S67	NRR	
0545	Coleophora saturatella Stt.		S69	Res.	VLLD
0546	Coleophora genistae Stt.		S69	NRR	
0547	Coleophora discordella Zell.		S69	Res.	LCMD
0532	Coleophora albidella D.& S.		S67	Res.	LCLD
0533	Coleophora anatipennella Hb.	Pistol Case-bearer	S67	Res.	WSMD
0534	Coleophora currucipennella Zell.		S67	NRR	

0535	Coleophora ibipennella Zell. (*ardeaepennella* Scott)		S68	Res.	WSMD
0536	Coleophora betuletella H. & W (*ibipennella* sensu auctt.)		S68	Res.	LCMD
0537	Coleophora palliatella Zinck.		S68	Res.	LCLD
0541	Coleophora pyrrhulipennella Zell.		S68	NRR	
0539	Coleophora conspicuella Zell.		S68	Res.	LCMD
0540	*Coleophora vibicigerella Zell.*		*S68*	*NRR*	
0543	Coleophora vulnerariae Zell.		S68	Unc.	
0544	Coleophora albicosta Haw.		S68	Res.	LCHD
0526	Coleophora laricella Hb.	Larch Case-bearer	S67	Res.	LCMD
0525	Coleophora solitariella Zell.		S67	Res.	LCMD
0550	Coleophora silenella H.-S.		S69	Res.	VLLD
0553	Coleophora striatipennella Nyl.		S69	Res.	LCMD
0555	Coleophora follicularis Vallot (*troglodytella* Dup.)		S69	Res.	LCMD
0556	Coleophora trochilella Dup.		S69	Res.	LCMD
0556a	Coleophora linosyridella Fuchs		S69	Res.	VLLD
0557	Coleophora gardesanella Toll (*machinella* Bradl.)		S69	Res.	VLLD
0559	Coleophora peribenanderi Toll		S69	Res.	LCMD
0560	Coleophora paripennella Zell.		S70	Res.	LCMD
0562	Coleophora asteris Mühl.		S70	Res.	LCMD
0563	Coleophora argentula Steph.		S70	Res.	WSHD
0564	Coleophora virgaureae Stt.		S70	NRR	
0565	Coleophora saxicolella Dup. (*benanderi* Kanerva)		L121	Res.	LCMD
0566	Coleophora sternipennella Zett.		S70	Res.	VLLD
0567	Coleophora adspersella Ben.		S70	Res.	LCMD
0568	Coleophora versurella Zell.		S70	Res.	VLMD
0569	Coleophora squamosella Stt.		S70	Res.	VLLD
0573	Coleophora atriplicis Meyr.		S70	Res.	LCHD
0574	Coleophora deviella Zell. (*suaedivora* Meyr.)		S71	Res.	VLMD
0574a	Coleophora aestuariella Bradl.		L121	Res.	VLMD
0575	Coleophora salinella Stt.		S71	Res.	LCMD
0576	Coleophora artemisiella Scott		S71	Res.	LCLD
0577	Coleophora artemisicolella Bru.		S71	Res.	WSMD
0578	Coleophora otidipennella Hb. (*murinipennella* Dup.)		S71	Res.	LCHD
0581	Coleophora taeniipennella H.-S.		S71	Res.	LCMD
0582	Coleophora glaucicolella Wood		S71	Res.	LCHD
0583	Coleophora tamesis Waters		L122	Res.	VLLD
0584	Coleophora alticolella Zell.		S71	Res.	WSHD
0585	Coleophora maritimella Newm.		S71	Res.	VLLD
0586	Coleophora adjunctella Hodgk.		S71	Res.	VLLD
0587	Coleophora caespititiella Zell.		S71	Res.	LCMD

Recently recorded from six 10km squares and is likely to be more widespread

0588	Coleophora salicorniae Wocke	S71	Res.	LCMD
0589	Coleophora clypeiferella Hofm.	S72	Res.	VLLD
0527	Coleophora wockeella Zell.	S67	NRR	

Depressariidae

0666	Semioscopis avellanella Hb.	S78	NRR	
0667	Semioscopis steinkellneriana D.& S.	S78	Res.	LCMD
0668	Enicostoma lobella D.& S.	S78	Res.	LCLD
0670	Depressaria daucella D.& S.	S78	NRR	
0671	Depressaria ultimella Stt.	S78	Res.	LCLD

0672	Depressaria pastinacella Dup.	S78	Res.	WSHD
0673	Depressaria pimpinellae Zell.	S79	Res.	LCMD
0674	Depressaria badiella Hb.	S79	Res.	LCLD
0676	Depressaria pulcherrimella Stt.	*	Res.	VLLD
0677	Depressaria douglasella Stt.	S79	Res.	VLLD
0678	Depressaria weirella Stt.	S79	Res.	LCMD
0680	Depressaria aegopodiella Hb. (albipunctella Hb.)	S79	Unc.	
0682	Depressaria chaerophylli Zell.	S79	Res.	VLLD
0683	Depressaria depressana Fabr.	S79	NRR	
0688	Agonopterix heracliana Linn.	S79	Res.	WSHD
0689	Agonopterix ciliella Stt.	*	Res.	VLLD
0690	Agonopterix cnicella Treit.	S79	NRR	
0691	Agonopterix purpurea Haw.	S80	Res.	LCLD
0692	Agonopterix subpropinquella Stt.	S80	Res.	WSMD
0693	*Agonopterix putridella D.& S.*	*S80*	*Res.*	*VLMD*
0694	Agonopterix nanatella Stt.	L122	Res.	VLLD
0695	Agonopterix alstromeriana Cl.	S80	Res.	WSHD
0696	Agonopterix propinquella Treit.	S80	Res.	LCLD
0697	Agonopterix arenella D.& S.	S80	Res.	WSHD
0698	Agonopterix kaekeritziana Linn. (liturella D.& S.)	S80	Res.	LCMD
0701	Agonopterix ocellana Fabr.	S80	Res.	VLMD
0702	Agonopterix assimilella Treit.	S80	Res.	WSMD
0703	Agonopterix atomella D.& S. (pulverella Hb.)	S80	NRR	
0704	Agonopterix scopariella Hein.	S81	Res.	LCMD
0705	Agonopterix ulicetella Stt.	S81	Res.	LCMD
0706	Agonopterix nervosa Haw.	S81	Res.	WSMD
0709	Agonopterix liturosa Haw.	S81	Res.	WSMD
0710	Agonopterix conterminella Zell.	S81	Res.	VLLD
0711	Agonopterix curvipunctosa Haw.	S81	NRR	
0713	Agonopterix angelicella Hb.	S81	Res.	VLLD
0714	Agonopterix yeatiana Fabr.	S82	Res.	VLMD

Elachistidae

0590	Perittia obscurepunctella Stt.	S72	Res.	VLMD
0592	Stephensia brunnichella Linn.	S72	Res.	VLMD
0593	Elachista regificella Sirc.	S72	NRR	
0594	Elachista gleichenella Fabr.	S73	Res.	LCMD
0595	Elachista biatomella Stt.	S73	Res.	VLLD
0596	Elachista poae Stt.	S73	Res.	LCMD
0597	Elachista atricomella Stt.	S73	Res.	LCMD
0599	Elachista alpinella Stt.	S73	Res.	LCMD
0600	Elachista luticomella Zell.	*	Res.	VLLD
0601	Elachista albifrontella Hb.	S73	Res.	WSHD
0602	Elachista apicipunctella Stt.	S73	Res.	LCHD
0603	Elachista subnigrella Dougl.	S73	Res.	VLLD
0606	Elachista humilis Zell.	S73	Res.	LCMD
0607	Elachista canapennella Hb. (pulchella Haw.)	S73	Res.	LCMD
0608	Elachista rufocinerea Haw.	S73	Res.	WSHD
0609	Elachista monosemiella Rössler (cerusella Hb.)	S74	Res.	WSMD
0610	Elachista argentella Cl.	S74	Res.	WSHD
0611	Elachista triatomea Haw.	S74	Res.	LCLD
0613	Elachista subocellea Steph.	S74	Res.	VLLD

0617	Elachista megerlella Hb.		S74	Res.	LCMD
0619	Elachista unifasciella Haw.		S74	Res.	VLLD
0620	Elachista gangabella Zell.		S74	Res.	LCMD
0623	Elachista bisulcella Dup.		S74	Res.	LCMD
0625	Biselachista cinereopunctella Haw.		S74	NRR	
0626	Biselachista serricornis Stt.		S74	NRR	
0627	Biselachista scirpi Stt.		S74	Res.	LCMD
0629	Biselachista utonella Frey		S74	NRR	
0631	Cosmiotes freyerella Hb.		S75	Res.	LCMD
0632	Cosmiotes consortella Stt.		S75	Res.	LCMD
0633	Cosmiotes stabilella Stt.		S75	Res.	VLLD

Ethmiidae

0717	Ethmia terminella Fletch.		*	Vag.	R
0718	Ethmia dodecea Haw.		*	Vag.	R
0719	Ethmia funerella Fabr.		L122	Vag.	R
0720	Ethmia bipunctella Fabr.		S82	Vag.	R

Blastobasidae

| 0873 | Blastobasis lignea Wals. | | S94 | Res. | LCMD |
| 0874 | Blastobasis decolorella Woll. | | S94 | Res. | WSHD |

Momphidae

0880	Mompha langiella Hb.		S95	NRR	
0881	Mompha terminella H.& W.		S95	NRR	
0883	Mompha raschkiella Zell.		S95	Res.	WSHD
0884	Mompha miscella D.& S.		S95	NRR	
0885	Mompha conturbatella Hb.		S96	Res.	LCLD
0886	Mompha ochraceella Curt.		S96	Res.	LCMD
0887	Mompha lacteella Steph.		L125	Res.	LCLD
0888	Mompha propinquella Stt.		S96	Res.	LCMD
0889	Mompha divisella H.-S.		S96	Res.	VLLD
0890	Mompha subdivisella Bradl.		*	Res.	VLLD
0891	Mompha nodicolella Fuchs		S96	Res.	LCMD
0892	Mompha subbistrigella Haw.		S96	Res.	LCHD
0893	Mompha epilobiella D.& S.		S96	Res.	WSHD
0903	Glyphipteryx linneella Cl.		S97	Res.	VLLD
0904	Spuleria flavicaput Haw.		S97	Res.	LCMD
0905	Blastodacna hellerella Dup.		S97	Res.	WSHD
0906	Blastodacna atra Haw.	Apple Pith Moth	S97	Res.	VLLD
0907	Dystebenna stephensi Stt.		S97	Res.	VLLD

Cosmopterigidae

0899	Pancalia leuwenhoekella Linn.		S97	NRR	
0900	Pancalia latreillella Curt.		S97	NRR	
0894	Cosmopterix zieglerella Hb.		S96	Res.	LCMD
0896	Cosmopterix orichalcea Stt.		S96	NRR	
0897	Cosmopterix lienigiella L.& Z.		S96	Res.	VLLD
0898	Limnaecia phragmitella Stt.		S96	Res.	LCMD
0908	Sorhagenia rhamniella Zell.		S97	Res.	VLLD
0909	Sorhagenia lophyrella Dougl.		S97	Res.	VLLD
0910	Sorhagenia janiszewskae Riedl		S98	Res.	VLLD

Gelechiidae

0866	Brachmia blandella Fabr.		S93	Res.	WSMD
0867	Brachmia inornatella Dougl.		S93	Res.	VLLD
0868	Brachmia rufescens Haw.		S93	Res.	WSHD
0862	Dichomeris marginella Fabr.	Juniper Webber	S93	Res.	LCMD
0856	Anarsia spartiella Schr.		S92	Res.	LCMD
0858	Hypatima rhomboidella Linn.		S92	Res.	WSMD
0859	Psoricoptera gibbosella Zell.		S92	Res.	VLLD
0861	Telephila schmidtiellus Heyd.		S93	Res.	VLMD
0840	Reuttia subocellea Steph.		S91	Res.	VLLD
0841	Sophronia semicostella Hb.		S91	Res.	VLLD
0843	Aproaerema anthyllidella Hb.		S91	Res.	LCMD
0844	Syncopacma larseniella Gozm.		L124	Res.	LCMD
0847	Syncopacma taeniolella Zell.		S91	NRR	
0848	Syncopacma albipalpella H.-S.		S91	NRR	
0849	Syncopacma cinctella Cl.		L124	Res.	VLLD
0852	Anacampsis temerella L.& Z.		S92	NRR	
0853	Anacampsis populella Cl.		S92	Res.	WSMD
0854	Anacampsis blattariella Hb.		S92	Res.	LCMD
0855	Acompsia cinerella Cl.		S92	Res.	VLLD
0724	Metzneria lappella Linn.		S83	Res.	VLMD
0725	Metzneria aestivella Zell.		L122	Res.	VLLD
0726	Metzneria metzneriella Stt.		S83	Res.	LCLD
0727a	Metzneria aprilella H.-S.		L122	Res.	LCLD
0728	Paltodora cytisella Curt.		S83	NRR	
0729	Isophrictis striatella D.& S.		S83	Res.	LCLD
0730	Apodia bifractella Dup.		S83	Res.	LCMD
0731	Eulamprotes atrella D.& S.		S83	Res.	LCMD
0732	Eulamprotes unicolorella Dup.		S83	Res.	LCLD
0733	Eulamprotes wilkella Linn.		S83	Res.	VLLD
0735	Monochroa tenebrella Hb.		S83	Res.	LCLD
0736	Monochroa lucidella Steph.		S83	Res.	VLLD
0737	Monochroa palustrella Dougl.		S84	Res.	LCLD
0738	*Monochroa tetragonella Stt.*		*L123*	*NRR*	
0740	Monochroa hornigi Stdgr		L123	Res.	VLLD
0741	Monochroa suffusella Dougl.		S84	NRR	
0742	Monochroa lutulentella Zell.		S84	Res.	VLLD
0744	*Monochroa arundinetella Stt.*		*S84*	*NRR*	
0744a	Monochroa moyses Uffen (*Monochroa sp.*)		L123	Res.	VLMD
0746	Chrysoesthia drurella Fabr.		S84	Res.	LCMD
0747	Chrysoesthia sexguttella Thunb.		S84	Res.	WSMD
0748	Ptocheuusa paupella Zell.		S84	Res.	LCMD
0752	Aristotelia ericinella Zell.		S84	Res.	VLMD
0753	Aristotelia brizella Treit.		S85	Res.	LCMD
0755	Stenolechia gemmella Linn.		S85	Res.	LCMD
0756	Parachronistis albiceps Zell.		S85	Res.	LCMD
0757	Recurvaria nanella D.& S.		S85	Res.	LCLD
0758	Recurvaria leucatella Cl.		S85	Res.	LCMD
0759	Coleotechnites piceaella Kearf.		S85	NRR	
0760	Exoteleia dodecella Linn.		S85	Res.	VLLD
0762	Athrips mouffetella Linn.		S85	Res.	LCMD
0764	Pseudotelphusa scalella Scop.		S85	Res.	VLMD

0765	Teleiodes vulgella Hb.		S85	Res.	WSMD
0766	Teleiodes scriptella Hb.		S86	Res.	LCLD
0767	Teleiodes decorella Haw.		S86	Res.	VLLD
0768	Teleiodes notatella Hb.		S86	Res.	LCLD
0770	Teleiodes proximella Hb.		S86	Res.	LCMD
0771	Teleiodes alburnella Zell.		S86	Res.	LCLD
0772	Teleiodes fugitivella Zell.		S86	Res.	LCMD
0773	Teleiodes paripunctella Thunb.		S86	Res.	VLLD
0774	Teleiodes luculella Hb.		S86	Res.	LCMD
0775	Teleiodes sequax Haw.		S86	Res.	VLLD
0776	Teleiopsis diffinis Haw.		S87	Res.	LCLD
0777	Bryotropha basaltinella Zell.		L123	Res.	VLLD
0779	Bryotropha affinis Haw.		S87	Res.	WSMD
0780	Bryotropha similis Stt.		S87	Res.	VLLD
0781	Bryotropha mundella Dougl.		S87	Res.	VLLD
0782	Bryotropha senectella Zell.		S87	Res.	LCMD
0786	Bryotropha desertella Dougl.		S87	Res.	LCMD
0787	Bryotropha terrella D.& S.		S87	Res.	WSHD
0789	Bryotropha domestica Haw.		S87	Res.	LCMD
0790	Chionodes fumatella Dougl.		L123	Res.	LCLD
0792	Mirificarma mulinella Zell.		S87	Res.	WSMD
0793	Mirificarma lentiginosella Zell.		S87	Res.	VLLD
0796	Aroga velocella Zell.		S88	Res.	LCMD
0797	Neofaculta ericetella Geyer		S88	Res.	VLMD
0799	Neofriseria singula Stdgr		S88	Res.	VLMD
0800	Gelechia rhombella D.& S.		S88	Res.	LCLD
0801	Gelechia scotinella H.-S.		S88	NRR	
0801a	Gelechia senticetella Stdgr		*	Unc.	
0802a	Gelechia sororculella Hb.		S88	Res.	LCLD
0804	Gelechia cuneatella Dougl.		S88	NRR	
0806	Gelechia nigra Haw.		S88	Res.	VLLD
0807	Gelechia turpella D.& S.		S89	NRR	
0808	Platyedra subcinerea Haw.		S89	Res.	VLLD
0809	Pexicopia malvella Hb.	Hollyhock Seed Moth	S89	Res.	VLLD
0810	Scrobipalpa suaedella Rich.		S89	Res.	LCHD
0811	Scrobipalpa samadensis plantaginella Stt.		S89	NRR	
0812	Scrobipalpa instabilella Dougl.		S89	Res.	LCHD
0813	Scrobipalpa salinella Zell.		S89	Res.	LCMD
0814	Scrobipalpa ocellatella Boyd	Beet Moth	S89	Res.	LCMD
0815	Scrobipalpa nitentella Fuchs		S89	Res.	LCMD
0816	Scrobipalpa obsoletella F.v.R.		S90	Res.	LCMD
0818	Scrobipalpa atriplicella F.v.R.		S90	Res.	LCMD
0819	Scrobipalpa costella H.& W.		S90	Res.	WSMD
0820	Scrobipalpa artemisiella Treit.	Thyme Moth	S90	NRR	
0822	Scrobipalpa acuminatella Sirc.		S90	Res.	WSMD
0823	Scrobipalpula psilella H.-S.		S90	NRR	
0826	Caryocolum vicinella Dougl.		L124	Res.	VLLD
0827	Caryocolum alsinella Zell.		*	Res.	VLLD
0828	Caryocolum viscariella Stt.		S90	Res.	WSMD
0829	Caryocolum marmoreum Haw.		S90	NRR	
0830	Caryocolum fraternella Dougl.		S90	Res.	LCMD
0831	Caryocolum proximum Haw.		L124	Res.	VLLD

0832	Caryocolum blandella Dougl.		S91	Res. LCMD
0834	Caryocolum tricolorella Haw.		S91	Res. LCMD

Symmocidae

0870	Oegoconia quadripuncta Haw.		L124	Res. VLLD
0871	Oegoconia deauratella H.- S.		S93	Res. LCMD
0871a	Oegoconia caradjai P.-G.& C.		L125	Res. LCMD

Scythrididae

0911	Scythris grandipennis Haw.		S98	Res. VLLD
0914	Scythris crassiuscula Hb. (*fletcherella* Meyr.)		S98	NRR
0915	Scythris picaepennis Haw.		S98	NRR
0918	Scythris limbella Fabr.		S98	Res. VLLD
0919	Scythris cicadella Zell.		S98	NRR

Cossidae

0162	*Cossus cossus Linn.*	*Goat Moth*	*L39*	*Res. VLLD*
0160	Phragmataecia castaneae Hb.	Reed Leopard	L38	NRR
0161	Zeuzera pyrina Linn.	Leopard Moth	L39	Res. WSMD

Tortricidae

1013	Olindia schumacherana Fabr.		S107	NRR
1014	Isotrias rectifasciana Haw.		S107	Res. LCMD
0921	Phtheochroa inopiana Haw.		S99	Res. LCLD
0923	Phtheochroa sodaliana Haw.		S100	Res. VLLD
0924	Hysterophora maculosana Haw.		S100	Res. LCMD
0925	Phtheochroa rugosana Hb.		S100	Res. LCMD
0929	Gynnidomorpha vectisana H.& W.		S100	Res. LCMD
0930	Gynnidomorpha alismana Rag.		S100	Res. LCMD
0932	Phalonidia affinitana Dougl.		S100	Res. LCMD
0926	Phalonidia manniana F.v.R.		S100	Res. LCLD
0935	Cochylimorpha alternana Steph. (*Stenodes* Guen.)		S100	NRR
0936	Cochylimorpha straminea Haw.		S100	Res. LCMD
0937	Agapeta hamana Linn.		S101	Res. WSHD
0938	Agapeta zoegana Linn.		S101	Res. WSMD
0939	Aethes tesserana D.& S.		S101	Res. LCMD
0941	Aethes hartmanniana Cl.		S101	Res. LCLD
0942	Aethes piercei Obraz.		S101	NRR
0943	Aethes margarotana Dup.		S101	NRR
0944	Aethes williana Brahm		S101	Res. LCMD
0945	Aethes cnicana Westw.		S101	Res. LCMD
0946	Aethes rubigana Treit.		S101	Res. LCMD
0947	Aethes smeathmanniana Fabr.		S101	Res. WSMD
0948	Aethes margaritana Haw.		S101	NRR
0949	Aethes dilucidana Steph.		S102	Res. LCMD
0950	Aethes francillana Fabr.		S102	Res. LCLD
0951	Aethes beatricella Wals.		S102	Res. LCMD
0952	Commophila aeneana Hb.		S102	Res. LCLD
0954	Eupoecilia angustana Hb.		S102	Res. LCMD
0955	Eupoecilia ambiguella Hb.	Vine Moth	S102	NRR
0956	Cochylidia implicitana Wocke		S102	Res. LCMD
0957	Cochylidia heydeniana H.-S.		S102	Res. VLLD

0958	Cochylidia subroseana Haw.		S103	NRR	
0959	Cochylidia rupicola Curt.		S103	NRR	
0960	Falseuncaria ruficiliana Haw.		S103	NRR	
0962	Cochylis roseana Haw.		S103	Res.	WSMD
0963	Cochylis flaviciliana Westw.		S103	NRR	
0964	Cochylis dubitana Hb.		S103	Res.	LCMD
0965	Cochylis hybridella Hb.		S103	Res.	WSMD
0966	Cochylis atricapitana Steph.		S103	Res.	LCMD
0968	Cochylis nana Haw.		S103	Res.	LCMD
0969	Pandemis corylana Fabr.	Chequered Fruit-tree Tortrix	S104	Res.	WSHD
0970	Pandemis cerasana Hb.	Barred Fruit-tree Tortrix	S104	Res.	WSHD
0971	Pandemis cinnamomeana Treit.		S104	Res.	VLLD
0972	Pandemis heparana D.& S.	Dark Fruit-tree Tortrix	S104	Res.	WSHD
0973	Pandemis dumetana Treit.		*	Res.	VLLD
0974	Argyrotaenia ljungiana Thunb. (pulchellana Haw.)		S105	Res.	LCMD
0976	Archips oporana Linn.		S105	NRR	
0977	Archips podana Scop.	Large Fruit-tree Tortrix	S105	Res.	WSHD
0979	Archips crataegana Hb.	Brown Oak Tortrix	S105	Res.	LCLD
0980	Archips xylosteana Linn.	Variegated Golden Tortrix	S105	Res.	WSHD
0981	Archips rosana Linn.	Rose Tortrix	S105	Res.	LCMD
0982	Choristoneura diversana Hb.		S105	Res.	VLLD
0983	Choristoneura hebenstreitella Müll.		S105	Res.	VLLD
0985	Cacoecimorpha pronubana Hb.	Carnation Tortrix	S105	Res.	WSHD
0986	Syndemis musculana Hb.		S105	Res.	WSHD
0987	Ptycholomoides aeriferanus H.-S.		S106	Res.	LCLD
0988	Aphelia viburnana D.& S.	Bilberry Tortrix	S106	Res.	LCMD
0989	Aphelia paleana Hb.	Timothy Tortrix	S106	Res.	WSMD
0992	Clepsis rurinana Linn.		S106	NRR	
0993	Clepsis spectrana Treit.	Cyclamen Tortrix	S106	Res.	WSHD
0994	Clepsis consimilana Hb.		S106	Res.	WSHD
0998	Epiphyas postvittana Walk.	Light Brown Apple Moth	S106	Res.	VLLD
0999	Adoxophyes orana F.v.R.	Summer Fruit Tortrix	S107	Res.	LCLD
1000	Ptycholoma lecheana Linn.		S107	Res.	LCMD
1001	Lozotaeniodes formosanus Geyer		S107	Res.	LCMD
1002	Lozotaenia forsterana Fabr.		S107	Res.	WSMD
1006	Epagoge grotiana Fabr.		S107	Res.	WSMD
1007	Capua vulgana Fröl.		S107	Res.	LCLD
1010	Ditula angustiorana Haw.	Red-barred Tortrix	S107	Res.	WSHD
1011	Pseudargyrotoza conwagana Fabr.		S107	Res.	WSMD
1015	Eulia ministrana Linn.		S108	Res.	LCMD
1016	Cnephasia longana Haw.		S108	Res.	WSMD
1018	Cnephasia communana H.-S.		S108	Res.	LCLD
1019	Cnephasia conspersana Dougl.		S108	Res.	VLLD
1020	Cnephasia stephensiana Doubl.	Grey Tortrix	S108	Res.	WSHD
1021	Cnephasia asseclana D.& S. (interjectana Haw.)Flax Tortrix		S108	Res.	WSHD
1022	Cnephasia pasiuana Hb.		S108	Res.	LCMD
1023	Cnephasia genitalana P.& M.		S108	Res.	VLLD
1024	Cnephasia incertana Treit.	Light Grey Tortrix	S108	Res.	WSHD
1025	Tortricodes alternella D.& S.		S108	Res.	LCMD
1026	Exapate congelatella Cl.		S108	NRR	
1027	Neosphaleroptera nubilana Hb.		S109	Res.	LCMD
1029	Eana osseana Scop.		S109	Res.	VLLD

1030	Eana incanana Steph.		S109	Res.	LCMD
1032	Aleimma loeflingiana Linn.		S109	Res.	LCMD
1033	Tortrix viridana Linn.	Green Oak Tortrix	S109	Res.	WSHD
1034	Spatalistis bifasciana Hb.		S109	Res.	VLLD
1035	Acleris bergmanniana Linn. (*Croesia* Hb.)		S109	Res.	LCMD
1036	Acleris forsskaleana Linn. (*Croesia* Hb.)		S109	Res.	WSMD
1037	Acleris holmiana Linn. (*Croesia* Hb.)		S109	Res.	LCMD
1038	Acleris laterana Fabr.		S109	Res.	LCMD
1039	Acleris comariana L.& Z.	Strawberry Tortrix	S110	Res.	LCLD
1041	Acleris sparsana D.& S.		S110	Res.	WSMD
1042	Acleris rhombana D.& S.	Rhomboid Tortrix	S110	Res.	WSHD
1043	Acleris aspersana Hb.		S110	Res.	LCLD
1044	Acleris ferrugana D.& S.		S110	Res.	LCMD
1045	Acleris notana Don.		S110	Res.	LCMD
1046	Acleris shepherdana Steph.		S110	NRR	
1047	Acleris schalleriana Linn.		S110	Res.	LCLD
1048	Acleris variegana D.& S.	Garden Rose Tortrix	S110	Res.	WSHD
1050	Acleris boscana Fabr.		S110	Res.	LCMD
1052	Acleris umbrana Hb.		S110	NRR	
1053	Acleris hastiana Linn.		S111	Res.	LCMD
1054	Acleris cristana D.& S.		S111	Res.	WSMD
1055	Acleris hyemana Haw.		S111	NRR	
1057	Acleris rufana D.& S.		S111	NRR	
1058	Acleris lorquiniana Dup.		S111	NRR	
1060	Acleris maccana Treit.		S111	NRR	
1061	Acleris literana Linn.		S111	Res.	VLLD
1062	Acleris emargana Fabr.		S111	Res.	WSMD
1063	Celypha striana D.& S.		S112	Res.	WSMD
1064	Celypha rosaceana Schläg.		S112	Res.	LCMD
1067	Celypha cespitana Hb.		S113	Res.	LCMD
1068	Olethreutes rivulana Scop.		S113	Res.	VLLD
1076	Olethreutes lacunana D.& S.		S113	Res.	WSHD
1080	Olethreutes arcuella Cl.		S113	NRR	
1079	Piniphila bifasciana Haw.		S113	Res.	LCMD
1082	Hedya pruniana Hb.	Plum Tortrix	S113	Res.	WSHD
1083	Hedya dimidioalba Retz. (*nubiferana* Haw.)				
		Marbled Orchard Tortrix	S113	Res.	WSHD
1084	Hedya ochroleucana Fröl.		S113	Res.	LCMD
1085	Hedya atropunctana Zett.		S113	NRR	
1086	Hedya salicella Linn.		S114	Res.	LCMD
1087	Orthotaenia undulana D.& S.		S114	Res.	LCMD
1088	Pseudosciaphila branderiana Linn.		S114	Res.	LCMD
1089	Apotomis semifasciana Haw.		S114	NRR	
1091	Apotomis lineana D.& S.		S114	Res.	LCLD
1092	Apotomis turbidana Hb.		S114	Res.	LCMD
1093	Apotomis betuletana Haw.		S114	Res.	LCMD
1094	Apotomis capreana Hb.		S115	Res.	LCLD
1095	Apotomis sororculana Zett.		S115	NRR	
1097	Endothenia gentianaeana Hb.		S115	Res.	WSMD
1098	Endothenia oblongana Haw.		S115	Res.	LCMD
1099	Endothenia marginana Haw.		S115	Res.	LCLD
1100	Endothenia pullana Haw.		S115	NRR	

1101	Endothenia ustulana Haw.		S115	Unc.	
1102	Endothenia nigricostana Haw.		S115	Res.	LCMD
1103	Endothenia ericetana H.& W.		S115	Res.	LCLD
1104	Endothenia quadrimaculana Haw.		S115	Res.	LCLD
1106	Lobesia reliquana Hb.		L126	Res.	VLLD
1108	Lobesia abscisana Doubl.		S116	Res.	LCMD
1109	Lobesia littoralis H.& W.		S116	Res.	LCMD
1110	Bactra furfurana Haw.		S116	Res.	LCMD
1111	Bactra lancealana Hb.		S116	Res.	LCMD
1112	Bactra robustana Christ.		S116	Res.	LCMD
1113	Eudemis profundana D.& S.		S116	Res.	LCMD
1115	Ancylis achatana D.& S.		S117	Res.	LCHD
1117	Ancylis unguicella Linn.		S117	Unc.	
1118	Ancylis uncella D.& S.		S117	NRR	
1119	Ancylis geminana Don.		S117	NRR	
1119a	Ancylis diminutana Haw.		S117	Res.	VLLD
1120	Ancylis mitterbacheriana D.& S.		S117	Res.	LCMD
1121	Ancylis upupana Treit.		S117	NRR	
1122	Ancylis obtusana Haw.		S117	NRR	
1123	Ancylis laetana Fabr.		S117	Res.	LCMD
1125	Ancylis unculana Haw.		*	Res.	VLLD
1126	Ancylis badiana D.& S.		S118	Res.	LCMD
1128	Ancylis myrtillana Treit.		S118	NRR	
1129	Ancylis apicella D.& S.		S118	NRR	
1130	Epinotia pygmaeana Hb.		S118	Res.	VLMD
1132	Epinotia subocellana Don.		S118	Res.	LCMD
1133	Epinotia bilunana Haw.		S118	Res.	LCMD
1134	Epinotia ramella Linn.		S118	Res.	LCMD
1135	Epinotia demarniana F.v.R.		S118	Res.	LCLD
1136	Epinotia immundana F.v.R.		S118	Res.	LCMD
1137	Epinotia tetraquetrana Haw.		S118	Res.	LCMD
1138	Epinotia nisella Cl.		S119	Res.	LCMD
1139	Epinotia tenerana D.& S.	Nut Bud Moth	S119	Res.	LCMD
1140	Epinotia nigricana H.-S.		S119	NRR	
1142	Epinotia tedella Cl.		S119	Res.	LCMD
1143	Epinotia fraternana Haw.		S119	Res.	LCMD
1144	Epinotia signatana Dougl.		S119	Res.	VLLD
1145	Epinotia nanana Treit.		S119	Res.	LCMD
1147	Epinotia cruciana Linn.	Willow Tortrix	S119	Res.	LCMD
1150	Epinotia abbreviana Fabr.		S119	Res.	WSMD
1151	Epinotia trigonella Linn. (stroemiana Fabr.)		S120	Res.	LCLD
1152	Epinotia maculana Fabr.		S120	Res.	LCMD
1153	Epinotia sordidana Hb.		S120	Res.	LCLD
1154	Epinotia caprana Fabr.		S120	Res.	LCLD
1155	Epinotia brunnichana Linn.		S120	Res.	LCHD
1156	Epinotia solandriana Linn.		S120	Res.	LCLD
1157	Crocidosema plebejana Zell.		L126	Vag. R	
1159	Rhopobota naevana Hb.	Holly Tortrix	S120	Res.	LCHD
1161	Rhopobota stagnana D.& S.		S120	NRR	
1163	Zeiraphera ratzeburgiana Ratz.		S121	Res.	LCMD
1164	Zeiraphera rufimitrana H.-S.		S121	NRR	
1165	Zeiraphera isertana Fabr.		S121	Res.	WSHD

1166	Zeiraphera diniana Guen.	Larch Tortrix	S121	Res.	VLMD
1167	Gypsonoma aceriana Dup.		S121	Res.	LCMD
1168	Gypsonoma sociana Haw.		S121	Res.	LCLD
1169	Gypsonoma dealbana Fröl.		S121	Res.	WSHD
1170	Gypsonoma oppressana Treit.		S121	Res.	LCMD
1171	Gypsonoma minutana Hb.		S121	Res.	LCLD
1173	Gibberifera simplana F.v.R.		S121	NRR	
1174	Epiblema cynosbatella Linn.		S121	Res.	WSMD
1175	Epiblema uddmanniana Linn.		S122	Res.	WSHD
1176	Epiblema trimaculana Haw.		S122	Res.	LCMD
1177	Epiblema rosaecolana Doubl.		S122	Res.	LCMD
1178	Epiblema roborana D.& S.		S122	Res.	LCMD
1179	Epiblema incarnatana Hb.		S122	NRR	
1180	Epiblema tetragonana Steph.		S122	NRR	
1182	Epiblema turbidana Treit.		L126	Res.	VLLD
1183	Epiblema foenella Linn.		S122	Res.	WSMD
1184	Epiblema scutulana D.& S.		S122	Res.	LCMD
1184a	Epiblema cirsiana Zell.		S122	Res.	LCMD
1186	Epiblema sticticana Fabr. (farfarae Fletch.)		S122	Res.	LCMD
1187	Epiblema costipunctana Haw.		S122	Res.	LCMD
1188	Pelochrista caecimaculana Hb.		S122	Res.	VLMD
1191	Eucosma catoptrana Rebel		S123	Res.	LCMD
1192	Eucosma conterminana H.-S.		S123	Res.	LCMD
1193	Eucosma tripoliana Barr.		S123	Res.	LCMD
1194	Eucosma aemulana Schläg.		S123	NRR	
1195	Eucosma lacteana Treit. (maritima H.& W.)		S123	Res.	LCLD
1197	Eucosma campoliliana D.& S.		S123	Res.	LCMD
1198	Eucosma pauperana Dup.		S124	Res.	VLLD
1199	Eucosma pupillana Cl.		S124	Res.	VLLD
1200	Eucosma hohenwartiana D.& S.		S124	Res.	WSHD
1200a	Eucosma fulvana Steph.		S124	Res.	LCMD
1201	Eucosma cana Haw.		S124	Res.	WSHD
1202	Eucosma obumbratana L.& Z.		S124	Res.	LCMD
1204	Thiodia citrana Hb.		S124	Res.	LCMD
1205	Spilonota ocellana D.& S.	Bud Moth	S124	Res.	WSHD
1205a	Spilonota laricana Hein.		*	Vag.	R
1207	Clavigesta purdeyi Durr.	Pine Leaf-mining Moth	S124	Res.	LCMD
1208	Blastesthia posticana Zett.		S125	Res.	VLMD
1209	Blastesthia turionella Linn.	Pine Bud Moth	S125	NRR	
1210	Rhyacionia buoliana D.& S.	Pine Shoot Moth	S125	Res.	LCLD
1211	Rhyacionia pinicolana Doubl.		S125	Res.	LCMD
1212	Rhyacionia pinivorana L.& Z.	Spotted Shoot Moth	S125	Res.	LCMD
1215	Cryptophlebia leucotreta Meyr.	False Codling Moth	S125	Acc.	R
1216	Enarmonia formosana Scop.	Cherry-bark Moth	S125	Res.	LCMD
1217	Eucosmomorpha albersana Hb.		S125	NRR	
1219	Lathronympha strigana Fabr.		S125	Res.	WSMD
1220	Collicularia microgrammana Guen.		S125	Res.	VLLD
1221	Strophedra weirana Dougl.		S126	Res.	LCLD
1222	Strophedra nitidana Fabr.		S126	Res.	LCLD
1223	Pammene splendidulana Guen.		S126	Res.	LCMD
1225	Pammene obscurana Steph.		L126	Res.	VLLD
1227	Pammene inquilina Fletch.		S126	Res.	VLLD

1228	Pammene argyrana Hb.		S126	Res.	LCMD
1229	Pammene albuginana Guen.		S126	Res.	VLMD
1231	Pammene spiniana Dup.		S126	NRR	
1232	Pammene populana Fabr.		S127	NRR	
1233	Pammene aurantiana Stdgr		S127	Res.	LCLD
1234	Pammene regiana Zell.		S127	Res.	WSMD
1235	Pammene trauniana D.& S.		S127	Res.	VLLD
1236	Pammene fasciana Linn.		S127	Res.	LCMD
1236a	Pammene herrichiana Hein.		S127	Res.	VLLD
1237	Pammene germmana Hb.		S127	Res.	LCLD
1238	Pammene ochsenheimeriana L.& Z.		S127	Unc.	
1239	Pammene rhediella Cl.	Fruitlet Mining Tortrix	S127	Res.	LCMD
1241	Cydia compositella Fabr.		S127	Res.	LCMD
1242	Cydia internana Guen.		S128	Res.	VLMD
1245	Cydia janthinana Dup.		S128	Res.	LCMD
1243	*Cydia pallifrontana L.& Z.*		*L127*	*Res.*	*VLMD*
1246	Cydia tenebrosana Dup.		S128	Res.	LCMD
1247	Cydia funebrana Treit.	Plum Fruit Moth	S128	Res.	LCMD
1248	Cydia molesta Busck	Oriental Fruit Moth	S128	Acc. R	
1251	Cydia jungiella Cl.		S128	Res.	LCMD
1254	Cydia strobilella Linn.		S128	NRR	
1255	Cydia succedana D.& S		S128	Res.	WSHD
1255a	Cydia medicaginis Kuzn.		*	Res.	VLLD
1256	Cydia servillana Dup.		S128	Res.	LCMD
1257	Cydia nigricana Fabr.	Pea Moth	S128	Res.	LCMD
1259	Cydia fagiglandana Zell.		S129	Res.	VLMD
1260	Cydia splendana Hb.		S129	Res.	WSHD
1261	Cydia pomonella Linn.	Codling Moth	S129	Res.	WSHD
1264	*Cydia leguminana L.& Z.*		*129*	*NRR*	
1269	Cydia conicolana Heyl.		S129	Res.	VLLD
1271	Cydia gallicana Guen.		S129	Res.	LCMD
1272	Cydia aurana Fabr.		S129	Res.	LCLD
1273	Dichrorampha petiverella Linn.		S129	Res.	WSHD
1274	Dichrorampha alpinana Treit.		S129	Res.	LCMD
1275	Dichrorampha flavidorsana Knaggs		S129	Res.	LCLD
1276	Dichrorampha plumbagana Treit.		S130	Res.	LCHD
1278	Dichrorampha sequana Hb.		S130	Res.	LCMD
1279	Dichrorampha acuminatana L.& Z.		S130	Res.	LCMD
1280	Dichrorampha consortana Steph.		S130	Res.	VLLD
1281	Dichrorampha simpliciana Haw.		S130	Res.	LCMD
1282	Dichrorampha sylvicolana Hein.		S130	Res.	VLLD
1284	Dichrorampha gueneeana Obraz.		S130	Res.	WSMD
1285	Dichrorampha plumbana Scop.		S130	Res.	WSHD
1286	Dichrorampha sedatana Busck		S130	Res.	LCMD
1287	Dichrorampha aeratana P.& M.		S131	Res.	LCLD

Sesiidae

0370	Sesia apiformis Cl.	Hornet Moth	L40	Res.	LCLD
0371	Sesia bembeciformis Hb.	Lunar Hornet Moth	L40	Res.	LCLD
0372	Paranthrene tabaniformis Rott.	Dusky Clearwing	L40	NRR	
0373	Synanthedon tipuliformis Cl.	Currant Clearwing	L40	Res.	VLLD
0374	Synanthedon vespiformis Linn.	Yellow-legged Clearwing	L40	Res.	LCLD

0375	Synanthedon spheciformis D.& S.	White-barred Clearwing	L41	NRR	
0378	Synanthedon andrenaeformis Lasp.	Orange-tailed Clearwing	L41	Res.	VLLD
0379	Synanthedon myopaeformis Borkh.	Red-belted Clearwing	L41	Res.	VLLD
0380	Synanthedon formicaeformis Esp.	Red-tipped Clearwing	L41	Vag.	R
0381	Synanthedon culiciformis Linn.	Large Red-belted Clearwing	L41	NRR	
0382	Bembecia scopigera Scop.	Six-belted Clearwing	L41	Res.	VLLD
0384	Bembecia chrysidiformis Esp.	Fiery Clearwing	L41	NRR	

Choreutidae

0385	Anthopila fabriciana Linn.		S54	Res.	WSHD
0387	Prochoreutis sehestediana Fabr.		L120	Res.	VLLD
0388	Prochoreutis myllerana Fabr.		S54	Res.	VLLD
0389	Choreutis pariana Cl.	Apple Leaf Skeletonizer	S54	Res.	LCLD

Zygaenidae

0163	Adscita statices Linn.	Forester	L39	NRR	
0169	Zygaena filipendulae Linn.	Six-spot Burnet	L39	Res.	WSMD
0170	Zygaena trifolii Esp.	Five-spot Burnet	L39	NRR	
0171	Zygaena lonicerae Schev.	Narrow Bordered Six-spot Burnet	L39	Res.	WSLD

Limacodidae

0173	Apoda limacodes Hufn.	Festoon	L40	Res.	VLMD
0174	*Heterogenea asella D.& S.*	*Triangle*	*L40*	*Res.*	*VLLD*

Schreckensteiniidae

0485	Schreckensteinia festaliella Hb.		S62	Res.	LCMD

Epermeniidae

0477	Phaulernis dentella Zell.		*	Res.	VLLD
0478	Phaulernis fulviguttella Zell.		S62	NRR	
0479	Cataplectica farreni Wals.		S62	Res.	VLLD
0480	Cataplectica profugella Stt.		S62	Res.	VLLD
0481	Epermenia falciformis Haw. (*illigerella* sensu auctt.)		S62	Res.	LCMD
0483	Epermenia chaerophyllella Goeze		S62	Res.	WSMD

Alucitidae

1288	Alucita hexadactyla Linn.	Twenty-plume Moth	S131	Res.	LCMD

Pterophoridae

1488	Agdistis bennetii Curt.		S152	Res.	LCHD
1490	Oxyptilus parvidactylus Haw.		S152	Res.	VLLD
1493	Buckleria paludum Zell.		S152	NRR	
1494	Capperia britanniodactyla Gregs.		S152	Res.	VLLD
1495	Marasmarcha lunaedactyla Haw.		S152	Res.	LCMD
1496	Cnaemidophorus rhododactyla D.& S.		S152	Res.	LCLD
1497	Amblyptilia acanthadactyla Hb.		S152	Res.	VLLD
1498	Amblyptilia punctidactyla Haw.		S152	NRR	
1500	Platyptilia calodactyla D.& S.		S153	Res.	LCLD
1501	Platyptilia gonodactyla D.& S.		S153	Res.	LCMD
1503	Platyptilia ochrodactyla D.& S.		S153	Res.	VLLD
1504	Platyptilia pallidactyla Haw.		S153	Res.	WSMD
1507	Stenoptilia zophodactylus Dup.		S153	Res.	LCLD

1508	Stenoptilia bipunctidactyla Scop.		S153	Res.	LCMD
1509	Stenoptilia pterodactyla Linn.		S153	Res.	LCMD
1512	Pterophorus baliodactylus Zell.		S153	Res.	VLLD
1513	Pterophorus pentadactyla Linn.	White Plume Moth	S153	Res.	WSMD
1514	Pterophorus galactodactyla D.& S.		S153	Res.	LCLD
1517	Adaina microdactyla Hb.		S154	Res.	LCMD
1518	Leioptilus lienigianus Zell.		S154	Res.	LCMD
1519	Leioptilus carphodactyla Hb.		L129	Res.	VLMD
1522	Leioptilus tephradactyla Hb.		S154	NRR	
1523	Oidaematophorus lithodactyla Treit.		S154	Res.	LCMD
1524	Emmelina monodactyla Linn.		S154	Res.	WSHD

Pyralidae

1425	Galleria mellonella Linn.	Wax Moth	S145	Res.	LCLD
1426	Achroia grisella Fabr.	Lesser Wax Moth	S145	Res.	LCLD
1427	Corcyra cephalonica Stt.	Rice Moth	S145	NRR	
1428	Aphomia sociella Linn.	Bee Moth	S145	Res.	WSMD
1429	*Melissoblaptes zelleri Joann.*		*S145*	*Vag.*	*O*
1430	Paralipsa gularis Zell.	Stored Nut Moth	S145	NRR	
1424	Endotricha flammealis D.& S.		S144	Res.	WSHD
1424a	Endotricha consobrinalis Zell.		*	Acc.	R
1413	Hypsopygia costalis Fabr.	Gold Triangle	S144	Res.	WSMD
1414	Synaphe punctalis Fabr.		S144	Res.	LCMD
1415	Orthopygia glaucinalis Linn.		S144	Res.	LCMD
1417	Pyralis farinalis Linn.	Meal Moth	S144	Res.	LCLD
1420	Aglossa caprealis Hb.	Small Tabby	S144	Res.	LCLD
1421	Aglossa pinguinalis Linn.	Large Tabby	S144	Res.	LCLD
1432	Anerastia lotella Hb.		S146	Res.	LCMD
1433	Cryptoblabes bistriga Haw.		S146	Res.	LCLD
1434	Cryptoblabes gnidiella Mill.		S146	NRR	
1450	Metriostola betulae Goeze		S148	Res.	LCLD
1448	Selagia argyrella D.& S.		*	NRR	
1449	Microthrix similella Zinck.		S148	NRR	
1451	Pyla fusca Haw.		S148	Res.	LCMD
1451a	Etiella zinckenella Treit.		*	Mig.	R
1452	Phycita roborella D.& S.		S148	Res.	WSHD
1441	Onocera semirubella Scop.		S147	Vag.	R
1442	Pempelia palumbella D.& S. (*Onocera* Steph.)		S147	NRR	
1443	Pempelia genistella Dup.			Res.	VLHD
1445	Pempelia formosa Haw. (*Onocera* Steph.)		S148	Res.	LCMD
1447	*Sciota hostilis Steph. (Nephopteryx Hb.)*		*S148*	*NRR*	
1447a	Sciota adelphella F.v.R.		*	Res.	VLLD
1457	Hypochalcia ahenella D.& S.		S149	Res.	VLLD
1454a	Dioryctria schuetzeella Fuchs		*	Res.	LCLD
1454	Dioryctria abietella D.& S.		S148	Res.	LCLD
1455	Dioryctria mutatella Fuchs		S148	Res.	LCMD
1453	Pima boisduvaliella Guen.		S148	Vag.	R
1465	Nephopterix angustella Hb. (*Alispa* Zell.)		S149	Res.	VLMD
1462	Pempeliella diluta Haw.		S149	NRR	
1435	Acrobasis tumidana D.& S.		S147	Unc.	
1436	Acrobasis repandana Fabr.		S147	Res.	LCMD
1437	Acrobasis consociella Hb.		S147	Res.	LCMD

1438	Numonia suavella Zinck. (*Eurhodope* Hb.)		S147	Res.	LCLD
1439	Numonia advenella Zinck. (*Eurhodope* Hb.)		S147	Res.	LCMD
1440	Numonia marmorea Haw. (*Eurhodope* Hb.)		S147	Res.	LCMD
1486	Apomyelois bistriatella Hulst		S151	Res.	VLLD
1460	Ectomyelois ceratoniae Zell.	Locus Bean Moth	S149	NRR	
1458	Myelois cribrella Hb.	Thistle Ermine	S149	Res.	WSMD
1464	Gymnancyla canella D.& S.		S149	Res.	VLMD
1461	Assara terebrella Zinck.		*	Res.	VLMD
1469	Euzophera cinerosella Zell.		S149	Res.	LCLD
1470	Euzophera pinguis Haw.		S150	Res.	WSMD
1472	Euzophera bigella Zell.		L128	Acc.	R
1468	Nyctegretis lineana Scop. (*achatinella* Hb.)		S149	NRR	
1467	Ancylosis oblitella Zell.		S149	Mig.	F
1480	Homoeosoma nebulella D.& S.		S150	NRR	
1481	Homoeosoma sinuella Fabr.		S150	Res.	WSMD
1482	Homoeosoma nimbella Dup.		S150	Unc.	
1483	Phycitodes binaevella Hb.		S151	Res.	LCMD
1484	Phycitodes saxicola Vaugh.		S151	Res.	LCMD
1485	Phycitodes maritima Tengst. (*carlinella* Hein.)		S151	Res.	LCMD
1289	Euchromius ocellea Haw.		*	Mig.	R
1290	Chilo phragmitella Hb.		S132	Res.	LCMD
1292	Calamotropha paludella Hb.		S132	Res.	LCMD
1293	Chrysoteuchia culmella Linn.		S132	Res.	WSHD
1294	Crambus pascuella Linn.		S132	Res.	WSHD
1296	Crambus silvella Hb.		S132	NRR	
1299	Crambus hamella Thunb.		S133	Vag.	R
1301	Crambus lathoniellus Zinck. (*nemorella* Hb.)		S133	Res.	WSHD
1302	Crambus perlella Scop.		S133	Res.	WSHD
1303	Agriphila selasella Hb.		S133	Res.	WSMD
1304	Agriphila straminella D.& S.		S133	Res.	WSHD
1305	Agriphila tristella D.& S.		S133	Res.	WSHD
1306	Agriphila inquinatella D.& S.		S133	Res.	LCMD
1307	Agriphila latistria Haw.		S133	Res.	LCMD
1309	Agriphila geniculea Haw.		S133	Res.	WSHD
1313	Catoptria pinella Linn.		S134	Res.	WSMD
1314	Catoptria margaritella D.& S.		*	Mig.	R
1316	Catoptria falsella D.& S.		S134	Res.	WSMD
	Increase in range. Now recorded from twenty-six 10km squares, SME gave only four widespread recent sites.				
1317	Catoptria verellus Zinck.		S134	Unc.	'
1321	Thisanotia chrysonuchella Scop.		S134	Res.	VLLD
1322	Pediasia fascelinella Hb.		S134	Vag. R	
1323	Pediasia contaminella Hb.		S134	Res.	LCLD
1324	Pediasia aridella Thunb.		S134	Res.	LCMD
1325	Platytes alpinella Hb.		S134	Res.	LCMD
	SME gave a single, old record from south Essex. Now recorded from eight 10km squares.				
1326	Platytes cerussella D.& S.		S135	Res.	LCMD
1331	Acentria ephemerella D.& S.	Water Veneer	S136	Res.	WSHD
1345	Elophila nymphaeata Linn.	Brown China-mark	S138	Res.	LCMD
1350	Nymphula stagnata Don.	Beautiful China-mark	S138	Res.	LCLD
1348	Parapoynx stratiotata Linn.	Ringed China-mark	S138	Res.	LCMD

1354	Cataclysta lemnata Linn.	Small China-mark	S138	Res.	LCMD
1332	Scoparia subfusca Haw.		S136	Res.	LCMD
1333	Scoparia pyralella D.& S.		S136	Res.	WSHD
1334	Scoparia ambigualis Treit.		S136	Res.	WSHD
1334a	Scoparia basistrigalis Knaggs		S136	Res.	LCLD
1335	Scoparia ancipitella La Harpe (*ulmella* Knaggs)		S137	NRR	
1338	Dipleurina lacustrata Panz. (*Eudonia crataegella* Hb.)		S137	Res.	LCMD
1336	Eudonia pallida Curt.		S137	Res.	LCMD
1340	Eudonia truncicolella Stt.		S137	Res.	LCLD
1342	Eudonia angustea Curt.		S137	Res.	LCMD
1344	Eudonia mercurella Linn.		S137	Res.	WSHD
1328	Schoenobius gigantella D.& S.		S135	Res.	LCMD
1329	Donacaula forficella Thunb. (*Schoenobius* Meyr.)		S135	Res.	LCMD
1330	Donacaula mucronellus D.& S.		S136	Res.	LCLD
1356	Evergestis forficalis Linn.	Garden Pebble	S138	Res.	WSHD
1357	Evergestis extimalis Scop.		S139	Res.	LCMD
1358	Evergestis pallidata Hufn.		S139	Res.	LCMD
1361	Pyrausta aurata Scop.		S140	Res.	WSMD
1362	Pyrausta purpuralis Linn.		S140	Res.	LCLD
1363	Pyrausta ostrinalis Hb.		S140	NRR	
1365	Pyrausta cespitalis D.& S.		S140	Res.	LCMD
1366	Pyrausta nigrata Scop.		S140	NRR	
1368	Margaritia sticticalis Linn.		S140	Mig.	O
1369	Uresiphita polygonalis D.& S. (*limbalis* D.& S.)		S140	Mig.	R
1370	Sitochroa palealis D.& S.		S140	Mig.	F
1371	Sitochroa verticalis Linn.		S140	Res.	LCMD
1373	Microstega pandalis Hb.	Bordered Pearl	S140	Res.	LCLD
1374	Microstega hyalinalis Hb.		L127	Res.	VLMD
1375	Ostrinia nubilalis Hb.	European Corn-borer	S141	Res.	WSLD
1376	Eurrhypara hortulata Linn.	Small Magpie	S141	Res.	WSMD
1377	Perinephela lancealis D.& S.		S141	Res.	LCMD
1378	Phyctaenia coronata Hufn.		S141	Res.	WSMD
1380	Phyctaenia perlucidalis Hb.		S141	Res.	LCMD
1384	Phyctaenia stachydalis Germ.		S141	NRR	
1381	Anania funebris Ström.		S141	NRR	
1382	Anania verbascalis D.& S.		S141	Res.	LCMD
1385	Ebulea crocealis Hb.		S142	Res.	LCMD
1386	Opsibotys fuscalis D.& S.		S142	Res.	LCLD
1387	Nascia cilialis Hb.		S142	Res.	LCLD
1388	Udea lutealis Hb. (*elutalis* D.& S.)		S142	Res.	WSMD
1390	Udea prunalis D.& S.		S142	Res.	LCMD
1392	Udea olivalis D.& S.		S142	Res.	WSMD
1395	Udea ferrugalis Hb.		S142	Mig.	F
1398	Nomophila noctuella D.& S.	Rush Veneer	S142	Mig.	F
1399	Dolicharthria punctalis D.& S.		S143	NRR	
1401	Maruca testulalis Geyer	Mung Moth	S143	Acc.	R
1402	Diasemia reticularis Linn. (*litterata* Scop.)		S143	Mig.	R
1403	Diasemiopsis ramburialis Dup.		S143	Mig.	R
1405	Pleuroptya ruralis Scop.	Mother of Pearl	S143	Res.	WSHD
1408	Palpita unionalis Hb.		S143	Mig.	R
1479	Plodia interpunctella Hb.	Indian Meal Moth	S150	Acc.	R
1473	Ephestia elutella Hb.	Cacao Moth	S150	Res.	LCMD

1474	Ephestia parasitella unicolorella Stdgr		S150	Res.	LCMD
1475	Ephestia kuehniella Zell.	Mediterranean Flour Moth S150		Res.	LCLD
1476	Ephestia cautella Walk.	Dried Currant Moth	S150	Res.	VLLD
1477	Ephestia figulilella Gregs.	Raisin Moth	S150	NRR	

Geometridae

1661	Archiearis parthenias Linn.	Orange Underwing	L54	Res.	VLLD
1662	Archiearis notha Hb.	Light Orange Underwing	L54	Res.	VLLD
1884	Abraxas grossulariata Linn.	Magpie	L71	Res.	WSMD
1885	Abraxas sylvata Scop.	Clouded Magpie	L71	Res.	VLLD
1887	Lomaspilis marginata Linn.	Clouded Border	L71	Res.	WSHD
1888	Ligdia adustata D.& S.	Scorched Carpet	L71	Res.	WSMD
1889	Semiothisa notata Linn.	Peacock Moth	L71	Res.	LCMD
1890	Semiothisa alternaria Hb.	Sharp-angled Carpet	L72	Res.	LCLD
1891	Semiothisa signaria Hb.	Dusky Peacock	L72	Mig.	R
1893	Semiothisa liturata Cl.	Tawny-barred Angle	L72	Res.	LCMD
1894	Semiothisa clathrata Linn.	Latticed Heath	L72	Res.	WSMD
1896	Semiothisa brunneata Thunb.	Rannoch Looper	L72	NRR	
1897	Semiothisa wauaria Linn.	V-Moth	L72	Res.	LCLD
1899	Isturgia limbaria Fabr.	Frosted Yellow	L72	NRR	
1901	Cepphis advenaria Hb.	Little Thorn	L72	NRR	
1902	Petrophora chlorosata Scop.	Brown Silver-lines	L72	Res.	WSMD
1903	Plagodis pulveraria Linn.	Barred Umber	L72	Res.	VLLD
1904	Plagodis dolabraria Linn.	Scorched Wing	L72	Res.	WSMD
1905	Pachycnemia hippocastanaria Hb.	Horse Chestnut	L72	NRR	
1906	Opisthograptis luteolata Linn.	Brimstone Moth	L72	Res.	WSHD
1907	Epione repandaria Hufn.	Bordered Beauty	L73	Res.	WSMD
1909	Pseudopanthera macularia Linn.	Speckled Yellow	L73	Res.	LCMD
1910	Apeira syringaria Linn.	Lilac Beauty	L73	Res.	WSLD
1911	Ennomos autumnaria Werneb.	Large Thorn	L73	Res.	WSMD
1912	Ennomos quercinaria Hufn.	August Thorn	L73	Res.	LCLD
1913	Ennomos alniaria Linn.	Canary-shouldered Thorn	L73	Res.	WSHD
1914	Ennomos fuscantaria Haw.	Dusky Thorn	L73	Res.	WSMD
1915	Ennomos erosaria D.& S.	September Thorn	L73	Res.	WSLD
1917	Selenia dentaria Fabr.	Early Thorn	L73	Res.	WSHD
1918	Selenia lunularia Hb.	Lunar Thorn	L73	Res.	LCLD
1919	Selenia tetralunaria Hufn.	Purple Thorn	L73	Res.	WSMD
1920	Odontopera bidentata Cl.	Scalloped Hazel	L73	Res.	WSMD
1921	Crocallis elinguaria Linn.	Scalloped Oak	L74	Res.	WSHD
1922	Ourapteryx sambucaria Linn.	Swallow-tailed Moth	L74	Res.	WSHD
1923	Colotois pennaria Linn.	Feathered Thorn	L74	Res.	WSMD
1924	Angerona prunaria Linn.	Orange Moth	L74	Res.	LCMD
1925	Apocheima hispidaria D.& S.	Small Brindled Beauty	L74	Res.	LCMD
1926	Apocheima pilosaria D.& S.	Pale Brindled Beauty	L74	Res.	WSHD
1927	Lycia hirtaria Cl.	Brindled Beauty	L74	Res.	WSMD
1930	Biston strataria Hufn.	Oak Beauty	L74	Res.	WSMD
1931	Biston betularia Linn.	Peppered Moth	L74	Res.	WSHD
1932	Agriopis leucophaearia D.& S.	Spring Usher	L74	Res.	WSMD
1933	Agriopis aurantiaria Hb.	Scarce Umber	L74	Res.	WSMD
1934	Agriopis marginaria Fabr.	Dotted Border	L75	Res.	WSMD
1935	Erannis defoliaria Cl.	Mottled Umber	L75	Res.	WSHD
1936	Menophra abruptaria Thunb.	Waved Umber	L75	Res.	WSMD

1937	Peribatodes rhomboidaria D.& S.	Willow Beauty	L75	Res.	WSHD
1937a	Peribatodes secundaria Esp.	Feathered Beauty	*	Vag.	R
1939	Cleora cinctaria D.& S.	Ringed Carpet	L75	NRR	
1940	Deileptenia ribeata Cl.	Satin Beauty	L75	NRR	
1941	Alcis repandata Linn.	Mottled Beauty	L75	Res.	WSHD
1943	Hypomecis roboraria D.& S.	Great Oak Beauty	L75	Res.	VLLD
1944	Serraca punctinalis Scop.	Pale Oak Beauty	L75	Res.	WSMD
1945	Cleorodes lichenaria Hufn.	Brussels Lace	L75	NRR	
1947	Ectropis bistortata Goeze	Engrailed	L75	Res.	WSMD
1948	Ectropis crepuscularia D.& S.	Small Engrailed	L75	Res.	LCLD
1949	Paradarisa consonaria Hb.	Square Spot	L76	NRR	
1950	Paradarisa extersaria Hb.	Brindled White-spot	L76	Res.	LCLD
1951	Aethalura punctulata D.& S.	Grey Birch	L76	Res.	LCLD
1952	Ematurga atomaria Linn.	Common Heath	L76	Unc.	R
1954	Bupalus piniaria Linn.	Bordered White	L76	Res.	LCMD
1955	Cabera pusaria Linn.	Common White Wave	L76	Res.	WSHD
1956	Cabera exanthemata Scop.	Common Wave	L76	Res.	WSMD
1957	Lomographa bimaculata Fabr.	White-pinion Spotted	L76	Res.	LCMD
1958	Lomographa temerata D.& S.	Clouded Silver	L76	Res.	WSHD
1959	Aleucis distinctata H.-S.	Sloe Carpet	L76	Res.	LCLD
1960	Thera primaria Haw.	Early Moth	L76	Res.	WSMD
1961	Campaea margaritata Linn.	Light Emerald	L76	Res.	WSHD
1962	Hylaea fasciaria Linn.	Barred Red	L76	Res.	LCLD
1964	Gnophos obscurata D.& S.	Annulet	L77	NRR	
1966	Siona lineata Scop.	Black-veined Moth	L77	NRR	
1967	Aspitates gilvaria D.& S.	Straw Belle	L77	NRR	
1968	Aspitates ochrearia Rossi	Yellow Belle	L77	Res.	LCMD
1969	Dyscia fagaria Thunb.	Grey Scalloped Bar	L77	NRR	
1663	Alsophila aescularia D.& S.	March Moth	L54	Res.	WSHD
1664	*Aplasta ononaria Fuessl.*	*Rest Harrow*	*L55*	*NRR*	
1665	Pseudoterpna pruinata Hufn.	Grass Emerald	L55	Res.	LCLD
1666	Geometra papilionaria Linn.	Large Emerald	L55	Res.	WSMD
1667	Comibaena bajularia D.& S.	Blotched Emerald	L55	Res.	WSLD
1668	*Thetidia smaragdaria Fabr.*	*Essex Emerald*	*L55*	*NRR*	
1669	Hemithea aestivaria Hb.	Common Emerald	L55	Res.	WSMD
1670	Chlorissa viridata Linn.	Small Grass Emerald	L55	NRR	
1672	Thalera fimbrialis Scop.	Sussex Emerald	L55	NRR	
1673	Hemistola chrysoprasaria Esp.	Small Emerald	L55	Res.	WSLD
1674	Jodis lactearia Linn.	Little Emerald	L55	Res.	WSLD
1676	Cyclophora annulata Schulze	Mocha	L55	Vag.	R
1677	Cyclophora albipunctata Hufn.	Birch Mocha	L56	Res.	LCLD
1678	Cyclophora puppillaria Hb.	Blair's Mocha	L56	Mig	R
1679	Cyclophora porata Linn.	False Mocha	L56	Res.	VLMD
1680	Cyclophora punctaria Linn.	Maiden's Blush	L56	Res.	LCMD

Still spreading from the south and growing numerically stronger.

1681	Cyclophora linearia Hb.	Clay Triple-lines	L56	Res.	LCLD
1682	Timandra griseata Peters.	Blood-vein	L56	Res.	WSMD
1687	Scopula ornata Scop.	Lace Border	L56	Vag.	R
1688	*Scopula rubiginata Hufn.*	*Tawny Wave*	*L56*	*Vag.*	*R*
1689	Scopula marginepunctata Goeze	Mullein Wave	L56	Res.	LCMD
1690	Scopula imitaria Hb.	Small Blood-vein	L57	Res.	WSMD
1691	Scopula emutaria Hb.	Rosy Wave	L57	Res.	LCLD

1692	Scopula immutata Linn.	Lesser Cream Wave	L57	Res.	LCLD
1693	Scopula floslactata Haw.	Cream Wave	L57	Res.	LCMD
1696	*Idaea ochrata Scop.*	*Bright Wave*	*L57*	*Unc.*	*R*
1699	Idaea vulpinaria H.-S.	Least Carpet	L57	Res.	LCMD

Abundant in some southern areas and becoming increasingly so in north Essex, especially near the coast.

1702	Idaea biselata Hufn.	Small Fan-footed Wave	L57	Res.	WSHD
1705	Idaea fuscovenosa Goeze	Dwarf Cream Wave	L57	Res.	WSMD
1707	Idaea seriata Schr.	Small Dusty Wave	L57	Res.	WSMD
1708	Idaea dimidiata Hufn.	Single-dotted Wave	L57	Res.	WSHD
1709	Idaea subsericeata Haw.	Satin Wave	L57	Res.	LCLD
1711	Idaea trigeminata Haw.	Treble Brown Spot	L57	Res.	WSMD
1712	Idaea emarginata Linn.	Small Scallop	L57	Res.	WSMD
1713	Idaea aversata Linn.	Riband Wave	L58	Res.	WSHD
1715	Idaea straminata Borkh.	Plain Wave	L58	Res.	LCLD
1716	Rhodometra sacraria Linn.	Vestal	L58	Mig.	O
1717	Lythria purpuraria Linn.	Purple-barred Yellow	L58	NRR	
1718	Phibalapteryx virgata Hufn.	Oblique Striped	L58	Vag.	R
1719	Orthonama vittata Borkh.	Oblique Carpet	L59	Vag.	R
1720	Orthonama obstipata Fabr.	Gem	L59	Mig.	O
1722	Xanthorhoe designata Hufn.	Flame Carpet	L59	Res.	LCLD
1724	Xanthorhoe spadicearia D.& S.	Red Twin-spot Carpet	L59	Res.	WSHD
1725	Xanthorhoe ferrugata Cl.	Dark-barred Twin-spot Carpet	L59	Res.	WSMD
1726	Xanthorhoe quadrifasiata Cl.	Large Twin-spot Carpet	L59	Res.	WSMD
1727	Xanthorhoe montanata D.& S.	Silver-ground Carpet	L59	Res.	WSHD
1728	Xanthorhoe fluctuata Linn.	Garden Carpet	L59	Res.	WSHD
1731	Scotopteryx bipunctaria D.& S.	Chalk Carpet	L59	Vag.	R
1732	Scotopteryx chenopodiata Linn.	Shaded Broad-bar	L59	Res.	WSHD
1733	Scotopteryx mucronata Scop.	Lead Belle	L59	NRR	
1734	Scotopteryx luridata Hufn.	July Belle	L60	NRR	
1735	Catarhoe rubidata D.& S.	Ruddy Carpet	L60	Res.	LCLD
1736	Catarhoe cuculata Hufn.	Royal Mantle	L60	Res.	VLLD
1738	Epirrhoe alternata Müll.	Common Carpet	L60	Res.	WSHD
1739	Epirrhoe rivata Hb.	Wood Carpet	L60	Res.	LCLD
1742	Camptogramma bilineata Linn.	Yellow Shell	L60	Res.	WSHD
1745	Larentia clavaria Haw.	Mallow	L60	Res.	WSMD
1746	Anticlea badiata D.& S.	Shoulder Stripe	L60	Res.	WSMD
1747	Anticlea derivata D.& S.	Streamer	L60	Res.	WSMD
1748	Mesoleuca albicillata Linn.	Beautiful Carpet	L60	Res.	LCLD
1749	Pelurga comitata Linn.	Dark Spinach	L60	Res.	WSMD
1750	Lampropteryx suffumata D.& S.	Water Carpet	L60	Res.	WSMD
1752	Cosmorhoe ocellata Linn.	Purple Bar	L61	Res.	WSMD
1753	Nebula salicata Hb.	Striped Twin-spot Carpet	L61	Mig.	R
1754	Eulithis prunata Linn.	Phoenix	L61	Res.	LCLD
1755	Eulithis testata Linn.	Chevron	L61	Res.	LCLD
1757	Eulithis mellinata Fabr.	Spinach	L61	Res.	WSMD
1758	Eulithis pyraliata D.& S.	Barred Straw	L61	Res.	WSHD
1759	Ecliptopera silaceata D.& S.	Small Phoenix	L61	Res.	WSMD
1760	Chloroclysta siterata Hufn.	Red-green Carpet	L61	Vag.	R
1761	Chloroclysta miata Linn.	Autumn Green Carpet	L61	NRR	
1762	Chloroclysta citrata Linn.	Dark Marbled Carpet	L61	Res.	LCLD
1764	Chloroclysta truncata Hufn.	Common Marbled Carpet	L62	Res.	WSHD

1765	Cidaria fulvata Forst.	Barred Yellow	L62	Res.	WSMD
1766	Plemyria rubiginata D.& S.	Blue-bordered Carpet	L62	Res.	WSMD
1767	Thera firmata Hb.	Pine Carpet	L62	Vag.	R
1768	Thera obeliscata Hb.	Grey Pine Carpet	L62	Res.	WSHD
1769	Thera britannica Turn.	Spruce Carpet	L62	Res.	LCMD
1771	Thera juniperata Linn.	Juniper Carpet	L62	Res.	LCLD
1773	Electrophaes corylata Thunb.	Broken-barred Carpet	L62	Res.	WSMD
1774	Colostygia olivata D.& S.	Beech-green Carpet	L62	NRR	
1775	Colostygia multistrigaria Haw.	Mottled Grey	L63	Unc.	VLLD
1776	Colostygia pectinataria Knoch	Green Carpet	L63	Res.	WSLD
1777	Hydriomena furcata Thunb.	July Highflier	L63	Res.	WSHD
1778	Hydriomena impluviata D.& S.	May Highflier	L63	Res.	LCLD
1779	Hydriomena ruberata Freyer	Ruddy Highflier	L63	NRR	
1781	Horisme vitalbata D.& S.	Small Waved Umber	L63	Res.	WSMD
1782	Horisme tersata D.& S.	Fern	L63	Res.	LCMD
1784	Melanthia procellata D.& S.	Pretty Chalk Carpet	L63	Res.	LCLD
1785	Pareulype berberata D.& S.	Barberry Carpet	L63	NRR	
1786	Spargania luctuata D.& S.	White-banded Carpet	L63	NRR	
1787	Rheumaptera hastata Linn.	Argent & Sable	L63	NRR	
1788	Rheumaptera cervinalis Scop.	Scarce Tissue	L63	Res.	LCLD
1789	Rheumaptera undulata Linn.	Scallop Shell	L63	Res.	LCLD
1790	Triphosa dubitata Linn.	Tissue	L64	Res.	LCLD
1791	Philereme vetulata D.& S.	Brown Scallop	L64	Res.	LCLD
1792	Philereme transversata Hufn.	Dark Umber	L64	Res.	LCLD
1793	Euphyia biangulata Haw.	Cloaked Carpet	L64	Res.	VLLD
1794	Euphyia unangulata Haw.	Sharp-angled Carpet	L64	Res.	LCMD
1795	Euphyia dilutata D.& S.	November Moth	L64	Res.	WSHD
1796	Euphyia christyi Allen	Pale November Moth	L64	Res.	VLMD
1799	Operophtera brumata Linn.	Winter Moth	L64	Res.	WSHD
1800	Operophtera fagata Scharf.	Northern Winter Moth	L64	Res.	LCLD
1802	Perizoma affinitata Steph.	Rivulet	L65	Res.	WSMD
1803	Perizoma alchemillata Linn.	Small Rivulet	L65	Res.	WSHD
1804	Perizoma bifaciata Haw.	Barred Rivulet	L65	Res.	LCLD
1807	Perizoma albulata D.& S.	Grass Rivulet	L65	Vag.	R
1808	Perizoma flavofasciata Thunb.	Sandy Carpet	L65	Res.	WSMD
1809	Perizoma didymata Linn.	Twin-spot Carpet	L65	Res.	WSMD
1811	Eupithecia tenuiata Hb.	Slender pug	L65	Res.	LCMD
1812	Eupithecia inturbata Hb.	Maple Pug	L65	Res.	LCLD
1813	Eupithecia haworthiata Doubl.	Haworth's Pug	L65	Res.	LCMD
1814	Eupithecia plumbeolata Haw.	Lead-coloured Pug	L65	Unc.	VLLD
1815	Eupithecia abietaria Goeze	Cloaked Pug	L65	NRR	
1816	Eupithecia linariata D.& S.	Toadflax Pug	L66	Res.	WSMD
1817	Eupithecia pulchellata Steph.	Foxglove Pug	L66	Res.	WSMD
1818	Eupithecia irriguata Hb.	Marbled Pug	L66	Vag.	R
1819	Eupithecia exiguata Hb.	Mottled Pug	L66	Res.	WSHD
1820	Eupithecia insigniata Hb.	Pinion-spotted Pug	L66	Vag.	R
1821	Eupithecia valerianata Hb.	Valerian Pug	L66	Vag.	R
1822	Eupithecia pygmaeata Hb.	Marsh Pug	L66	NRR	
1823	Eupithecia venosata Fabr.	Netted Pug	L66	Res.	LCLD
1825	Eupithecia centaureata D.& S.	Lime-speck Pug	L66	Res.	WSMD
1826	Eupithecia trisignaria H.-S.	Triple-spotted Pug	L66	Res.	VLLD
1827	Eupithecia intricata Zett.	Freyer's Pug	L66	Res.	LCMD

1828	Eupithecia satyrata Hb.	Satyr Pug	L66	Vag.	R
1829	Eupithecia cauchiata Dup.	Doubleday's Pug	L67	NRR	
1830	Eupithecia absinthiata Cl.	Wormwood Pug	L67	Res.	WSMD
1832	Eupithecia assimilata Doubl.	Currant Pug	L67	Res.	LCMD
1833	Eupithecia expallidata Doubl.	Bleached Pug	L67	Vag.	R
1834	Eupithecia vulgata Haw.	Common Pug	L67	Res.	WSMD
1835	Eupithecia tripunctaria H.-S.	White-spotted Pug	L67	Res.	WSMD
1836	Eupithecia denotata Hb.	Campanula Pug	L67	NRR	
1837	Eupithecia subfuscata Haw.	Grey Pug	L67	Res.	WSMD
1838	Eupithecia icterata Vill.	Tawny-speckled Pug	L67	Res.	WSMD
1839	Eupithecia succenturiata Linn.	Bordered Pug	L67	Res.	WSMD
1840	Eupithecia subumbrata D.& S.	Shaded Pug	L67	Res.	LCMD
1841	Eupithecia millefoliata Rössler	Yarrow Pug	L67	Res.	LCLD
1842	Eupithecia simpliciata Haw.	Plain Pug	L67	Res.	LCLD
1844	Eupithecia indigata Hb.	Ochreous Pug	L68	Unc.	VLLD
1845	Eupithecia pimpinellata Hb.	Pimpinel Pug	L68	Res.	LCLD
1846	Eupithecia nanata Hb.	Narrow-winged Pug	L68	Res.	LCLD
1847	*Eupithecia extensaria Freyer*	*Scarce Pug*	*L68*	*Unc.*	*VLLD*
1849	Eupithecia fraxinata Crewe	Ash Pug	L68	Res.	LCLD
1851	Eupithecia virgaureata Doubl.	Golden-rod Pug	L68	Unc.	VLLD
1852	Eupithecia abbreviata Steph.	Brindled Pug	L68	Res.	WSHD
1853	Eupithecia dodoneata Guen.	Oak-tree Pug	L68	Res.	WSMD
1854	Eupithecia pusillata D.& S.	Juniper Pug	L69	Res.	LCLD
1855	Eupithecia phoeniceata Ramb.	Cypress Pug	L69	Res.	VLLD
1856	Eupithecia lariciata Freyer	Larch Pug	L69	Res.	LCLD
1857	Eupithecia tantillaria Boisd.	Dwarf Pug	L69	Res.	LCLD
1858	Chloroclystis v-ata Haw.	V-Pug	L69	Res.	WSMD
1859	Chloroclystis chloerata Mab.	Sloe Pug	L69	Res.	LCMD
1860	Chloroclystis rectangulata Linn.	Green Pug	L69	Res.	WSMD
1862	Gymnoscelis rufifasciata Haw.	Double-striped Pug	L69	Res.	WSHD
1863	Anticollix sparsata Treit.	Dentated Pug	L69	NRR	
1864	Chesias legatella D.& S.	Streak	L69	Res.	LCMD
1865	Chesias rufata Fabr.	Broom-tip	L70	Res.	LCMD
1867	Aplocera plagiata Linn.	Treble-bar	L70	Res.	LCLD
1868	Aplocera efformata Guen.	Lesser Treble-bar	L70	Res.	VLLD
1870	Odezia atrata Linn.	Chimney Sweeper	L70	NRR	
1872	Discoloxia blomeri Curt.	Blomer's Rivulet	L70	NRR	
1874	Euchoeca nebulata Scop.	Dingy Shell	L70	Res.	LCMD
1875	Asthena albulata Hufn.	Small White Wave	L70	Res.	LCMD
1876	Hydrelia flammeolaria Hufn.	Small Yellow Wave	L70	Res.	WSMD
1877	Hydrelia sylvata D.& S.	Waved Carpet	L70	NRR	
1878	Minoa murinata Scop.	Drab Looper	L70	NRR	
1879	Lobophora halterata Hufn.	Seraphim	L70	Res.	LCLD
1880	Trichopteryx polycommata D.& S.	Barred Tooth-striped	L70	NRR	
1881	Trichopteryx carpinata Borkh.	Early Tooth-striped	L70	Res.	VLLD
1882	Pterapherapteryx sexalata Retz.	Small Seraphim	L71	Res.	LCMD
1883	Acasis viretata Hb.	Yellow-barred Brindle	L71	Res.	WSMD

Drepanidae

1652	Thyatira batis Linn.	Peach Blossom	L53	Res.	WSLD
1653	Habrosyne pyritoides Hufn.	Buff Arches	L53	Res.	WSHD
1654	Tethea ocularis Linn.	Figure of Eighty	L53	Res.	WSMD

1655	Tethea or D.& S.	Poplar Lutestring	L53	Res.	LCLD
1656	Tetheella fluctuosa Hb.	Satin Lutestring	L53	Vag.	R
1657	Ochropacha duplaris Linn.	Common Lutestring	L53	Res.	LCMD
1658	Cymatophorima diluta D.& S.	Oak Lutestring	L53	Res.	VLMD
1659	Achlya flavicornis Linn.	Yellow Horned	L53	Res.	LCLD
1660	Polyploca ridens Fabr.	Frosted Green	L54	Res.	WSMD
1645	Falcaria lacertinaria Linn.	Scalloped Hook-tip	L52	Res.	LCMD
1646	Drepana binaria Hufn.	Oak Hook-tip	L53	Res.	WSHD
1647	Drepana cultraria Fabr.	Barred Hook-tip	L53	Res.	LCLD
1648	Drepana falcataria Linn.	Pebble Hook-tip	L53	Res.	WSMD
1649	Drepana curvatula Borkh.	Dusky Hook-tip	*	Mig.	R
1651	Cilix glaucata Scop.	Chinese Character	L53	Res.	WSMD

Hesperiidae

1532	Erynnis tages Linn.	Dingy Skipper	L42	Unc.	R
1534	Pyrgus malvae Linn.	Grizzled Skipper	L42	Res.	VLLD
1526	Thymelictus sylvestris Poda	Small Skipper	L41	Res.	WSHD
1527	Thymelictus lineola Ochs.	Essex Skipper	L42	Res.	WSHD
1529	Hesperia comma Linn.	Silver-spotted Skipper	L42	NRR	
1531	Ochlodes venata B.& G.	Large Skipper	L42	Res.	WSHD

Papilionidae

| 1539 | Papilio machaon Linn. | Swallowtail | L42 | Mig. | R |

Pieridae

1541	Leptidea sinapis Linn.	Wood White	L43	Vag.	R
1543	Colias hyale Linn.	Pale Clouded Yellow	L43	Mig.	R
1545	Colias croceus Geoff.	Clouded Yellow	L43	Mig.	O
1546	Gonepteryx rhamni Linn.	Brimstone	L43	Res.	WSMD
1548	Aporia crataegi Linn.	Black-veined White	L43	Mig.	R
1549	Pieris brassicae Linn.	Large White	L44	Res.	WSHD
1550	Pieris rapae Linn.	Small White	L44	Res.	WSHD
1551	Pieris napi Linn.	Green-veined White	L44	Res.	WSHD
1552	Pontia daplidice Linn.	Bath White	L44	NRR	
1553	Anthocharis cardamines Linn.	Orange-tip	L44	Res.	WSMD

Nymphalidae

1614	Pararge aegeria Linn.	Speckled Wood	L49	Res.	WSMD
1615	Lasiommata megera Linn.	Wall	L50	Res.	WSMD
1620	Melanargia galathea Linn.	Marbled White	L50	Res.	VLLD
1621	Hipparchia semele Linn.	Grayling	L50	Res.	VLLD
1625	Pyronia tithonus Linn.	Gatekeeper	L50	Res.	WSHD
1626	Maniola jurtina Linn.	Meadow Brown	L50	Res.	WSHD
1629	Aphantopus hyperantus Linn.	Ringlet	L50	Res.	WSMD
1627	Coenonympha pamphilus Linn.	Small Heath	L50	Res.	WSHD
1600	Boloria selene D.& S.	Small Pearl-bordered Fritillary	L48	NRR	
1601	Boloria euphrosyne Linn.	Pearl-bordered Fritillary	L48	Int.	VLLD
1602	Boloria dia Linn.	Weaver's Fritillary	L48	NRR	
1603	Argynnis lathonia Linn.	Queen of Spain Fritillary	L48	Mig.	R
1606	Argynnis adippe D.& S.	High Brown Fritillary	L48	Vag.	R
1607	Argynnis aglaja Linn.	Dark Green Fritillary	L48	Vag.	R
1608	Argynnis paphia Linn.	Silver-washed Fritillary	L49	Vag.	R

1610	Eurodryas aurinia Rott.	Marsh Fritillary	L49	NRR	
1611	Melitaea didyma Esp.	Spotted Fritillary	*	Acc.	R
1613	Mellicta athalia Rott.	Heath Fritillary	L49	Int.	VLMD
1584	Ladoga camilla Linn.	White Admiral	L47	Res.	VLMD
1590	Vanessa atalanta Linn.	Red Admiral	L47	Mig.	F
1591	Cynthia cardui Linn.	Painted Lady	L47	Mig.	F
1593	Aglais urticae Linn.	Small Tortoiseshell	L47	Res.	WSHD
1594	Nymphalis polychloros Linn.	Large Tortoiseshell	L47	Mig.	R
1596	Nymphalis antiopa Linn.	Camberwell Beauty	L47	Mig.	R
1597	Inachis io Linn.	Peacock	L47	Res.	WSHD
1598	Polygonia c-album Linn.	Comma	L48	Res.	WSMD
1585	Apatura iris Linn.	Purple Emperor	L47	Vag.	R
1630	Danaus plexippus Linn.	Milkweed	L51	Mig.	R

Lycaenidae

1555	Callophrys rubi Linn.	Green Hairstreak	L44	Res.	LCMD
1556	Thecla betulae Linn.	Brown Hairstreak	L44	Vag.	R
1557	Quercusia quercus Linn.	Purple Hairstreak	L45	Res.	WSMD
1558	Satyrium w-album Knoch	White-letter Hairstreak	L45	Res.	WSLD
1561	Lycaena phlaeas Linn.	Small Copper	L45	Res.	WSMD
1567	Lampides boeticus Linn.	Long-tailed Blue	L45	NRR	
1569	Cupido minimus Fuessl.	Small Blue	L45	NRR	
1571	Plebejus argus Linn.	Silver-studded Blue	L45	NRR	
1572	Aricia agestis D.& S.	Brown Argus	L45	Res.	LCLD
1574	Polyommatus icarus Rott.	Common Blue	L45	Res.	WSMD
1575	Lysandra coridon Poda	Chalk Hill Blue	L45	Vag.	R
1576	Lysandra bellargus Rott.	Adonis Blue	L46	NRR	
1578	Cyaniris semiargus Rott.	Mazarine Blue	L46	NRR	
1580	Celastrina argiolus Linn.	Holly Blue	L46	Res.	WSMD
1582	Hamearis lucina Linn.	Duke of Burgundy Fritillary	L46	NRR	

Lasiocampidae

1642	Gastropacha quercifolia Linn.	Lappet	L52	Res.	WSLD
1631	Poecilocampa populi Linn.	December Moth	L51	Res.	WSMD
1632	Trichiura crataegi Linn.	Pale Eggar	L51	Res.	WSLD
1633	Eriogaster lanestris Linn.	Small Eggar	L51	NRR	
1634	Malacosoma neustria Linn.	Lackey	L51	Res.	WSHD
1635	*Malacosoma castrensis Linn.*	*Ground Lackey*	*L51*	*Res.*	*LCMD*
1636	Lasiocampa trifolii D.& S.	Grass Eggar	L52	NRR	
1637	Lasiocampa quercus Linn.	Oak Eggar	L52	Res.	WSMD
1638	Macrothylacia rubi Linn.	Fox Moth	L52	Res.	LCLD
1640	Euthrix potatoria Linn.	Drinker	L52	Res.	WSHD

Saturniidae

| 1643 | Pavonia pavonia Linn. | Emperor Moth | L52 | Res. | WSMD |

Sphingidae

1979	Mimas tiliae Linn.	Lime Hawk-moth	L78	Res.	WSMD
1980	Smerinthus ocellata Linn.	Eyed Hawk-moth	L78	Res.	WSMD
1981	Laothoe populi Linn.	Poplar Hawk-moth	L78	Res.	WSMD
1972	Agrius convolvuli Linn.	Convolvulus Hawk-moth	L77	Mig.	O
1973	Acherontia atropus Linn.	Death's-head Hawk-moth	L77	Mig.	O

1976	Sphinx ligustri Linn.	Privet Hawk-moth	L78	Res.	WSLD
1978	Hyloicus pinastri Linn.	Pine Hawk-moth	L78	Res.	VLLD

There have been twelve post-LMBE records, adding to the speculation that H. pinastri is now resident in Essex.

1982	Hemaris tityus Linn.	Narrow-bordered Bee Hawk-moth	L78	NRR	
1983	Hemaris fuciformis Linn.	Broad-bordered Bee Hawk-moth	L78	Unc.	R
1984	Macroglossum stellatarum Linn.	Humming-bird Hawk-moth	L78	Mig.	O
1985	Daphnis nerii Linn.	Oleander Hawk-moth	L78	Mig.	R
1986	Hyles euphorbiae Linn.	Spurge Hawk-moth	L78	Mig.	R
1987	Hyles gallii Rott.	Bedstraw Hawk-moth	L79	Mig.	O
1990	Hyles livornica Esp. (*lineata* Fabr.)	Striped Hawk-moth	L79	Mig.	R
1991	Deilephila elpenor Linn.	Elephant Hawk-moth	L79	Res.	WSHD
1992	Deilephila porcellus Linn.	Small Elephant Hawk-moth	L79	Unc.	O
1993	Hippotion celerio Linn.	Silver-striped Hawk-moth	L79	NRR	

Notodontidae

2022	Thaumetopoea processionea Linn.	Oak Processionary	*	Mig.	R
2017	Clostera pigra Hufn.	Small Chocolate-tip	L81	Vag.	R
2018	Clostera anachoreta D.& S.	Scarce Chocolate-tip	L81	Mig.	R
2019	Clostera curtula Linn.	Chocolate-tip	L81	Res.	LCMD
1995	Cerura vinula Linn.	Puss Moth	L79	Res.	WSLD
1996	Furcula bicuspis Borkh.	Alder Kitten	L79	NRR	
1997	Furcula furcula Cl.	Sallow Kitten	L80	Res.	WSHD
1998	Furcula bifida Brahm	Poplar Kitten	L80	Res.	LCLD
2000	Notodonta dromedarius Linn.	Iron Prominent	L80	Res.	WSMD
2002	Tritophia tritophus D.& S.	Three-humped Prominent	L80	NRR	
2003	Eligmodonta ziczac Linn.	Pebble Prominent	L80	Res.	WSMD
2005	Peridea anceps Goeze	Great Prominent	L80	Res.	LCLD
2006	Pheosia gnoma Fabr.	Lesser Swallow Prominent	L80	Res.	WSMD
2007	Pheosia tremula Cl.	Swallow Prominent	L80	Res.	WSMD
2008	Ptilodon capucina Linn.	Coxcomb Prominent	L80	Res.	WSMD
2009	Ptilodontella cucullina D.& S.	Maple Prominent	L80	Res.	WSLD
2010	Odontosia carmelita Esp.	Scarce Prominent	L80	Vag.	R
2011	Pterostoma palpina Cl.	Pale Prominent	L80	Res.	WSHD
2014	Drymonia dodonaea D.& S.	Marbled Brown	L81	Res.	LCMD
2015	Drymonia ruficornis Hufn.	Lunar Marbled Brown	L81	Res.	LCMD
2016	Gluphisia crenata Esp.	Dusky Marbled Brown	L81	NRR	
1994	Phalera bucephala Linn.	Buff-tip	L79	Res.	WSMD
1999	Stauropus fagi Linn.	Lobster Moth	L80	Res.	LCLD

Lymantriidae

2025	Orgyia recens Hb.	Scarce Vapourer	L82	NRR	
2026	Orgyia antiqua Linn.	Vapourer	L82	Res.	WSHD
2027	Dicallomera fascelina Linn.	Dark Tussock	L82	NRR	
2028	Calliteara pudibunda Linn.	Pale Tussock	L82	Res.	WSMD
2029	Euproctis chrysorrhoea Linn.	Brown-tail	L82	Res.	WSMD
2030	Euproctis similis Fuessl.	Yellow-tail	L82	Res.	WSHD
2031	Leucoma salicis Linn.	White Satin Moth	L82	Res.	WSMD
2032	Arctornis l-nigrum Müll.	Black V Moth	L82	NRR	
2033	Lymantria monacha Linn.	Black Arches	L82	Res.	LCMD
2034	Lymantria dispar Linn.	Gypsy Moth	L83	NRR	

Arctiidae

2035	Thumatha senex Hb.	Round-winged Muslin	L83	Res.	LCMD
2036	Setina irrorella Linn.	Dew Moth	L83	NRR	
2037	Miltochrista miniata Forst.	Rosy Footman	L83	Res.	LCMD
2038	Nudaria mundana Linn.	Muslin Footman	L83	Vag.	R
2039	Atolmis rubricollis Linn.	Red-necked Footman	L83	Vag.	R
2040	Cybosia mesomella Linn.	Four-dotted Footman	L84	Res.	VLLD
2041	*Pelosia muscerda Hufn.*	*Dotted Footman*	*L84*	*Mig.*	*R*
2043	Eilema sororcula Hufn.	Orange Footman	L84	Res.	VLLD
2044	Eilema griseola Hb.	Dingy Footman	L84	Res.	LCMD
2046	Eilema pygmaeola Doubl.	Pigmy Footman	L84	Mig.	R
2047	Eilema complana Linn.	Scarce Footman	L84	Res.	WSHD
2049	Eilema deplana Esp.	Buff Footman	L84	Res.	VLMD
2050	Eilema lurideola Zinck.	Common Footman	L84	Res.	WSHD
2051	Lithosia quadra Linn.	Four-spotted Footman	L84	Mig.	R
2052	Spiris striata Linn.	Feathered Footman	L85	Mig.	R
2054	Utetheisa pulchella Linn.	Crimson Speckled	L85	Mig.	R
2056	Parasemia plantaginis Linn.	Wood Tiger	L85	NRR	
2057	Arctia caja Linn.	Garden Tiger	L85	Res.	WSMD
2058	Arctia villica Linn.	Cream-spot Tiger	L85	Res.	LCMD
2059	Diacrisia sannio Linn.	Clouded Buff	L85	Vag.	R
2060	Spilosoma lubricipeda Linn.	White Ermine	L85	Res.	WSMD
2061	Spilosoma lutea Hufn.	Buff Ermine	L85	Res.	WSHD
2062	*Spilosoma urticae Esp.*	*Water Ermine*	*L85*	*Res.*	*LCLD*
2063	Diaphora mendica Cl.	Muslin Moth	L85	Res.	WSMD
2064	Phragmatobia fuliginosa Linn.	Ruby Tiger	L85	Res.	WSHD
2068	Callimorpha dominula Linn.	Scarlet Tiger	L86	NRR	
2069	Tyria jacobaeae Linn.	Cinnabar	L86	Res.	WSMD

Noctuidae

2277	Moma alpium Osb.	Scarce Merveille du Jour	L100	NRR	
2278	Acronicta megacephala D.& S.	Poplar Grey	L100	Res.	WSMD
2279	Acronicta aceris Linn.	Sycamore	L100	Res.	WSMD
2280	Acronicta leporina Linn.	Miller	L100	Res.	LCMD
2281	Acronicta alni Linn.	Alder Moth	L101	Res.	LCLD
2283	Acronicta tridens D.& S.	Dark Dagger	L101	Res.	WSMD
2284	Acronicta psi Linn.	Grey Dagger	L101	Res.	WSHD
2289	Acronicta rumicis Linn.	Knot Grass	L101	Res.	WSMD
2290	Simyra albovenosa Goeze	Reed Dagger	L101	Res.	LCMD
2291	Craniophora ligustri D.& S.	Coronet	L101	Vag.	R
2293	Cryphia domestica Hufn.	Marbled Beauty	L101	Res.	WSHD
2488	Pechipogo strigilata Linn.	Common Fan-foot	L114	NRR	
2489	Herminia tarsipennalis Treit.	Fan-foot	L115	Res.	WSMD
2491	Herminia tarsicrinalis Knoch	Shaded Fan-foot	*	Res.	VLLD
2492	Herminia grisealis D.& S.	Small Fan-foot	L115	Res.	WSMD
2493	Macrochilo cribrumalis Hb.	Dotted Fan-foot	L115	Res.	LCMD
2494	*Paracolax tristalis Fabr.*	*Clay Fan-foot*	*L115*	*Res.*	*VLLD*
2495	*Trisateles emortualis D.& S.*	*Olive Crescent*	*L115*	*Res.*	*VLLD*
2482	Schrankia taenialis Hb.	White-line Snout	L114	Res.	VLLD
2484	Schrankia costaestrigalis Steph.	Pinion-streaked Snout	L114	Res.	LCLD
2451	Catocala fraxini Linn.	Clifden Nonpareil	L112	Mig.	R
2452	Catocala nupta Linn.	Red Underwing	L112	Res.	WSMD

2453	Catocala electa View.	Rosy Underwing	L112	NRR	
2454	Catocala promissa D.& S.	Light Crimson Underwing	L112	NRR	
2455	Catocala sponsa Linn.	Dark Crimson Underwing	L112	NRR	
2456	Minucia lunaris D.& S.	Lunar Double-striped	L113	Mig.	R
2460	Dysgonia algira Linn.	Passenger	L113	Mig.	R
2462	Callistege mi Cl.	Mother Shipton	L113	Res.	WSMD
2463	Euclidia glyphica Linn.	Burnet Companion	L113	Res.	VLLD
2464	Catephia alchymista D.& S.	Alchymist	L113	NRR	
2465	*Tyta luctuosa D.& S.*	*Four-spotted*	*L113*	*Vag.*	*R*
2466	Lygephila pastinum Treit.	Blackneck	L113	Res.	LCLD
2469	Scoliopteryx libatrix Linn.	Herald	L113	Res.	WSMD
2473	Laspeyria flexula D.& S.	Beautiful Hook-tip	L113	Res.	WSMD
2470	Phytometra viridaria Cl.	Small Purple-barred	L113	Vag.	R
2477	Hypena proboscidalis Linn.	Snout	L114	Res.	WSMD
2480	Hypena rostralis Linn.	Buttoned Snout	L114	Res.	VLLD
2474	Rivula sericealis Scop.	Straw Dot	L113	Res.	WSHD
2475	Parascotia fuliginaria Linn.	Waved Black	L114	Res.	LCLD
2428	Chrysodeixis chalcites Esp.	Golden Twin-spot	L110	Mig.	R
2430	Ctenoplusia limbirena Guen.	Scar Bank Gem	L111	NRR	
2432	Trichoplusia ni Hb.	Ni Moth	L111	Mig.	R
2434	Diachrysia chrysitis Linn.	Burnished Brass	L111	Res.	WSMD
2436	Macdunnoughia confusa Steph.	Dewick's Plusia	L111	Mig.	R
2437	Polychrysia moneta Fabr.	Golden Plusia	L111	Res.	WSLD
2439	Plusia festucae Linn.	Gold Spot	L111	Vag.	O
2441	Autographa gamma Linn.	Silver Y	L111	Mig.	C
2442	Autographa pulchrina Haw.	Beautiful Golden Y	L111	Res.	WSMD
2443	Autographa jota Linn.	Plain Golden Y	L111	Res.	WSMD
2444	Autographa bractea D.& S.	Gold Spangle	*	Mig.	R
2447	Syngrapha interrogationis Linn.	Scarce Silver Y	L111	Mig.	R
2448	Syngrapha circumflexa Linn.	Essex Y	L112	Mig.	R
2450	Abrostola tripartita Hufn. (*triplasia* sensu auctt.)	Spectacle	L112	Res.	WSHD
2449	Abrostola triplasia Linn. (*trigemina* Werneb.)	Dark Spectacle	L112	Res.	VLLD
2407	Eublemma ostrina Hb.	Purple Marbled	*	Mig.	R
2408	Eublemma parva Hb.	Small Marbled	*	Mig.	R
2410	Protodeltote pygarga Hufn.	Marbled White Spot	L109	Res.	WSMD
2412	Deltote uncula Cl.	Silver Hook	L109	NRR	
2413	*Deltote bankiana Fabr.*	*Silver Barred*	*L109*	*Mig.*	*R*
2414	*Emmelia trabealis Scop.*	*Spotted Sulphur*	*L109*	*NRR*	
2211	Cucullia absinthii Linn.	Wormwood	L96	Res.	LCLD
2213	Cucullia artemisiae Hufn.	Scarce Wormwood	L96	NRR	
2214	Cucullia chamomillae D.& S.	Chamomile Shark	L96	Res.	WSLD
2216	Cucullia umbratica Linn.	Shark	L96	Res.	WSLD
2217	Cucullia asteris D.& S.	Star-wort	L96	Res.	LCLD
2219	Cucullia lychnitis Ramb.	Striped Lychnis	L96	NRR	
2221	Cucullia verbasci Linn.	Mullein	L96	Res.	WSLD
2223	Calophasia lunula Hufn.	Toadflax Brocade	L97	NRR	
2225	Brachylomia viminalis Fabr.	Minor Shoulder-knot	L97	Res.	WSMD
2227	Brachionycha sphinx Hufn.	Sprawler	L97	Res.	LCLD
2229	Dasypolia templi Thunb.	Brindled Ochre	L97	NRR	
2230	Aporophyla australis Boisd.	Feathered Brindle	L97	Res.	VLLD
2231	Aporophyla lutulenta D.& S.	Deep-brown Dart	L97	Res.	WSMD
2232	Aporophyla nigra Haw.	Black Rustic	L97	Res.	LCMD

Regarded by LMBE as being very rare, A. nigra has since spread along the eastern coast as far north as Harwich and there are additional records inland, including one at Saffron Walden in 1996. The Bradwell light trap yielded eighty-five specimens during 1994 alone.

2233	Lithomoia solidaginis Hb.	Golden-rod Brindle	L97	NRR	
2235	Lithophane semibrunnea Haw.	Tawny Pinion	L97	Res.	WSLD
2236	Lithophane hepatica Cl.	Pale Pinion	L97	NRR	
2237	Lithophane ornitopus Hufn.	Grey Shoulder-knot	L97	Res.	WSMD
2240	Lithophane leautieri Boisd.	Blair's Shoulder-knot	L97	Res.	WSMD
2241	Xylena vetusta Hb.	Red Sword-grass	L98	Mig.	O
2242	Xylena exsoleta Linn.	Sword-grass	L98	Vag.	R
2243	Xylocampa areola Esp.	Early Grey	L98	Res.	WSHD
2245	Allophyes oxacanthae Linn.	Green-brindled Crescent	L98	Res.	WSHD
2247	Dichonia aprilina Linn.	Merveille du Jour	L98	Res.	WSMD
2248	Dryobotodes eremita Fabr.	Brindled Green	L98	Res.	WSHD
2250	Mniotype adusta Esp.	Dark Brocade	L98	Vag.	R
2252	Polymixis flavicincta D.& S.	Large Ranunculus	L98	Res.	WSMD
2254	Antitype chi Linn.	Grey Chi	*	NRR	
2255	Eumichtis lichenea Hb.	Feathered Ranunculus	L98	Res.	LCHD

Dramatic increase since LMBE, especially inland. On the coast it can be one of the commonest autumn moths, a trap at Jaywick reporting one hundred and fifty plus during September 1989.

2256	Eupsila transversa Hufn.	Satellite	L99	Res.	WSMD
2257	Jodia croceago D.& S.	Orange Upperwing	L99	NRR	
2258	Conistra vaccinii Linn.	Chestnut	L99	Res.	WSHD
2259	Conistra ligula Esp.	Dark Chestnut	L99	Res.	WSLD
2262	Agrochola circellaris Hufn.	Brick	L99	Res.	WSMD
2263	Agrochola iota Cl.	Red-line Quaker	L99	Res.	WSMD
2264	Agrochola macilenta Hb.	Yellow-line Quaker	L99	Res.	WSMD
2265	Agrochola helvola Linn.	Flounced Chestnut	L99	Res.	WSMD
2266	Agrochola litura Linn.	Brown-spot Pinion	L99	Res.	WSHD
2267	Agrochola lychnidis D.& S.	Beaded Chestnut	L99	Res.	WSHD
2269	Atethmia centrago Haw.	Centre-barred Sallow	L99	Res.	WSMD
2270	Omphaloscelis lunosa Haw.	Lunar Underwing	L99	Res.	WSHD
2271	Xanthia citrago Linn.	Orange Sallow	L100	Res.	LCLD
2272	Xanthia aurago D.& S.	Barred Sallow	L100	Res.	WSMD
2273	Xanthia togata Esp.	Pink-barred Sallow	L100	Res.	WSMD
2274	Xanthia icteritia Hufn.	Sallow	L100	Res.	WSHD
2275	Xanthia gilvago D.& S.	Dusky-lemon Sallow	L100	Res.	WSLD
2276	Xanthia ocellaris Borkh.	Pale-lemon Sallow	L100	Res.	VLLD
2020	Diloba caeruleocephala Linn.	Figure of Eight	L81	Res.	WSHD
2397	Panemeria tenebrata Scop.	Small Yellow Underwing	L108	Res.	WSMD
2399	Pyrrhia umbra Hufn.	Bordered Sallow	L109	Res.	LCLD
2400	Heliothis armigera Hb.	Scarce Bordered Straw	L109	Mig.	O
2401	*Heliothis viriplaca Hufn.*	*Marbled Clover*	*L109*	*Vag.*	*R*
2403	Heliothis peltigera D.& S.	Bordered Straw	L109	Mig.	O
2297	Amphipyra pyramidea Linn.	Copper Underwing	L101	Res.	WSHD
2298	Amphipyra berbera Rungs	Svensson's copper Underwing	L102	Res.	LCLD
2299	Amphipyra tragopoginis Cl.	Mouse Moth	L102	Res.	WSHD
2300	Mormo maura Linn.	Old Lady	L102	Res.	WSMD
2301	Dypterygia scabriuscula Linn.	Bird's Wing	L102	Res.	WSLD
2302	Rusina ferruginea Esp.	Brown Rustic	L102	Res.	WSMD

2303	Thalpophila matura Hufn.	Straw Underwing	L102	Res.	WSMD
2304	Trachea atriplicis Linn.	Orache Moth	L102	Mig.	R
2305	Euplexia lucipara Linn.	Small Angle Shades	L102	Res.	WSMD
2306	Phlogophora meticulosa Linn.	Angle Shades	L102	Res.	WSHD
2311	Ipimorpha retusa Linn.	Double Kidney	L102	NRR	
2312	Ipimorpha subtusa D.& S.	Olive	L102	Res.	WSLD
2313	Enargia paleacea Esp.	Angle-striped Sallow	L103	Mig.	R
2268	Parastichtis suspecta Hb.	Suspected	L99	Res.	LCLD
2314	Parastichis ypsillon D.& S.	Dingy Shears	L103	Res.	WSMD
2315	Dicycla oo Linn.	Heart Moth	L103	NRR	
2316	Cosmia affinis Linn.	Lesser-spotted Pinion	L103	Res.	WSLD
2317	*Cosmia diffinis Linn.*	*White-spotted Pinion*	*L103*	*Res.*	*VLLD*
2318	Cosmia trapezina Linn.	Dun-bar	L103	Res.	WSHD
2319	Cosmia pyralina D.& S.	Lunar-spotted Pinion	L103	Res.	WSMD
2321	Apamea monoglypha Hufn.	Dark Arches	L103	Res.	WSHD
2322	Apamea lithoxylaea D.& S.	Light Arches	L103	Res.	WSHD
2323	Apamea sublustris Esp.	Reddish Light Arches	L103	Vag.	R
2325	Apamea oblonga Haw.	Crescent Striped	L103	Res.	LCMD
2326	Apamea crenata Hufn.	Clouded-bordered Brindle	L104	Res.	WSMD
2327	Apamea epomidion Haw.	Clouded Brindle	L104	Res.	WSLD
2328	Apamea lateritia Hufn.	Scarce Brindle	*	Unc.	R
2330	Apamea remissa Hb.	Dusky Brocade	L104	Res.	WSHD
2331	Apamea unanimis Hb.	Small Clouded Brindle	L104	Res.	WSLD
2333	Apamea anceps D.& S.	Large Nutmeg	L104	Res.	WSHD
2334	Apamea sordens Hufn.	Rustic Shoulder-knot	L104	Res.	WSMD
2335	Apamea scolopacina Esp.	Slender Brindle	L104	Res.	WSMD
2336	Apamea ophiogramma Esp.	Double Lobed	L104	Res.	WSMD
2337	Oligia strigilis Linn.	Marbled Minor	L104	Res.	WSHD
2338	Oligia versicolor Borkh.	Rufous Minor	L104	Res.	VLLD
2339	Oligia latruncula D.& S.	Tawny Marbled Minor	L104	Res.	WSHD
2340	Oligia fasciuncula Haw.	Middle-barred Minor	L104	Res.	WSMD
2341	Mesoligia furuncula D.& S.	Cloaked Minor	L105	Res.	WSHD
2342	Mesoligia liturosa Haw.	Rosy Minor	L105	Res.	WSMD
2343	Mesapamea secalis Linn.	Common Rustic	L105	Res.	WSHD
2343b	Mesapamea didyma Esp.	Lesser Common Rustic	L105	Res.	WSMD
2345	Photedes minima Haw.	Small Dotted Buff	L105	Res.	WSLD
2347	Photedes extrema Hb.	Concolorous	L105	Vag.	R
2348	Photedes elymi Treit.	Lyme Grass	L105	Res.	VLMD
2349	Photedes fluxa Hb.	Mere Wainscot	L105	Vag.	R
2350	Photedes pygmina Haw.	Small Wainscot	L106	Res.	LCMD
2352	Eremobia ochroleuca D.& S.	Dusky Sallow	L106	Res.	WSMD
2353	Luperina testacea D.& S.	Flounced Rustic	L106	Res.	WSHD
2354	Luperina nickerlii Freyer	Sandhill Rustic	L106	Res.	LCMD
2357	Amphipoea lucens Freyer	Large Ear	*	Acc.	R
2358	Amphipoea fucosa Freyer	Saltern Ear	L106	Res.	LCMD
2360	Amphipoea oculea Linn.	Ear Moth	L106	Res.	WSMD
2361	Hydraecia micacea Esp.	Rosy Rustic	L106	Res.	WSMD
2362	Hydraecia petasitis Doubl.	Butterbur	L106	Unc.	VLLD
2364	Gortyna flavago D.& S.	Frosted Orange	L106	Res.	WSMD
2365	*Gortyna borelii Pierr.*	*Fisher's Estuarine Moth*	*L106*	*Res.*	*VLMD*
2367	Celaena haworthii Curt.	Haworth's Minor	L106	NRR	
2368	Celaena leucostigma Hb.	Crescent	L107	Res.	LCLD

2369	Nonagria typhae Thunb.	Bulrush Wainscot	L107	Res.	WSMD
2370	Archanara geminipuncta Haw.	Twin-spotted Wainscot	L107	Res.	LCMD
2371	Archanara dissoluta Treit.	Brown-veined Wainscot	L107	Res.	VLLD
2373	Archanara sparganii Esp.	Webb's Wainscot	L107	Res.	LCMD
2375	Rhizedra lutosa Hb.	Large Wainscot	L107	Res.	WSMD
2376	Sedina buettneri Her.	Blair's Wainscot	*	Mig.	R
2377	Arenostola phragmitidis Hb.	Fen Wainscot	L107	Res.	WSMD
2379	Coenobia rufa Haw.	Small Rufous	L107	Res.	LCMD
2380	Charanyca trigrammica Hufn.	Treble Lines	L107	Res.	LCMD
2381	Hoplodrina alsines Brahm	Uncertain	L107	Res.	WSHD
2382	Hoplodrina blanda D.& S.	Rustic	L107	Res.	WSHD
2384	Hoplodrina ambigua D.& S.	Vine's Rustic	L108	Res.	WSMD
2385	Spodoptera exigua Hb.	Small Mottled Willow	L108	Mig.	O
2387	Caradrina morpheus Hufn.	Mottled Rustic	L108	Res.	WSHD
2389	Caradrina clavipalpis Scop.	Pale Mottled Willow	L108	Res.	WSMD
2391	Chilodes maritimus Tausch.	Silky Wainscot	L108	Res.	LCLD
2396	Elapheria venustula Hb.	Rosy Marbled	L108	Unc.	VLLD
2142	Anarta myrtilli Linn.	Beautiful Yellow Underwing	L91	NRR	
2145	Discestra trifolii Hufn.	Nutmeg	L91	Res.	WSHD
2147	Hada plebeja Linn. (nana Hufn.)	Shears	L91	Res.	WSMD
2148	Polia bombycina Hufn.	Pale Shining Brown	L91	Unc. VLLD	
2149	Polia trimaculosa Esp.	Silvery Arches	L91	NRR	
2150	Polia nebulosa Hufn.	Grey Arches	L91	Res.	WSMD
2152	Sideridis albicolon Hb.	White Colon	L92	Res.	VLLD
2153	Heliophobus reticulata Goeze	Bordered Gothic	L92	Vag.	R
2154	Mamestra brassicae Linn.	Cabbage Moth	L92	Res.	WSHD
2155	Melanchra persicariae Linn.	Dot Moth	L92	Res.	WSHD
2156	Lacanobia contigua D.& S.	Beautiful Brocade	L92	Vag.	R
2157	Lacanobia w-latinum Hufn.	Light Brocade	L92	Res.	WSMD
2158	Lacanobia thalassina Hufn.	Pale-shouldered Brocade	L92	Res.	WSMD
2159	Lacanobia suasa D.& S.	Dog's Tooth	L92	Res.	WSMD
2160	Lacanobia oleracea Linn.	Bright-line Brown-eye	L92	Res.	WSHD
2163	Ceramica pisi Linn.	Broom Moth	L92	Res.	WSMD
2164	Hecatera bicolorata Hufn.	Broad-barred White	L92	Res.	WSMD
2165	*Hecatera dysodea D.& S.*	*Small Ranunculus*	*L92*	*NRR*	
2166	Hadena rivularis Fabr.	Campion	L93	Res.	WSMD
2167	Hadena perplexa D.& S.	Tawny Shears	L93	Res.	LCLD
2170	Hadena compta D.& S.	Varied Coronet	L93	Res.	WSMD
2171	Hadena confusa Hufn.	Marbled Coronet	L93	Vag.	R
2173	Hadena bicruris Hufn.	Lychnis	L93	Res.	WSHD
2176	Cerapteryx graminis Linn.	Antler Moth	L93	Res.	WSHD
2177	Tholera cespitis D.& S.	Hedge Rustic	L93	Res.	WSLD
2178	Tholera decimalis Poda	Feathered Gothic	L93	Res.	WSMD
2179	Panolis flammea D.& S.	Pine Beauty	L93	Res.	WSMD
2181	Egira conspicillaris Linn.	Silver Cloud	L93	NRR	
2182	Orthosia cruda D.& S.	Small Quaker	L93	Res.	WSHD
2183	Orthosia miniosa D.& S.	Blossom Underwing	L93	Res.	LCLD
2184	Orthosia opima Hb.	Northern Drab	L94	Res.	VLMD
2185	Orthosia populeti Fabr.	Lead-coloured Drab	L94	Res.	LCLD
2186	Orthosia gracilis D.& S.	Powdered Quaker	L94	Res.	WSMD
2187	Orthosia cerasi Fabr.	Common Quaker	L94	Res.	WSHD
2188	Orthosia incerta Hufn.	Clouded Drab	L94	Res.	WSHD

2189	Orthosia munda D.& S.	Twin-spotted Quaker	L94	Res.	WSMD
2190	Orthosia gothica Linn.	Hebrew Character	L94	Res.	WSHD
2191	Mythimna turca Linn.	Double Line	L94	NRR	
2192	Mythimna conigera D.& S.	Brown-line Bright-eye	L94	Res.	WSMD
2193	Mythimna ferrago Fabr.	Clay	L94	Res.	WSHD
2194	Mythimna albipuncta D.& S.	White-point	L95	Mig.	O
2195	Mythimna vitellina Hb.	Delicate	L95	Mig.	R
2196	Mythimna pudorina D.& S.	Striped Wainscot	L95	Res.	VLLD
2197	Mythimna straminea Treit.	Southern Wainscot	L95	Res.	WSMD
2198	Mythimna impura Hb.	Smoky Wainscot	L95	Res.	WSHD
2199	Mythimna pallens Linn.	Common Wainscot	L95	Res.	WSHD
2200	Mythimna favicolor Barr.	Mathew's Wainscot	L95	Res.	LCMD
2201	Mythimna litoralis Curt.	Shore Wainscot	L95	NRR	
2202	Mythimna l-album Linn.	L-album Wainscot	L95	Mig.	R
2203	Mythimna unipuncta Haw.	White-speck	L95	Mig.	O
2204	Mythimna obsoleta Hb.	Obscure Wainscot	L95	Res.	LCLD
2205	Mythimna comma Linn.	Shoulder-striped Wainscot	L96	Res.	WSMD
2208	Mythimna loreyi Dup.	Cosmopolitan	*	Mig.	R
2209	Senta flammea Curt.	Flame Wainscot	L96	Vag.	R
2081	Euxoa tritici Linn.	White-line Dart	L87	Res.	LCMD
2082	Euxoa nigricans Linn.	Garden Dart	L87	Res.	WSMD
2083	Euxoa cursoria Hufn.	Coast Dart	L87	Mig.	R
2085	Agrotis vestigialis Hufn.	Archer's Dart	L87	Res.	VLMD
2087	Agrotis segetum D.& S.	Turnip Moth	L87	Res.	WSHD
2088	Agrotis clavis Hufn.	Heart & Club	L87	Res.	WSLD
2089	Agrotis exclamationis Linn.	Heart & Dart	L87	Res.	WSHD
2091	Agrotis ipsilon Hufn.	Dark Sword-grass	L87	Mig.	O
2092	Agrotis puta Hb.	Shuttle-shaped Dart	L87	Res.	WSHD
2093	Agrotis ripae Hb.	Sand Dart	L88	Res.	VLMD
2097	Actinotia polyodon Cl.	Purple Cloud	L88	Mig.	R
2098	Axylia putris Linn.	Flame	L88	Res.	WSHD
2099	Actebia praecox Linn.	Portland Moth	L88	Mig.	R
2102	Ochropleura plecta Linn.	Flame Shoulder	L88	Res.	WSHD
2105	Rhyacia simulans Hufn.	Dotted Rustic	L88	Res.	WSLD
	Drastic reduction since LMBE: only five records from 1987 to 1994.				
2107	Noctua pronuba Linn.	Large Yellow Underwing	L88	Res.	WSHD
2108	Noctua orbona Hufn.	Lunar Yellow Underwing	L88	Vag.	R
2109	Noctua comes Hb.	Lesser Yellow Underwing	L88	Res.	WSHD
2110	Noctua fimbriata Screb.	Broad-bordered Yellow Underwing	L89	Res.	WSMD
2111	Noctua janthe Borkh. (*janthina* sensu auctt.) Less.				
		Broad-bordered Yellow U'wing	L89	Res.	WSHD
2112	Noctua interjecta Hb.	Least Yellow Underwing	L89	Res.	WSMD
2113	Spaelotis ravida D.& S.	Stout Dart	L89	Res.	WSLD
	No post-LMBE records. The species may no longer be resident in Essex.				
2114	Graphiphora augur Fabr.	Double Dart	L89	Res.	WSMD
2117	Paradiarsia glareosa Esp.	Autumnal Rustic	L89	Res.	LCMD
2118	Lycophotia porphyrea D.& S.	True Lover's Knot	L89	Res.	LCMD
2119	Peridroma saucia Hb.	Pearly Underwing	L89	Mig.	O
2120	Diarsia mendica Fabr.	Ingrailed Clay	L89	Res.	WSHD
2021	Diarsia dahlii Hb.	Barred Chestnut	L89	NRR	
2122	Diarsia brunnea D.& S.	Purple Clay	L90	Res.	WSLD
2123	Diarsia rubi View.	Small Square-spot	L90	Res.	WSHD

2126	Xestia c-nigrum Linn.	Setaceous Hebrew Character	L90	Res.	WSHD
2127	Xestia ditrapezium D.& S.	Triple-spotted Clay	L90	Res.	LCLD
2128	Xestia triangulum Hufn.	Double Square-spot	L90	Res.	WSHD
2130	Xestia baja D.& S.	Dotted Clay	L90	Res.	WSLD
2131	Xestia rhomboidea Esp.	Square-spotted Clay	L90	Res.	VLLD
2132	Xestia castanea Esp.	Neglected Rustic	L90	Vag.	R
2133	Xestia sexstrigata Haw.	Six-striped Rustic	L90	Res.	WSMD
2134	Xestia xanthographa D.& S.	Square-spot Rustic	L90	Res.	WSHD
2136	Naenia typica Linn.	Gothic	L90	Res.	WSLD
2137	Eurois occulta Linn.	Great Brocade	L90	Mig.	O
2138	Anaplectoides prasina D.& S.	Green Arches	L91	Res.	LCLD
2139	Cerastis rubricosa D.& S.	Red Chestnut	L91	Res.	WSHD
2140	Cerastis leucographa D.& S.	White-marked	L91	Vag.	R
2418	Earias clorana Linn.	Cream-bordered Green Pea	L110	Res.	LCLD
2422	Pseudoips prasinana Linn. (fagana Fabr.)Green Silver-lines		L110	Res.	WSMD
2421	Bena bicolorana Fuess. (prasinana sensu auctt.)				
		Scarce Silver-lines	L110	Res.	WSLD
2423	Nycteola revayana Scop.	Oak Nycteoline	L110	Res.	WSMD
2424b	Pardasena virgulana Mab.	Grey Square	*	NRR	R
2075	Meganola strigula D.& S.	Small Black Arches	L86	NRR	
2076	Meganola albula D.& S.	Kent Black Arches	L86	Vag.	O

LMBE gave three localities in south-east Essex. There have been seven additional sites, during 1985 to 1991. At Bradwell the species occurred every year from 1982 to 1991, but there has been no record since.

2077	Nola cucullatella Linn.	Short-cloaked Moth	L86	Res.	WSMD
2078	Nola confusalis H.-S.	Least Black Arches	L86	Res.	LCLD
2079	Nola aerugula Hb.	Scarce Black Arches	L86	Mig.	R
2425	Colocasia coryli Linn.	Nut-tree Tussock	L110	Res.	LCMD

Appendix (Records in literature but not admitted to the County List)

0003	Micropterix aureatella Scop.	
0051	Stigmella fragariella Heyd.	form of *S. aurella*
0052	Stigmella dulcella Hein.	form of *S. splendidissimella*
0069	Stigmella auritella Skåla	form of *S. salicis*
0489	Coleophora albella Thunb.	
0498	Coleophora alnifoliae Bar.	
0561	Coleophora therinella Tengst.	
1283	Dichrorampha montanana Dup.	
1536	Parnassius apollo Linn.	Apollo
1544	Colias alfacariensis Berger	Berger's Clouded Yellow
1559	Satyrium pruni Linn.	Black Hairstreak
1562	Lycaena dispar Haw.	Large Copper
1566	Lycaena hippothoe Linn.	Purple-edged Copper
—	Heliconias hecale Fabr.	
1583	Dryas julia Fabr.	Julia
1704	Idaea dilutaria Hb.	Silky Wave
1723	Xanthorhoe munitata Hb.	Red Carpet
1737	Epirrhoe tristata Linn.	Small Argent & Sable
1797	Epirrita autumnata Borkh.	Autumnal Moth
1824	Eupithecia egenaria H.-S.	Pauper Pug
1831	Eupithecia goossensiata Mab.	Ling Pug	form of *E. absinthiata*

1848	Eupithecia innotata Hufn.	Angle-barred Pug	form of *E. fraxinata*
1877	Hydrelia sylvata D.& S.	Waved Carpet	
1928	Lycia zonaria D.& S.	Belted Beauty	
2084	Agrotis cinerea D.& S.	Light Feathered Rustic	
2090	Agrotis trux Hb.	Crescent Dart	
2094	Agrotis crassa Hb.	Great Dart	
2096	Feltia subterranea Fabr.	Tawny Shoulder	
2135	Xestia agathina Dup.	Heath Rustic	
2172	Hadena albimacula Borkh.	White Spot	
2215	Cucullia lactucae D.& S.	Lettuce Shark	
2218	Cucullia gnaphalii Hb.	Cudweed	
2234	Scotochrosta pulla D.& S.	Ash Shoulder-knot	
2261	Jodia erythrocephala D.& S.	Red-headed Chestnut	
2295	Cryphia muralis Forst.	Marbled Green	
2329	Apamea furva D.& S.	Confused	
2372	Archanara neurica Hb.	White-mantled Wainscot	
2383	Hoplodrina superstes Ochs.	Powdered Rustic	
2386	Spodoptera littoralis Boisd.	Mediterranean Brocade	
2386b	Spodoptera eridania Stoll		
2429	Chrysodeixis acuta Walk.	Tunbridge Wells Gem	
2476	Hypena crassalis Fabr.	Beautiful Snout	

REFERENCES

Allfrey, P. 1975. Topping up. BBCS News **15**: 8-10.

Anon. [Corke, D.] 1961. Some notes on the butterflies in Epping Forest. *Bull. amat. Ent. Soc.* **20**: 11-12.

Argent, J.B. 1892. *Lycaena corydon* and *Colias edusa* and helice in Epping Forest. *Essex Nat.* **6**: 140-141.

Bailey G. 1994 The brown argus burgeons in Essex. *Butterfly Conservation News* **57**: 24-25.

Baldwin, S.A. 1986. *John Ray (1627-1705) Essex Naturalist.* Baldwin's Books, Witham.

Barker, S.; Warren, M. & Williams, M. 1996. *Hedgerows for hairstreaks.*. Butterfly Conservation (West Midlands branch).

Barnett, L.K. & Warren, M.S. 1995a. *Species Action Plan: silver-spotted skipper, Hesperia comma.* Butterfly Conservation, Wareham.

Barnett, L.K. & Warren, M.S. 1995b. *Species Action Plan: the swallowtail, Papilio machaon.* Butterfly Conservaton, Wareham.

Barnett, L.K. & Warren, M.S. 1995c. *Species Action Plan: small pearl-bordered fritillary, Boloria selene.* Butterfly Conservation, Wareham.

Barnett, L.K. & Warren, M.S. 1995d. *Species Action Plan: pearl-bordered fritillary, Boloria euphrosyne..* Butterfly Conservation, Wareham.

Barnett, L.K. & Warren, M.S. 1995e. *Species Action Plan: high brown fritillary Argynnis adippe.* Butterfly Conservation, Wareham.

Barnett, L.K. & Warren, M.S. 1995f. *Species Action Plan: marsh fritillary Eurodryas aurinia.* Butterfly Conservation, Wareham.

Barnett, L.K. & Warren, M.S. 1995g. *Species Action Plan: heath fritillary Mellicta athalia.* Butterfly Conservaton, Wareham.

Barnett, L.K. & Warren, M.S. 1996. *Species Action Plan:the silver-studded blue Plebejus argus.* Butterfly Conservaton, Wareham.

Bennett, T. & Perrin, V. 1994. The butterflies of Cambridgeshire: highlights of a county survey (1985-1992). *Nature in Cambridgeshire* **36**: 3-17.

Berger, L.A. 1948. A *Colias* new to Britain. (Lep. Pieridae). *Entomologist* **81**: 129-131.

Bradley, J.D. & Fletcher, D.S. 1979. *A recorder's log book or label list of British Butterflies and Moths.* Curwen Books, London.

Brakefield, P.M.; Shreeve, T.G. & Thomas, J.A. 1992. *Avoidance, concealment and defence.* In Dennis (1992) pp 93-119.

Brimblecome, P. 1987. *The big smoke: a history of air pollution in London since medieval times.* Methuen, London.

Buckell, F.J. & Prout, L.B. 1899-1902. The fauna of the London district. *Trans. Cy. Lond. ent. nat. Hist. Soc.* **8**: 51-63:, **10**: 62-74, **11**: 54-68.

Carrington, J.T. 1879. Localities for beginners: Wanstead Flats. *Entomologist* **12**: 162-165.

Chapman T.A. 1909 Why is *Cyaniris semiargus* no longer a British insect? *Entomologist's Rec. J. Var.* **21**: 132-133.

Chapman, J. & André, P. 1777. *A map of the county of Essex.* Reprinted Essex County Council, 1970.

Chatfield, J. 1987. *F.W. Frohawk his life and work.* Crowood Press, Marlborough.

Collins, N.M. 1987. *Butterfly Houses in Britain: the conservation implications.* International Union for the Conservation of Nature and Natural Resources, Huntingdon.

Common, A.F. 1947. *Pontia daplidice* in Essex. *Entomologist* **80:** 193

Corke, D. 1984. *The Nature of Essex.* Barracuda Books, Buckinham.

Corke, D. 1989. Of pheasants and fritillaries: is predation by pheasants (*Phasianus colchicus*) a cause of the decline in some British butterflies? *Br. J. Ent. Nat. Hist. Soc.* **2:** 1-14.

Corke, D. 1991. Stinging Nettle Butterflies. *British Wildlife* **2** (6): 325-334.

Corke, D. 1996. The butterflies of Epping Forest. *London Naturalist* **75:** 97-113.

Davies, B.N.K. 1989. Habitat creation for butterflies in a landfill site. *Entomologist* **108:** 109-122.

Davis, S. & Corke, D. 1992. *The status and conservation needs of butterflies in Essex.* unpublished report to Butterfly Conservation & Essex Wildlife Trust.

Dawson, J. 1997. Action for Butterflies: Butterfly Conservation: Cambridge and Essex Branch Counties Action Plan. DRAFT. Privately circulated.

Dennis, M.K. 1996. *Breeding Birds of Essex.* Essex Birdwatching Society.

Dennis, R.L.H. (ed) 1992. *The ecology of Butterflies in Britain.* OUP, Oxford.

Dennis, R.L.H. 1993. *Butterflies and climate change.* Manchester University Press.

Doubleday, E. 1836. Remarks on the entomology of Epping and its vicinity. *Entomological Magazine* **3:** 147-159, 283-292.

Doubleday, H. [Delta] 1837. Notes of captures. Entomological Magazine **4:** 230-234.

Doubleday, H. 1849. *A synonimic list of British Lepidioptera.* London.

Douglas, J.W. 1842. Captures of Lepidoptera in July during an excusrsion of four days, between Walton-on-the-Naze and Brightlingsea, Essex. *Entomologist* **1:** 384-385.

Emmet, A.M. & Heath, J. 1989. *The Moths and Butterflies of Great Britain and Ireland* **7**(1) *the Butterflies.* Harley Books, Colchester.

Emmet, A.M. & Heath, J. 1996. *The Moths and Butterflies of Great Britain and Ireland* **7**(2). Harley Books, Colchester.

Emmet, A.M. 1981. *The Smaller Moths of Essex.* Essex Naturalist 6. Essex Field Club.

Emmet, A.M. 1991. *The scientific names of the British Lepidoptera.* Harley Books, Colchester.

Emmet, A.M.; Pyman, G.A. & Corke, D. 1985. *The Larger Moths and Butterflies of Essex.* Essex Naturalist 8. Essex Field Club.

English,J.L. 1887. Entomological notes from an old pocket-book. *Essex Naturalist* **1:** 109-112.

Essex County Council. 1992. *The Essex Environment. A report on the state of the county's environment.* Essex County Council, Chelmsford.

Essex Field Club. 1882. Saturday, November 26th, 1881 - ordinary meeting. *Proc. Essex Field Club* **2:** 76-80.

Essex Field Club. 1890. *Hesperia lineola*, Ochs., a butterfly new to Essex and to . Britain. *Essex Naturalist* **4:** 191-192.

Essex Wildlife Trust. 1996. *Essex Wildlife 2000 a vision for the 21st century.* Essex Wildlife Trust, Colchester.

Firmin, J. et. al. 1975. *A Guide to the Butterflies and Larger Moths of Essex.* Essex Naturalists' Trust, Colchester.

Fitch, E.A. 1891. The Lepidoptera of Essex. Part 1 - Butterflies. *Essex Naturalist* **5:** 74-108.

References

Friedlein 1953. The butterflies and moths in North Fambridge area in 1952. *Essex Naturalist* **29:** 109-110.

Frohawk, F.W. 1924. *Natural History of British Butterflies.* Hutchinson, London.

Geiger, H.J.; Descimon, H. & Scholl, A. 1988. Evidence for speciation within nominal *Pontia daplidice* (Linnaeus, 1758) in southern Europe (Pieridae). *Nota Lepidopterologica* **11:** 7-20.

Gibson, G.S. 1862. The Flora of Essex. London.

Goodey, B. & Firmin, J.1992. *Lepidoptera of north east Essex.* Colchester Natural History Society.

Harris, M. 1766. *The Aurelian or natural history of English insects; namely, moths and butterflies. Together with the plants on which they feed .* London.

Harvey, A.A. 1924. *Nemobius lucina* in Essex. *Entomologist* **57:** 186.

Harwood, W.H. 1871. p57 in Newman, E. 1871.*The illustrated natural history of Britsh Butterflies.* London.

Harwood, W.H. 1903. Lepidoptera. *Victoria County History of Essex* **1:** 136-177.

Hawes, F.W. 1890. *Hesperia lineola* Ochsenheimer: an addition to the list of British butterflies. *Entomologist* **23:** 3-4.

Heath, J.; Pollard, E. & Thomas, J. 1984. *Atlas of Buttterflies in Britain and Ireland.* Viking, Harmondsworth.

Howarth, T.G. 1973. *South's British Butterflies.* Warne, London.

Jermyn, L. 1827. A butterfly collector's vade mecum. Ipswich & London.

Jermyn, S.T. 1974. *The Flora of Essex.* Essex Naturalists' Trust, Colchester.

Maes, D. & Dyck, H. van. 1996. *Een gedocumenteerde Rode lijst van de dagvlinders van Vlaanderen.* Inst. voor Natuurbehoud. Brussels, B.

Mathew, G.F. 1947. 1912. Notes from an Essex Lepidopterist's diary for 1911. *Entomologist* **45:** 153-155.

Mays, R. 1978. *Henry Doubleday the Epping naturalist.* Precision Press, Marlow.

McCay, H. 1991. Egg-laying requirements of woodland butterflies - brimstones (*Gonepteryx rhamni*) and alder buckthorn (*Frangula alnus*). *J. appl. Ecol.* **28:** 731-743.

Meldola, R. 1891. The Lepidoptera of Leyton and neighbourhood: a contribution to the county fauna. *Essex Naturalist* **5:** 153-170.

Mendel H. & Piotrowski, S.H. 1986. *The Butterflies of Suffolk and atlas & history.* Suffolk Naturalists' Trust, Ipswich.

Mera, A.W. 1929. Stray notes on the butterflies of Epping Forest. *Essex Naturalist* **22:** 201-202.

Morley, C. 1912. Obituary: Edward Arthur Fitch. *Entomologist* **45:** 235-236

Morris, F.O. 1865. *A history of British butterflies* edn 2. London.

Murray, J.B. 1997. *Hertfordshire and Middlesex Butterfly and Moth Report for 1996.* Butterfly Conservation Hertfordshire and Middlesex Branch.

Newman, E. 1871. *The illustrated natural history of British butterflies.* London.

Oates, M.R. & Warren. M. 1990. *A review of butterfly introductions in Britain and Ireland.* World Wide Fund for Nature, Godalming.

Office of Population Census Surveys. 1993. *1991 Census County Report (Essex).* HMSO

Payne, R.G. & Skinner, J.F. 1982. *Butterflies of Essex provisional maps.* Essex Bilogical Records Centres, Southend-on-Sea.

Perrin V. 1996. Preliminary report on the 1996 local butterfly season. *Newsletter: Butterfly Conservation, Cambridge and Essex branch* **27:** 2-3

Perrin, V. 1995. Survey officer's preliminary report on the 1995 season. *Newsletter: Butterfly Conservation, Cambridge and Essex branch.* **25**: 2.

Perrin, V. 1996. Cambs and Essex butterflies in 1995. *Newsletter, Butterfly Conservation (Cambridgeshire & Essex branch).* **26**: 2-5.

Philp, E.G. 1993. *The Butterflies of Kent.* Kent Field Club, Sittingbourne.

Pinniger, E.B. 1945. Report on the survey of the Cuckoo Pits area 1942-44: Order Lepidoptera. *London Naturalist* **24**: 62-64.

Plant, C.W. 1987. *The Butterflies of the London Area.* London Natural History Society.

Pollard E. 1979. Population ecology and changes in range of the white admiral butterfly Ladoga camilla L. in England. *Ecological Entomology* **4**: 61-74.

Pollard, E. & Cooke, A.S. 1994. Impact of muntjac deer *Muntiacus reevesi* on egg-laying sites of the white admiral butterfly *Ladoga camilla* in a Cambridgeshire wood. *Biological Conservation* **70**: 189-191.

Pollard, E. & Eversham, B.C. 1995. Butterfly monitoring 2 - interpreting the changes. In Pullin (1992) pp

Pollard, E. & Hall, M.L. 1980. Possible movements of *Gonepteryx rhamni* (L.) (Lepidoptera, Pieridae) between hibernating and breeding areas. *Entomologist's Gazette* **36**: 3.

Pollard, E. & Yates, T.J. 1993. *Monitoring Butterflies for Ecology and Conservation.* Chapman & Hall, London.

Pollard, E.; Hall, M.L. & Bibby, T.J. 1986. Monitoring the abundance of butterflies. Nature Conservancy Council, Peterborough.

Porter, K., Steel, C.A. & Thomas, J.A. 1992. *Butterflies and communities.* In Dennis (1992) pp 139-177.

Pratt, C.R. 1983. A modern review of the demise of *Aporia crataegi* L.: the black-veined white. *Entomologist's Rec. J. Var.* **95**: 45-52, 161-166, 232-237.

Pullin, A.S. 1995. *Ecology and Conservation of Butterflies.* Chapman & Hall, London.

Pyman, G.A. 1987. The larger moths and butterflies of Essex: a selection of recent records. *Essex Field Club Bulletin* **35**: 25-38.

Rackham, O. 1986. *The woods of south-east Essex.* Rochford District Council.

Rackham, O. 1989. *The Last Forest.* Dent, London.

Ray, J. 1710. *Historia Insectorum.* London.

Raynor, G.H. 1884. The Macro-lepidoptera of the district around Maldon. *Trans. Essex Field Club* **3**: 30-47.

Raynor, G.H. 1888. Food of *Vanessa polychloros. Entomologist* **21**: 255-256

Raynor, G.H. 1912. An old Essex collection. *Entomologist's Rec. J. Var.* **24**: 290-293.

Revels, R. 1994. The rise and fall of the holly blue butterfly. *British Wildlife* **5** (4): 236-239.

Sawford, B. 1987. *The Butterflies of Hertfordshire.* Castlemead, Ware.

Scott, J.A. 1986. *The Butterflies of North America.* Stanford University Press.

Spiller, A.J. 1890. On the ocurrence of *Hesperia lineola* in Essex. *Entomologist* **23**: 56-57.

Stephens, J.F. 1827-28. *Illustrtaions of British Entomology. (Haustellata)* 1 London.

Stewart, R. 1996. *Provisional Atlas of Suffolk Butterflies.* Suffolk Biological Records Centre, Ipswich.

Stokoe, W.J. 1944. *The caterpillars of the British butterflies.* Warne, London.

Swaay, C. van & Plate, C. 1996. Hoe gaat het met de Rode Lijst vlinders? *Vlinders* **11**: (3) 11-13.

Tax, M.H. 1989. *Atlas van den nederlandse dagvlinders.* Vlinderstichting, Wageningen, NL

Thomas, J. 1986. *Butterflies of the British Isles*. Hamlyn, London.

Thomas, J.A. & Lewington, R. 1991. *The Butterflies of Britain and Ireland*. Dorling Kindersley, London.

Tyssen, R. 1857. Captures in Epping Forest. *Entomologist's Weekly Intelligencer* **2**: 115.

Warren, M. 1984. The biology and status of the wood white butterfly, Leptidea sinapis L. in the British Isles. *Entomologist's Gazette* **35**: 207-223.

Warren, M.S. 1992. The conservation of British butterflies. In Dennis (1992) pp 246-274.

Warren. M. 1991. The successful conservation of an endangered species, the heath fritillary butterfly (*M. athalia*) in Britain. *Biological Conservation* **55**: 37-56.

Whalley, P. 1980. *Butterfly Watching*. Hamlyn, Feltham.

Whalley, P. 1982. *Butterflies*. Mitchell Beazley, London.

Whalley, P.1997. *Butterflies of Gwynedd*. First Hydro, Llanberis.

Williams 1953. Butterflies in the Brentwood are in 1952. *Essex Naturalist* **29**: 110-111.

Williams, E.F. 1950. Grayling, speckled wood and silver-studded blue butterflies. *Essex Naturalist* **28**: 210.

Worms C.G.M. de 1959. A supplement to the butterflies and moths of London and its surroundings. *London Naturalist* **38**: 46-80.

Worms, C.G.M. de 1950. The butterflies of London and its surroundings. *London Naturalist* **29**: 46-80.

Wurzell B. 1990. The long-tailed blue, *Lampides boeticus*, breeding in north London. *Bull. amat. Ent. Soc.* **49**: 254-256.

Wykes, N. 1979. Memoirs of an Aurelian. *Entomologist's Rec. J. Var.* **91**: 225-233.

INDEX

Figures in bold refer to colour plates.

COLOUR PLATES

The following colour plates are all, with the exception of the clouded yellow, photographed in Essex. The name of the photographer is indicated on the caption to each.

Every species of butterfly that breeds in Essex, or has done so during the 1990s, is illustrated with at least one photograph but this book is not intended as a field identification guide. If you need a guide for identification of butterflies seen in Essex you cannot do better than Jeremy Thomas's *Butterflies of the British Isles* (1986, Hamlyn).

Plate 1 (above). Large Skipper in High Woods Country Park. (Ted Benton)

Plate 2 (below left). Small Skipper. (Terry Spooner)

Plate 3 (below right). Essex Skipper. (Terry Spooner)

Plate 4 (above). Dingy Skipper in Friday Woods (its last haunt in Essex before its extinction). (Ted Benton)

Plate 5 (left). Grizzled Skipper at the Little Baddow Heath re-establishment site. (Iris Newbery)

Plate 6 (below). Grizzled Skipper var. *taras* at Langdon NR. (Stephen Davis)

Plate 7 (above). Clouded Yellow. (David Corke)

Plate 8 (right). Newly emerged Brimstone butterfly. (John Court)

Plate 9 (below). Fully grown Brimstone caterpillar. (John Court)

Plate 10 (above). Large White at Black Notley. (Carl Blamire)

Plate 11 (left). Small White near Brentwood. (Stephen Davis)

Plate 12 (below). Green-veined Whites mud-puddling, Galleyhill. (Iris Newbery)

Plate 13. Orange-tip in a Roydon churchyard. (Stephen Davis)

Plate 14 (above left). Green Hairstreak, Hitchcock's Meadow NR. (Iris Newbery)

Plate 15 (above right). Purple Hairstreak, newly emerged. (Iris Newbery)

Plate 16 (below). Purple Hairstreak female basking. (Terry Spooner)

ate 17 (above). White-letter Hairstreak, nr Colchester. (Stephen Davis)

ate 18 (below). Small Copper, Roydon. (Stephen Davis)

Plate 19 (above). Brown Argus, Colchester. (Ted Benton)

Plate 20 (below left). Brown Argus at rest. (Stephen Davis)

Plate 21 (below right). Common Blues. (Graham Bailey)

late 22 (above). Common Blue, Brightlingsea. (Carl Blamire)

late 23 (below). Holly Blue, Black Notley. (Carl Blamire)

Plate 24 (above). White Admiral, Belfairs. (Terry Spooner)

Plate 25 (below). Red Admiral, garden in Roydon. (Stephen Davis)

Plate 26 (above). Painted Lady, female, Curry Farm 1996. (Iris Newbery)

Plate 27 (below). Painted Lady, eggs massed on thistle, Curry Farm 1996. (Iris Newbery)

Plate 28 (above). Small Tortoiseshell caterpillars. (John Court)

Plate 29 (below). Small Tortoiseshell, Roydon. (Stephen Davis)

Plate 30 (above left). Peacock caterpillars. (Carl Blamire)

Plate 31 (above right). Peacock egg-laying on nettles. (Graham Bailey)

Plate 32 (below). Peacock basking. (Carl Blamire)

Plate 33 (above). Comma, basking. (Ted Benton)

Plate 34 (below left). Comma, underside. (Stephen Davis)

Plate 35 (below right). Comma caterpillar. (Terry Spooner)

ate 36 (above). Pearl-bordered Fritillary egg, Little Baddow NR. (Iris Newbery)

ate 37 (below). Pearl-bordered Fritillary at Little Baddow Heath NR. (Carl amire)

Plate 38 (above). Heath Fritillary on cow wheat, Thrift Wood NR. (Iris Newbery)

Plate 39 (below left). Heath Fritillary. (Graham Bailey)

Plate 40 (below right). Heath Fritillary caterpillars basking on dead leaves, Thrift Wood NR. (Stephen Davis)

ate 41 (above). Speckled Wood at Maldon Wick NR. (Carl Blamire)

ate 42 (below). Wall Brown, Roydon. (Stephen Davis)

Plate 43. Marbled Whites: Butterfly Photograph of the Year, 1991.
(Alan Sadgrove)

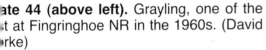

ate 44 (above left). Grayling, one of the
t at Fingringhoe NR in the 1960s. (David
rke)

ate 45 (above right). Gatekeeper at rest. (Carl Blamire)

ate 46 (below left). Female Gatekeeper. (Ted Benton)

ate 47 (below right). Male Gatekeeper. (Ted Benton)

Plate 48 (above left). Ringlet, Thrift Wood NR. (Stephen Davis)

Plate 49 (above right). Small Heath. (Ted Benton)

Plate 50 (below). Mating pair of Meadow Browns. (Carl Blamire)